The Physical Geography of China

This volume is published in cooperation with Research & Microfilm Publications, Inc., Washington, D. C., as a service to the scholarly community. The translation from the Russian was provided by the U.S. Joint Publications Research Service, and the publisher disclaims responsibility for its quality or accuracy.

PRAEGER SPECIAL STUDIES IN
INTERNATIONAL ECONOMICS AND DEVELOPMENT

The Physical Geography of China

Prepared by the
**Institute of Geography,
U.S.S.R. Academy of Sciences**

Volume II

FREDERICK A. PRAEGER, Publishers
New York · Washington · London

The purpose of the Praeger Special Studies is to make specialized research monographs in U.S. and international economics and politics available to the academic, business, and government communities. For further information, write to the Special Projects Division, Frederick A. Praeger, Publishers, 111 Fourth Avenue, New York, N.Y. 10003.

FREDERICK A. PRAEGER, PUBLISHERS
111 Fourth Avenue, New York, N.Y. 10003, U.S.A.
5, Cromwell Place, London S.W. 7, England

Published in the United States of America in 1969
by Frederick A. Praeger, Inc., Publishers

Library of Congress Catalog Card Number: 68-14541

Printed in the United States of America

The general subject areas of this two-volume publication, *The Physical Geography of China*, include the following:

72978

CONTENTS

The Physical Geography of China

CHAPTER 1 TOPOGRAPHY

N. M. Kazakova
USSR Adademy of Sciences
Institute of Geography

BASIC FEATURES OF OROGRAPHY

China is basically a mountainous nation; its relief is extremely diverse and is a complex combination of mountain chains with various altitudes, uplands, plateaus, intermontane and submontane plains with unique genesis and morphology. In terms of the character of the relief, China can be divided into the more elevated and dry western portion occupying a larger section of the nation's area than the less elevated but heavily wetted eastern portion.

A particular feature of the western Central Asiatic portion of China is the combination of extremely high mountains and broad highly uplifted plains, and the latter frequently lie in deep intermontane depressions. All of the basic orographic elements here are amazing in their enormous dimensions, stretching for hundreds of kilometers and thereby occupying very large areas. In the southwestern portion of China, reaching an altitude of more than 5,000 meters above sea level, lie the extremely high Tibetan Uplands. These uplands include the complex of upland plains, the Changtan, the lacustrine plains of Central Tibet, and a number of interior mountain ranges: The Kantissushan, Tangla, etc., and the border mountains: The Kunlun in the north and the Sino-Tibetan mountains in the east. To the north of the Kunlun stretch the Nanshan Mountains. All of the listed ranges and uplands, as is known, are the highest mountain systems in the world, the so-called High Asia; individual peaks rise up to 7,000-8,000 meters and more. The designated mountains consist of a number of mountain ranges and intermontane depressions, and the largest of them, the Tsaidam Depression, lies between the Kunlun and Nanshan at an elevation of about 3,000 meters above sea level.

The general plan in the strike of the orographic elements here is from west-northwest to east-southeast, that is, virtually in a latitudinal direction. Individual deviations from it can be noted in areas where these mountain systems abut the plain areas of the depressions, and also in the extreme southeastern portion of the Kunlun, where the Sino-Tibetan mountains have a meridional strike.

In the northwest of China, there predominate high plains; they strike in a direction from west to east forming an extensive Central Asian plain belt. This belt includes in the west the Tarim and Dzungar intermontane depressions which are separated by the high-mountain system of the Eastern Tien Shan, and in the center by the Kashun (Gashiun) Gobi, Alashan and Ordos which are separated one from the other by the relatively low mountains of the Peishan, Alashan (Holangshan) and Yinshan, and in the east the plains of the Eastern Gobi and Bargi. The predominating altitude of this belt of plains is about 1,200 meters and within them one can encounter individual low-mountain ranges and hillocky areas. The extreme northwestern portion of China, bordering on the USSR and Mongolia, is occupied by mountains which skirt on the west and north the Dzungar Plain.

The relief of the eastern portion of China, in contrast to the western, is marked by a predominance of medium altitude and low mountains and lowland plains. The altitudes of the mountains here rarely exceed 2,000 meters above sea level and the extent of them is significantly less than in the west. The predominating strike of the orographic lines is north-northeast to south-southwest, i.e., virtually meridional.

The following patterns can be noted in the distribution of mountains and plains on the territory of Eastern China. On the boundary with the western portion of China lies a belt of mountains--the Greater Khingan, the Jehol Uplands, the Shansi Mountains, the so-called Loess Province of hills and plateaus, the Ch'inling Range (as an exception to the latitudinal strike), the Kweichow Mountains, the Yunnan Uplands, and also the intermontane Szechwan Depression. To the east stretches a belt of lowland plains--the Sankiang, the northeastern (separated from the Zeya-Bureya Plain of the Soviet Union by the Lesser Khingan Mountains), the North China (or as it is frequently called, the Great China) plains, and the depressions of the middle and lower reaches of the Yangtze. To the south of the latter, the belt of depressions is broken and the relief here shows predominantly low mountains--the Nanling, etc.--with a predominant latitudinal strike. To the east of the listed depressions, once again on a meridional strike but no longer in a solid belt, lie the mountains of the Eastern Manchurian Range, the Liaotung, Shantung, the mountains of the southeastern coast, and also the mountains of Taiwan.

As a whole for the relief of China there is a characteristic step-like drop in the surface from west to east, the extensive development of upland and intermontane plains lying at a great altitude relative to sea level, a definite predominance in the strikes of the basic orographic lines and very great altitude fluctuations.

Within the limits of China one can in essence establish four basic altitude levels: the upper of 5,000 meters absolute altitude, two medium altitudes of 1,200 and 600 meters, and a lower level of less than 200 meters absolute altitude. These basic altitude levels are separated one from another by steps and represent as it were gigantic hypsometric steps descending from the enormous altitudes of the Tibetan Uplands to the depth of the Pacific Ocean. However, the endurance of these steps over the entire territory of the nation and their expression in the relief are not the same. Thus, for example, the upper step is strictly confined to the Tibetan Uplands and is represented by upland plains which are surrounded by mountain chains rising above them to an altitude of up to 2,000 meters, and in places more than 3,000 meters. The 1,200 meter step can be seen particularly well in the Central Asian part of China in the form of an extensive strip of high plains. In the east of the nation, this step has already been heavily deformed and is represented by a virtually uninterrupted chain of mountains (the ranges of the Greater Khingan, the T'aihangshan, the Kweichow, etc.) with absolute altitudes of up to 1,500-2,000 meters. These mountains lie predominantly from northeast to southwest and drop steeply in the east to lowland plains, thereby being in the present relief a major step known in literature under the name of "continental step."

The following step, the 600-meter altitude, can be followed particularly well in the southeast of China where it occupies a significant area and includes a complex of low mountain reliefs among which in various places there rise individual ranges and peaks; the elevation of the latter above the average elevation of the mountains rarely is more than 1,000 meters. This hypsometric level comes directly up to the seacoast and thus the lowest step here, as a rule, is absent or, for example, in the extreme south it is represented by a very narrow strip. The lower step of less than 200 meters in altitude includes the strip of depressions along the border portion of the Asiatic continent and is best of all expressed in the central portion of Eastern China and in the northeast of the nation.

The mountain systems within China lie along two basic directions--from west-northwest to east-southeast which is characteristic chiefly for the western half of the nation, and from north-northeast to south-southwest which is most typical for the eastern portion. Very characteristic for the relief of China, as has been noted, are the great fluctuations in altitude. Mountains may rise above the plains that they surround by 3,000-4,000 meters, and in places even more. The maximum amplitude in altitudes here is 9,000 meters, and the highest peak, Mount Chomolungma (Everest) lying in the Himalayas on the boundary of China and Nepal rises 8,848 meters above sea level; the lowest place, the Turfan Depression, located in the mountains of the Eastern Tien Shan, has an elevation of 154 meters below sea level.

The listed features in the orography of China have been caused by the entire course of the geological history and to a great degree depend upon the placement of the basic geotectonic units. The sharp contrasts in the orographic elements of China and the significant fluctuations in altitude have caused the vertical zonality of the relief. The diversity of the relief is even more intensified by the influence of the latitudinal zonality (China is extended along the meridian by approximately 35°) and by the various regional physical geographic conditions. The latter to a great degree depend upon the predominating directions in the orographic

lines which in a number of places of China are important
climatic boundaries.

The Geological Structure, Minerals and Developmental History of the Territory of China

The basic tectonic units of China are the Precambrian
Chinese Platform which in a significant portion has already
lost the properties of a platform, being involved and reworked by later mountain-forming movements, and also the
area of the Paleozoic, Mesozoic and Cenozoic folding.

The tectonic structure of the territory of China has
been soundly studied in the works of V. M. Sinitsyn (1948,
1955) who used the abundant material of Chinese geologists
and his own personal observations. According to the works
of the designated author, the tectonic structure of China in
general can be represented in the following form.

The entire eastern half, with a relatively narrow
branch in the west, is occupied by the Chinese Platform, the
birth of which dates to the Upper Proterozoic. The development of this platform occurred in a unique manner. Its middle portion or the Sinian shield lies to the north of the Ch'inling Range and was marked by a tendency of a predominant
uplift; for a major portion of geological time it was dry land.
The southern portion or the South China land area, on the
contrary, was marked by a tendency of predominant subsidence; a large portion of this territory (with the exception of
the coastal) for a long period of time was covered by seawater. The northern portion of the platform entered the
phase of continental development once and for all at the end
of the Permian Age and the southern at the end of the Triassic. At the end of the Mesozoic the entire territory of the
platform was seized by tectonic movements and as a result
a number of mountain systems developed within it separated
by relatively stable land masses. This, as geologists propose, is the chief distinguishing feature of the Chinese Platform.

The folded systems of the Eastern Tien Shan, the Kunlun and the Gobi region which surround the platform were
formed basically at the end of the Paleozoic as a result of
the Hercynian orogenesis. The development of the intra-

platform mountain systems dates to the Mesozoic Age while
the southern border of the Tibetan Uplands and the Island of
Taiwan were formed only in Tertiary times.

Analyzing a geological map of China showing the complex structure of the rock, beginning from the most ancient
times and ending with the modern era, and also the stratigraphic and tectonic data, shows the very complex history
of the geological development of this nation.

The detailed study of the geological structure is not
part of the plan for the given work, and therefore we will
take up here only those questions which could be of assist-
ance in helping to correctly understand the course of the formation of the contemporary relief of China and its minerals.

The Precambrian rock is encountered in various parts
of China and is very thick. Among this rock the Chinese
geologists have isolated archaic deposits consisting chiefly
of heavily metamorphized gneisses and crystalline schists,
intruded granites; mica schists, quartzites, marbles and
phyllites of the Wut'ai System (the Lower and Middle Proterozoic deposits), and also frequently pierced by magmatic
rock, and the Sinian deposits (Upper Proterozoic) represented by limestones, mica-clay schists, conglomerates,
sandstones and quartzites.

The archaic deposits are widely found within the
Sinian shield and in the maritime zone of the Southern
China land mass, and also in the axial zones of the Kunlun
and Kantissushan.

The Wut'ai complex forms major outcroppings in the
middle (the Shansi Mountains) and the western (Alashan and
Peishan) parts of the Sinian shield, in the Nanshan-
Ch'inling zone, in the axial zone of the Eastern Tien Shan
and in the fore chains of the Kunlun. To the south of the
Ch'inling Range the outcroppings of the Wut'ai rock are encountered more rarely and on relatively limited areas; they
are known in Southeastern Kiangso and in Kwangtung (Canton)
Province to the south of the Nanling Range. The Sinian deposits have developed both in the southern part of China
where they are represented chiefly by terrigenic facies of

rather great thickness, and in the north where they are
shown by a relatively shallow epicontinental series.

The Sinian deposits, in contrast to the earlier ones,
belong basically to the sedimentary complex and have been
slightly dislocated. Therefore, geologists suppose that in
the Sinian times over a larger portion of the territory of
China there was a replacing of the geosynclinal conditions
with platform conditions. The protracted period of tectonic
quiet caused the general levelness in the relief of the platform which, as we will see below, in certain portions of it
has remained up to the present. Here, judging from the
thickness of the sediments, within the platform in the Sinian
Age one can note individual syneclises and anteclises which
also to one degree or another are reflected in the structure
of the contemporary relief.

Thus, for example, the modern North China Plain occupies the western portion of the Sinian syneclise, and the
mountains of the southeastern coast, a portion of the Catho-
asiatic anteclise, etc.

The crystalline rock of the Precambrian has been
richly mineralized and the eye is struck by a clear predominance of iron ores. According to Huang Po-ch'in (1952),
among the important deposits of the pre-Sinian times one
should note the iron ore deposits of the Anshan, K'ung-
chaling and Miaoerhk'ou in Liaotung (the eastern portion of
Liaoning) and also the Luanhsien and the Hopeh. These deposits in his opinion have a sedimentary-metamorphic origin. In the Sinian times there were formed the sedimentary
iron ore deposits of Northern China; geologists suppose that
they have a shallow-water or littoral origin.

The Paleozoic deposits are represented in China by an
alternation of continental and marine facies and this shows
the frequent shift of marine transgressions and regressions.

According to the geological data, very great geological
changes occurred here at the beginning of the Ordovician.
At this time the former structural plan of this territory was
fundamentally disrupted and the bases of a new plan were put
down which to a significant degree is followed by the contemporary orography. Thus, on the site of the Eastern Tien

Shan, the Northern Nanshan and the Kunlun, between the
large deep faults there developed intensively subsided geo-
synclines which formed the moving framework of the Chinese
Platform. Between the Sinian shield and the South China
land mass, i.e., at the site of the present Ch'inling Range,
there also arose a strip of disturbances and geosynclinal
conditions were established. In the syneclise of Northeastern China there appeared gently sloping swells, the em-
bryos of the modern ranges, due to which the formerly whole
syneclise was broken up into smaller syneclises--the Ordos
and the P'ich'ihli (V. M. Sinitsyn, 1955).

The tectonic movements of the Paleozoic times (the
Caledonian and Hercynian) which within the platform had
basically a fluctuating character, are expressed chiefly in
the flexure of individual areas of the platform and this was
the beginning to its breaking-up into isolated land masses.
As a result there was a significant increase in the area of
dry land and the relief was more complex. In contradistinction to the predominance of lowland plain territories in the
Lower Paleozoic, in the Upper Paleozoic there developed a
number of elevated mountainous sections separated by depressions and this led to a much more intensive development of continental sedimentation. Among the deposits of
this age, there is a typical predominance of various continental facies and the lagoon bases closely related to them.
Here while in the Carboniferous and Lower Permian ages,
the entire eastern portion of China was characterized by a
humid climate which can be seen from the heavy accumulation of coals, in the Upper Permian Age the climatic situation here became even more differentiated. The humid
conditions with the accumulation of coals remained only in
the southern portion of Eastern China, while in the north the
climate became arid and there was the accumulation of redbeds.

In contrast to the Chinese Platform, in the geosynclinal areas surrounding it, the tectonic movements had
important orogenic significance. As a result of these movements, here were formed the large folded mountain structures of the Kunlun, Tien Shan and Mongolia.

The Upper Paleozoic times are marked by the intensive formation of minerals.   On the platform under the

conditions of a predominance of a continental and lagoon regime, there were formed coals, bauxites, iron and copper ores, and in the geosynclinal areas, minerals of endogenic origin.

Chinese geologists suppose that here in the Upper Paleozoic--in the Upper Carboniferous and Permian ages-- the most important coal-bearing suites of China were formed. Here the Carboniferous coals were distributed basically in the northern portion of China where they stretch from the Ch'inling Range along to Inner Mongolia (the thick coal-bearing suite of the Shihhotse). In the southern portion of China, there are few Carboniferous coals, and here the Permian coal suites predominate. The latter lie basically within the limits of the Hunan Uplands, the Kweichow Mountains, in the eastern portion of the Szechwan Depression, along the middle course of the Yangtze, and also in the mountains of the Nanling and in the eastern portion of the Tibetan Uplands.

The iron (hematite) ores in the northern portion of China lie in deposits of clay shales and limestones from the Upper Carboniferous. In the southern portion of China, or more precisely in the east of Hopeh Province and in the southeast of Szechwan, pisolite hematite lies in limestones of the Lower Permian; in Hunan Province in Upper Devonian shallow-water deposits, where frequently one can encounter strata of oolite hematite ores.

The bauxites of this age in Northern China are found on Shantung Peninsula where they lie above the Upper Carboniferous coal seams and Liaotung where they are confined to the coal suite of the Upper Permian. In Southern China bauxites are found more widely, chiefly in the central portions of Yunnan Province and Kweichow, lying among clay shales of the Carboniferous.

The sedimentary copper deposits are encountered in the form of concretions in the Permian coal-bearing suites of Szechwan and in the form of impregnations in the Triassic layers of the Kweichow.

Chinese geologists link the formation of a number of ore minerals to the igneous rock of the Hercynian cycle.

This age is responsible for the deposits of wolfram, molybdenum, gold, copper, lead, zinc and chrome lying in the northwest of the nation in the mountains of the Eastern Tien Shan, the Kunlun and Nanshan; the deposits of iron, copper, gold, lead, zinc, silver and in places nickel and cobalt, lying in the mountains of the southeast and also certain ore deposits in other parts of the nation (Huang Po-ch'in, 1952).

Judging from the distribution of the Triassic deposits and their facies on the territory of China, it may be supposed that in the Lower Mesozoic, the paleogeographic conditions in China remained basically the same as in the Permian Age. The northern half of China was dry land with large sedimentation troughs in the areas of the Ordos and P'ich'ihli syneclises, and depressions stretching along the Eastern Tien Shan and Kunlun in which red sands accumulated. In South China, the sea remained up to the Upper Triassic, and here clay shales and limestones were deposited. The highest mobility was found in the zone of the Tethys and the areas of Yunnan and Kweichow next to it; the thickness of the shale beds in places exceeds 2,000 meters.

All of the Upper Triassic deposits of China, both in the north and in the south, are characterized by a predominance of purple tones in their color. Moreover, in various regions of China (Szechwan, Yunnan, etc.), among the Triassic deposits one can find strata of rock salt, anhydrite and more rarely potassium salts (in the district of Ch'ieh-liukiang. All of this together shows that in China during this time there reigned a dry and perhaps even desert climate. The shallow interior seas of South China partially dried up, changing into extensive lagoons and lake basins.

As a result of the tectonic movements at the end of the Triassic (the Indosinian cycle) which were particularly intensive in Indochina but also reached the southern territories, all of the interior seas of China disappeared once and for all.

In general within the Chinese Platform, the tectonic movements of this cycle were expressed in the continuing downwarping of individual areas of dry land and the formation of new sags, and this brought about the development of

a mountain relief on the territory of the Chinese Platform.
The large intracontinental depressions at this time lay within
the Szechwan Basin, in the Ordos, in the foothills of the Nanshan, the Eastern Tien Shan and Western Kunlun, in the
Tsaidam, in Dzungaria, in the Turfan-Hami Depression,
and in the southern part of the Tibetan Uplands, i.e., basically where they are now. A number of depressions was
occupied by fresh lakes as can be seen from the findings of
freshwater fauna. Thus, for example, a large lake lay at
that time within the Ordos and on the site of the present
Szechwan Depression.

Thus, the Jurassic deposits which are widely found in
China, in the predominant majority are continental or freshwater. Only in the Himalayan zone within China and the
western portion of Yunnan do the Jurassic deposits show marine facies. The continental sediment consists basically of
clay shales, sandstones and conglomerates, which lie in
the above-mentioned intermontane and submontane depressions. For the deposits of this time there are typical thick
seams of hard coal. The abundant coal manifestations and
also the fossil flora with a predominance of ferns, bennetites
and cycads show that the climate in China at this time became warm and was abundantly wet.

Judging from the character of the deposits and the
thickness of them, geologists suppose that the relief of the
Lower and Middle Jurassic generally was reminiscent of the
modern relief, although the altitudes were different. On the
site of the present plains--the Tarim, Dzungar, Alashan,
Tsaidam, Ordos and Szechwan--then also there were extensive intracontinental plains divided by belts of elevations.
The latter, however, were not extensive systems and were
lower than the present elevations, but the ratios of their
altitudes in general were the same as at present. Thus, the
greatest altitude was also found in the northern and southern chains of the Eastern Tien Shan and the border ranges
of the Kunlun and Nanshan along the feet of which there
developed thick beds of conglomerates; the Peishan, Altyntag and Nanshan mountains were lower, and the Jurassic deposits here were shallower and virtually contained no conglomerates (V. M. Sinitsyn, 1961). Proceeding from the
character of the vegetation remains in the Lower and Middle
Jurassic deposits and from the particular features of their

stratification, the designated author proposes that on the elevations of this time there flourished a coniferous-ginkgo tayga on the plains under the conditions of an abundant moisture there predominated lake-swamp landscapes with the extensive development of ferns and the other above-listed moisture and heat-loving plants.

Beginning with the Upper Jurassic, the paleogeographic situation in China once again changed in the direction of intensifying the aridity of the climate. The latter can be seen particularly clearly in the western and Central Asian part of China; the vegetation remains in the Upper Jurassic deposits here are significantly sparser and represented exclusively by the xerophyte forms. In the eastern portion of China, humid conditions remained; however, the coal manifestations of this time are noted only in the northeast of the nation. In the south and southeast, as A. N. Kristofovich (1957) wrote, the Upper Jurassic deposits show only traces of xeromorphism. Characteristically, in the Upper Jurassic and Lower Cretaceous over the predominant area of China there were formed thick beds of red and varicolored sands of the laterite type. V. M. Sinitsyn supposes that the swamp-forest landscapes of the Lower and Middle Jurassic during the Upper Jurassic gave way to savannas.

The Cretaceous deposits are represented in China by continental freshwater sediments, predominantly by redbeds, volcanic rock and more rarely by marine sediments. The chief areas for the accumulation of continental beds were the above-mentioned inland depressions, the submontane troughs and also the maritime depression which was formed in the Cretaceous. The thickness of these deposits was very great, for example, in the Ordos and Szechwan it reached 2,000 meters, and in some places even rose to 3,500 meters. The volcanic rock widely developed in the eastern regions of the nation where it attained great thickness and overlay discordantly the lower-lying rock. The marine sediments of this age, according to Huang Po-ch'in (1952) have been found only in the region of Southern Tibet. The extensive development of redbeds among the Cretaceous deposits and the corresponding shift in the centers of coal accumulation further and further to the northeast show that the arid conditions gradually covered a greater and greater area.

At the end of the Jurassic and during the Cretaceous, the Chinese Platform experienced the Yenshan tectonic movements which were the strongest in its history. It may be supposed that they were the chief mountain-forming movement for this area of China and fundamentally changed its surface. The Yenshan movements were particularly strong within the limits of the South China land mass; mountain ranges even developed in the Szechwan Depression.

Within the limits of the Sinian shield, the Yenshan movements were weaker. Here in certain areas there developed broad belts of dislocations and elevations were formed with a block and folded-block structure. Judging from everything, they lay on the site of the present Eastern Manchurian Mountains, the T'aihangshan, Yinshan, Alashan, Peishan, the Kel'pin Mountains and the Kuruktag and bordered solid land masses such as the Shantung-Korean, Manchurian, Tarim and Ordos, the basement of which was not disturbed.

The interior depressions and submontane troughs began to subside, and this can be seen from the above-mentioned significant thickness of the Cretaceous deposits; in many of the depressions there were lakes, largely fresh. During this time the Tsaidam Depression was formed and the maritime portion of the modern North China Plain and areas of the northeast plain began to subside. This process of the subsidence of the earth's crust in maritime areas spread, evidently, from the seaside since, according to V. V. Belousov (1956), from the end of the Mesozoic, the depression of the Pacific Ocean began to subside rapidly.

In the shifted belts of the Eastern Tien Shan and Kunlun which were at that time uplifts, the Yenshan movements were marked by even greater differentiation and amplitude. This can be seen from the abundance of conglomerates in the deposits of the Upper Jurassic and Lower Cretaceous, and also by the frequent and significant fluctuations in the thickness of the sediments.

The tectonic movements of the Cretaceous Age were accompanied by extensive volcanic activity. Over a great expanse, beginning with the Greater Khingan in the north and down to Kwangtung Province in the south there were eruptions of enormous flows of lava with a varying composition--

andesites, dacites, trachytes, rhyolites. Here the andesites are characteristic basically for the northern part of China in the Yinshan Range and the border of Mongolia; * in Southern China they are encountered more rarely; rhyolites, on the contrary, are widely found both in Southern and Northern China.

This period of volcanic eruption in turn was accompanied by the introduction of intrusive bodies such as granites, granite-porphyries, granodiorites, etc., which were found not only in the maritime regions, but are also encountered in other parts of China, with the exception only of the areas with extensive depressions. Thus the Yenshan granites made up enormous areas of mountains in the southeastern maritime provinces of China, Kwangtung, Fukien and Chekiang; granite domes frequently formed mountains in the provinces of Shansi, Hunan and Kwangsi; moreover, the intrusive bodies of this age developed in the mountains of the northeast.

The movements in the Yenshan mountain structures continued also in the Tertiary and Quaternary ages, although the general tectonic structure of China, with the exception of the insular part, was not basically changed. All of the basic structural-orographic units in the continental portion of China were formed in the Mesozoic in their present outline.

V. M. Sinitsyn supposes that in the Lower Cretaceous, as in the Upper Jurassic, the landscapes of the plain territories of Central Asia and the larger portion of Eastern China were like modern subtropical savannas with a relatively sparse vegetation cover and individual thickets in moist areas. The eastern boundary of the savannas passed along the Alashan Range; this range was the western boundary for the distribution of the lower Cretaceous coals.

---

*Here and in other instances the term "Mongolia" is used in the physical geographic meaning accepted in scientific literature covering not only the territory of Inner Mongolia (China) but also the territory of the Mongolian People's Republic.

During the Upper Cretaceous, the savanna area spread greatly to the east, and the western portion of it assumed a more deserty quality. The composition of the flora, in comparison with the preceding age, changed. In the forests the bennetites disappeared, and there was a reduction in the amount of ferns, cycads and ginkgos, and the angiospermous plants appeared such as plane trees, magnolia, laurel, eucalyptus and various coniferous trees which could exist under less moist conditions (V. M. Sinitsyn, 1961).

The Upper Cretaceous Age was characterized by the formation of a whole series of minerals of both exogenic and endogenic genesis. In the lakes and other relief depressions, where thick beds of sedimentary deposits had been laid down, there were formed coals, oil, bog and hematite ores, gypsum and salt. The coals of the Jurassic Age encountered in China ubiquitously are most widely developed in the Ordos, Szechwan and in the Province of Sinkiang. The coals of the Lower Cretaceous Age are concentrated basically in Northeastern China and in the southern part of the Tibetan Uplands. They occupy the largest area within the Mongolian plains where they lie in a major Mesozoic basin crossing the territory of the Mongolian People's Republic. A number of small depressions containing Jurassic, Lower Cretaceous and Upper Cretaceous coals lie in the upper reaches of the Nun River and in the lower courses of the Sungari.

Oil and oil shales have been found in various levels of the Mesozoic deposits. Oil strata from this age are found most widely in the Szechwan, Ordos and Fuhsing depressions.

Bog ferriferous ores are encountered in many regions of China and they frequently lie among the Jurassic sedimentary beds. In the southern part of Szechwan one will also encounter hematite ores. Gypsum and salts are characteristic for the Cretaceous red layers of Szechwan Northwest China.

The Yenshan tectonic cycle was responsible for the development of many ore deposits in North China, for example, gold, lead, silver, wolfram, etc., and also the majority of deposits of magmatic origin in South China including the deposits of tin, wolfram, iron, copper, lead, antimony and mercury.

The Cenozoic deposits are represented in China chiefly by the formations of a fragmentary character. The Lower Tertiary (Paleogene) deposits have predominantly a lacustrine origin and are represented by red clays and sands. According to the data of Chinese geologists (Li Ssukuang and others), the Eocene deposits have been uncovered in a number of areas in Southern Shansi, Northern and Southern Honan, Shantung, Southern Shensi, Eastern Kansu, in the Eastern Ch'inling, along the valley of the Yangtze, in Kwangtung, Kwangsi, in the southeast and other areas. They are usually represented by sandstones of a dark red and brown hue, red clays and conglomerates, and are frequently interbedded with shales, marles and freshwater limestones. These red deposits in various regions of the nation have been given various names, but the lithological character of them is always basically the same. The Eocene Age of these deposits has been determined by the fauna of gastropods, and by the remains of mammals such as rodents, perissodactyls, etc., and in places by the remains of fossil flora. Intercalations of gypsum in a number of regions can also be encountered in these redbeds.

The Oligocene deposits are widely found to the north of the town of Kalgan, where they are represented by basalt mantles spreading into Mongolia. The lavas are usually intercalated with clays and sands and with fine partings of coals. The Oligocene deposits of the Ordos and Mongolia contain remnants of a gigantic hornless rhinoceros, the baluchitherium, a relative of the Indricotherium of Kazakhstan which evidently was widely distributed over the plains of Central Asia.

The Paleogene Age was characterized by relative tectonic quiet, and the relief over a larger portion of China was, evidently, rather flat; as V. M. Sinitsyn writes (1961), low plateau-like elevations alternated with extensive plains. This can be seen from the character of the continental sediments which are distinct from the Cretaceous by the lesser thickness and by a finer homogeneous composition. Here there predominated a general uplift, since even in the depressions of the Ordos and Szechwan the Paleogene deposits are absent. The latter were localized in individual small depressions. In the Far West in places there was a subsidence and in line with this the dimension of the interior depressions

increased and one of them, the Yarkend, was briefly pene-
trated by the sea from the Fergana. The extreme eastern
portion of the nation--the area of the present North China
Plain--continued to subside, and, judging from the distribution of sediments, the subsidence here covered a greater
and greater area.

The extensive development of red and frequently gypsum bearing deposits and the character of the fossil fauna
show that in the Paleogene, as in the Cretaceous, over the
larger portion of the territory of China there reigned a hot
and dry climate and evidently the savanna landscape predominated.

The clear predominance of deposits from a lake genesis makes it possible at the same time to suppose the existence at this time of numerous lacustrine basins which had
lasted possibly since the Mesozoic. This was particularly
typical for the western, Central Asiatic portion of China,
where the traces of the ancient lakes can be easily traced
in the modern relief. Moreover, the western portion of
China has, as is known, a great deal in common with the
nearby territories of Mongolia and within this area the fact
of the existence of an ancient lake-river network has been
convincingly shown by the geological data and work of
E. M. Murzayev (1952). The research has established that
here, in the Gobi, there were numerous isolated and clearly
expressed synclines with the fauna of limnetics and mammals of a lacustrine-delta and valley genesis.

In the eastern, and particularly in the northeastern,
part of China, aside from the lacustrine sediments one will
also encounter alluvial deposits with rather good roundness
and sorting and this indicates the extensive development of
a river network at this time.

At the end of the Paleogene there occurred strong as-
cending movements--the alpine orogenesis--which covered
the entire territory of China. As a result on the spot of the
Himalayan geosyncline which was uplifted and emerged from
under the water, there were formed the elevations of the
Himalayas and the Kantissushan, in truth, still not very high;
the Tien Shan, Kunlun and Nanshan also were uplifted; the
interior depressions such as the Dzungar, Tarim, Ordos and

Szechwan were also uplifted, but even less. The Yenshan structures in the eastern half of China also underwent uplifting, where mountain ridges were formed and only within the limits of the maritime depressions did the subsidence and sedimentation continue. Particularly characteristic for this era of tectonic movements were the disjunctive dislocations as a result of which in the mountains of China there were formed numerous faults and fissures of great scope. Faults were particularly numerous in the northern and northwestern part of China. Chinese geologists suppose that during this time there were formed the valleys of the major rivers, the Hwang Ho, Yangtse, Chekiang and certain others.

The movements of the Tertiary Age, like the Mesozoic, were accompanied by volcanic eruptions which were particularly significant in the eastern half of China. Within Inner Mongolia, to the north of the Great Wall of China, the basalt mantles stretch in the form of a more or less unbroken belt from the town of Khukh-Khoto in the west to the Greater Khingan in the east, forming what was an extensive lava plateau, the remains of which have been preserved excellently up to the present. The extensive basalt mantles are also found in the Eastern Manchuria Mountains, in many places of the Shantung Peninsula, along the southeastern coast of China, forming plateaus, mesas in the provinces of Kiangsu and Anhwei, and the Pescadores Islands and a number of other islands and peninsulas.

The Lower Tertiary Age was characterized by the formation of basically coal and oil. The coals of the Tertiary have been discovered in the eastern portion of the nation, within the Bargi, along the lower reaches of the Sungari, in the region of Lake Hangk'a, along the western foothills of the Eastern Manchurian Mountains and in the western portion of Taiwan. The coals of certain deposits, for example, the brown coals of the Dzhalaynor Basin close to the station of Manchuria and the hard coals of the Fushun mines close to the town of Shenyang (Mukden) have important industrial significance.

The oil deposits which are stratigraphically confined to the Tertiary rock have been found within the Tsaidam, Dzungar and a number of other smaller intermontane depressions of China.

As yet few minerals of endogenic genesis formed in this time have been discovered. The largest deposits are the deposits of gold and copper on Taiwan (Hsieh Chia-jung, 1953). Chinese geologists and, in particular, Huang Po-ch'in, feel that the Himalayan cycle in terms of the formation of magmatic minerals does not have basic significance in China.

The Neogene-Tertiary deposits are represented in China chiefly by gravel beds, sandy-clay formations and loess rock. These deposits reach particularly wide distribution within the Central Asiatic and eastern Chinese plains, and the loess rock has developed basically in the northern and northeastern parts of the nation.

Judging from the great thickness of the deposits of this age which have accumulated in various parts of China, the Neogene-Tertiary time was evidently a period for the manifestation of intensive erosion and sedimentation which was caused by the sharp intensification of the mountain-forming process. This process was accompanied by a general uplift of the land which had a discontinuous character both in terms of time and space.

Chinese geologists in making a detailed study of the Pliocene-Quaternary deposits of North China have come to the conclusion that over all of this time there occurred not less than six (and possibly more) stages of aggradation which alternated with significant interruptions in sedimentation (Yang Chung-chien, 1957). According to the scheme given by this author, in the Pliocene there were two stages of aggradation and in the Quaternary period four. In the Pliocene sandy deposits of lacustrine genesis accumulated (the lower and middle section of the Yushe suite) and the loess-like red clays (the Paote suite or Lower Pliocene with remains of the hipparion and the Chingle suite, the Middle Pliocene). In the Quaternary Age the Sanmen suite was formed, represented in its lower part by a sandy bed of lacustrine and fluvial facies (the Ni-ho-wan strata--the upper section of the Yushe suite) and the corresponding loess-like deposits of red loams; in the upper part there were cave and more rarely lacustrine and fluvial facies (the Chouk'outan beds) and the loess-like deposits of red loams with intercalations of buried soils and limestone concretions.

Above was deposited the typical yellow loess (the Huangt'u suite) and finally the recent deposits consisting of gravel, sand and redeposited loess.

Against the background of the general uplift of the land, individual parts of it were uplifted at a varying velocity and this has caused the sharp differentiation in the relief of China. Moreover, the disjunctive disturbances were also strong and the old faults and fissures revived, and new ones developed. Along the fissures in certain places lava erupted and here it was noted that the greatest volcanic activity was confined, as in the Mesozoic, to the border of the continent. Folding continued in places as can be seen from the deformation in the Quaternary rock observable in a number of ranges of China--the foothill ranges in the west of China, the Liupan-shan Range, etc.

The most intensive were the uplifts in the western half of China and in the neighboring lands. In the areas of the particularly strong uplifts here there developed the highest mountain systems, the Himalayas, Kunlun, Nanshan, the Eastern Tien Shan which consist of ranges separated by deep depressions and within the areas which have remained in the uplift, extensive highly uplifted plains. Water erosion revived strongly in the mountains and there was an intensification in the accumulation of friable beds in the submontane and intermontane depressions such as the Manass, Kuchar, Yarkend, Suichow and others, where the thickness of the sediments can be measured in thousands of meters. V. M. Sinitsyn (1959), in describing the deposits of the submontane depressions of Central Asia, points out that if the thickness of the Paleogene deposits here is not more than 400 meters, then the beds of the Miocene and Lower Pliocene are 1,500-3,000 meters thick, and the beds of the Upper Pliocene are 1,000-2,500 meters thick, and correspondingly the composition of the deposits becomes more rough. The growth of the mountains occurred not only in height but also in width due to their encompassing of the neighboring border areas of the plains. This can be seen by the subsequent rejuvenation of the structures in the foothill zone as one moves from the mountains to the plains, the shift of the detritus fans in the same direction, and certain other indications. The velocity of the uplift of the mountains during the Neogene-Quaternary Age was very great. V. M. Sinitsyn gives indices for the velocity of uplift in the Himalayas and Kunlun over the postglacial age (about 10,000 years) at an average of 13-14 cm. per year, and points out that even the plains where the movement amplitude is minimal, uplifted over this period by scores of meters.

In the eastern half of China, with the exception of the islands, the recent movements were less intensive, however, here there developed differential shifts, frequently very significant, although the amplitude of the latter was incomparably less than in the west. As a result of these movements there was formed a relief of medium-altitude mountains separated by plain areas. The latter lay both on the site of ancient stable land masses and within the newly formed impressions. The rivers of Eastern China, as the Chinese geologists propose, by the end of the Neogene had already cut broad valleys as is substantiated by the Lower Pliocene fauna (Prosiphneus and Hipparion richthofeni) characteristic for the red clays which compose the high terrace on the Hwang Ho River. According to V. G. Lebedev, in the Neogene the Hwang Ho had virtually the same configuration as at present, and skirted the Ordos over a chain of numerous depressions (V. G. Lebedev, 1961).

The eastern border of China underwent at the same time a great subsidence which was the cause of the formation of extensive depressions here and active sedimentation continued which had begun as early as the Cretaceous. The insular part of China maintained the properties of a geosyncline. The folding here occurred chiefly in the Pliocene Age, but it was not accompanied by a general regression of the sea and evidently was not accompanied by a loss of the geosynclinal properties. The marginal seas of Eastern Asia, as is supposed by N. M. Strakhov and other geologists, are an example of a modern and still living geosyncline.

Evidently the border seas of Asia such as the Sea of Japan, the Yellow Sea, the East China and South China seas date to the Neogene-Quaternary Age as did the framing of the recent contour of the dry land in Eastern China. According to the data of G. U. Lindberg (1946), the relief of the bottom of the border seas of Eastern Asia with its system of underwater valleys with divides between them and also the identicalness in the specific composition of the freshwater fish fauna inhabiting the present rivers of China, Korea and Japan make it possible to suppose the continental origin of the relief for the bottom of the Yellow and East China seas. Evidently the designated seas were formed in the period when in the neighboring geosynclinal zone there occurred sharp tectonic movements which led to the subsiding of the nearby platform territories and caused the occurrence of transgressions. Very intensive were the recent movements on the Island of Taiwan, and as a result of this in this period a larger portion of the island was changed into high mountains.

The types of deformations caused by the movements in recent times within the various structural-orographic units of China have differed--arch, monoclinal, broken, folded, and this in turn has also played a great role in the formation of the relief, having caused a number of its local features. Thus, for example, for the northern part of the Chinese Platform composed of dense metamorphic rock, there are characteristic rupture dislocations which are clearly expressed in the modern relief in the form of horsts, grabens and faults. In the southern portion of the platform composed of soft sedimentary rock, the rupture dislocations are expressed more weakly, and here are typical anticlinal and synclinal structures.

Judging from the varying relief of the deposits in the western and eastern parts of China and the organic remains contained in them, it can be felt that in the Upper Tertiary Age the differentiation of the climate which was noted in the Paleogene in line with the alpine tectogenesis continued to grow. Thus, in the Central Asian part of China a further change in the climate continued towards an increase in aridity, and at the same time it grew cooler. At the same time, in Eastern China the climate was significantly warmer and more moist.

Moreover, the differentiation of climatic conditions in the various areas of China increased even more in line with the intensifying contrast to the relief and this brought about a significant diversity of landscapes. The particular features of the latter were now caused not only by the provincial differences in the territory of China, but also by the vertical zonality in the mountains.

During the Quaternary Age the mountains of China were subjected to glaciation in the process of the continuing uplifting and in line with the general cooling in the world's climate. Judging from the distribution and the character of the glacial relief forms, the ancient glaciation was not very intense on this territory, although it covered a significantly greater area than at present. Chinese researchers have noticed places of ancient glaciation even in the relatively low mountains of Eastern China where present glaciation is absent.

At present, the data on ancient glaciation over the territory of China are still very incomplete, and therefore a whole series of questions related to this problem up to now remains open. A certain idea on the scope of ancient glaciation and its subsequent changes can be obtained, having compared data on the distribution of ancient glaciation reliefs with the data on present glaciation over this territory, since the latter is a continuation of Quaternary glaciation.

At present in Inner Asia, glaciation covers only the highest mountains such as the Karakorum, the Himalayas, Kunlun, Eastern Tien Shan, the Nanshan, the mountains of Tibet and the Mongolian Altai. The dimensions of the glaciation generally are not great and certainly do not correspond to the enormous altitude of the mountains. The reduction in the areas covered by internal snow and ice has occurred, on the one hand, from south to north which has been due to the reduction in the absolute altitudes of the mountains, and on the other, from west to east, i.e., towards the interior parts of Central Asia which has been caused by their greater aridness. In line with the latter, and this is very characteristic, among the highest mountains in the given territory the least degree of glaciation is found in the Kunlun and in the interior ranges of the Tibetan Uplands. Here, with the exception of the extreme western parts of the Kunlun and Eastern Tibet (the Kam area) which to a certain degree were subjected to oceanic influences, the glaciers lie at very great altitudes, almost nowhere do they descend below 5,000 meters above sea level.

During the glacial age the picture obviously was somewhat different. Proceeding from the presently existing data, it may be supposed that the heaviest glaciation was found at that time, if one can speak about the mountain systems as a whole, in the Mongolian Altai, the mountains of Border Dzungaria, the Tien Shan, where traces of ancient glacial relief are noted everywhere and at rather low hypsometric levels (down to 1, 500-2, 000 meters, and in places even down to 1, 000 meters above sea level). In the mountains lying further to the south such as the Kunlun and the interior ranges of the Tibetan Uplands, the degree of glaciation was evidently significantly less; the majority of researchers working in these regions feel that the ancient glacial relief was encountered almost nowhere here below altitudes of 3, 000-4, 000 meters.

This was mentioned by V. A. Obruchev who felt that in the era of maximal glaciation the greatest degree of glaciation was to be found for the mountains in the northern part of Central Asia, the Mongolian Altai (and more precisely the western portion of it), the mountains of the Hangkai, Hengt'ai, and Border Dzungaria where the firn fields and glaciers occupied large areas and were of a Scandinavian type. In the Eastern Tien Shan there were also enormous glaciers, in places of the Scandinavian type, and in other areas of the alpine type. In the southern belt of mountains in Central Asia, the Kunlun, Altyntag and Nanshan, glaciation also significantly exceeded the present, but the glaciers, with rare exceptions, belonged to the alpine type (V. A. Obruchev, 1951).

In terms of the dimensions of the ancient glaciation in the various mountain systems of the western half of China, as in terms of the number of glaciations, the opinions of the researchers working there split, and sometimes very significantly.

Thus, for example, on the question of ancient glaciation in the Kunlun, K. I. Bogdanovich (1892) and E. Norin (1941) have adhered to sharply differing points of view. Bogdanovich felt that ancient glaciations differed little from the present; the second researcher, on the contrary, supposed that ancient glaciation was so thick that the glaciers descended along the valleys even into the upland plains. Later researchers--N. A. Belyayevskiy (1948) and V. M. Sinitsyn (1959) agreeing with him--also felt that the dimensions of the ancient glaciers were significantly greater than

at present, but the data which they give do not substantiate
the conclusions of Norin since they draw the lower boundary
of glaciers up on the mountains at altitudes of 3, 300-4, 000
meters in the Western Kunlun and 4, 200 meters in the Eastern (Mount Ulugmuztag). E. M. Murzayev (1961) proposes
that although ancient glaciation in the Kunlun encompassed a
greater area than at present, nevertheless it was relatively
small due to the profound aridness of the mountains.

The opinions on ancient glaciation in Tibet also differ.
As B. V. Yusov recalls (1958), Sven Hedin, F. K. Ward and
Ye. V. Kozlov felt that glaciation in Tibet was not solid and
appeared only in its highest mountain chains, without covering the upland plains. At the same time, Ku Shen-hsiu (1955)
and also V. M. Sinitsyn (1959, 1961) wrote about the significant scale of glaciation in the Tibetan Uplands, where traces
of activity of ancient glaciers can be observed throughout.
According to the computations of V. M. Sinitsyn, the ancient
glaciers should have descended here down to 4, 400-4, 300
meters above sea level, and on the basis of this the given
researcher supposes that in the Early Quaternary Period the
Tibetan Uplands were virtually totally covered with snow and
ice. However, the thickness of this ice sheet was relatively
thin, and it was probably little mobile, since the pre-Ice Age
relief was little changed by glacial processes and the dimensions of the moraines were small. As the glaciers re-
treated, in the intermontane depressions which were freed
of ice, there arose extensive morainic aprons with enormous
lakes that gradually dried up with the passage of time.

Nor is there a single opinion on the number of glaciations in the Mongolian Altai. Thus, V. V. Sapozhnikov
(1911) proposed a double glaciation of these mountains, I. G.
Grane (1916) a fourfold, A. Kh. Ivanov (1949) a threefold
which is also adhered to by E M. Murzayev (1952). At the
same time, all of the researchers noted the greatest dimensions in the first glaciation which, in their opinion, had a
semimantle character and covered almost the entire Mongolian Altai. Subsequent glaciations were related to the
alpine type and confined only to the upper parts of the mountains. E. M. Murzayev and after him N. T. Kuznetsov
(1955) also pointed out that the two subsequent glaciations
within this mountain system evidently were not ubiquitous,

or more precisely, if they existed in the western part of the mountains, they could have scarcely occurred in the east. The proof of this was felt to be by the designated researchers the very weak traces (and in places the complete absence) of the second and particularly the third glaciation in the eastern part of the Mongolian Altai, although here under the conditions of a desert climate they should have lasted particularly well.

In the Tien Shan, according to B. A. Fedorovich and Yang T'inghsien (1961), there were four types of glaciation-- glaciation of the mountain masses, glaciation of the alpine type, mantle glaciation of the ranges and icecaps of the intra-montane depressions. The first three types occur at present and the fourth type was inherent to the Eastern Tien Shan only in the era of preceding glaciations. The designated researchers have come to the conclusion that in the Quaternary Age in the Eastern Tien Shan four glaciations occurred. The first two were maximal and their moraines emerged on the submontane plains, and the last two were much weaker-- traces of them can be found in the valleys high in the mountains.

Thus, there can be no doubt that in the Quaternary Age the mountains in the western part of China were covered with glaciation, but the degree of their glaciation was not the same. Particularly great dimensions are to be found in the ancient glaciation of the highest mountains of Asia--the Kunlun, Nanshan and Tibetan Uplands--but these in no way corresponded to the enormous altitude of the mountains, nor do the scales of present glaciation correspond to it. As has been correctly noted by E. M. Murzayev (1961), this can serve as proof that in the Ice Age arid conditions reigned here. The predominant type of glacier at that time was obviously the valley glacier.

In the eastern half of China, as has already been noted, present glaciation is absent, and the question of ancient glaciation on this territory for a long time has been under dispute. Certain foreign scientists (for example, Barbour and Deji) categorically denied the possibility of ancient glaciation on the low mountains in the eastern part of the nation, at the same time that Chinese researchers (Li Ssu-kuang,

Li Ch'en-san, Kao Yung-yuan and others) proved the presence of numerous traces of ancient glaciation here.

We might recall that the first traces of ancient glaciation were discovered by Li Ssu-kuang in 1933 in the mountains of the interfluve of the Yangtze and Ch'ient'angkiang at an altitude of about 1,500 meters, where he discovered a glacial relief represented by forms of glacial erosion and accumulation (Li Ssu-kuang, 1952). With further research, traces of ancient glaciation were found by Chinese scientists in many other regions of Eastern China. Thus, for example, ancient glacial reliefs have been noted for the Kweichow Mountains at an altitude of about 2,000 meters (Lee, 1947), in the western and eastern portions of the Tapashan Mountains at an altitude of 2,000 meters and lower (Li Ch'en-san and Kao Yung-yuan, 1942; Ko Lin-chih, 1943), in the Greater Khingan (Yen Ch'in-shang, 1950), in the mountains of the Yenshan (Chang Chung-yin, et al., 1951), in the maritime portion of Southeastern China (Chang Jen-chun, 1951), in the mountains of the T'aipaishan (Chang Pao-sheng, 1958), and in other areas. Traces of ancient glaciation are also well expressed in the mountains of Taiwan, where in the Chungyangshan Range at altitudes of more than 2,000 meters there are numerous glacial relief forms of the sink type (Li Ch'en-san, 1954).

On the question of the number of glaciations on this territory, as in the western parts of China, the opinions of the researchers differ. Thus, for the region of the Lower Yangtze and the Tapashan Mountains, they have supposed three glaciations: for the Greater Khingan two, for the Yangtze Basin four in mountains more than 1,200 meters high, and three in mountainous localities lying lower.

Thus, the question of the number of glaciations in China and their precise dating up to now has not been solved. One might naturally assume that in the mountains of various localities of China which differ sharply in terms of the absolute altitude and are located in unique climatic conditions, the number of glaciations or stages of one glaciation and their intensity differ. The solution to these questions requires additional factual information.

During the period that the glaciers thawed, when the runoff of the thawed glacier water was abundant there occurred a certain change in the climate towards greater wetness, there was a sharp increase in the inundation of the territory of China. Lakes which existed previously significantly increased in dimensions; moreover, on the plains and in the mountains there developed a number of new lakes and the river network developed rapidly.

A particularly large number of big lakes lay at that time within the limits of the intermontane depressions in the Central Asian part of China, the Tarim, Dzungar, Tsaidam and other basins, and this has made it possible for researchers working there to speak about a lacustrine stage in the Quaternary history of Central Asia (N. T. Kuznetsov, E. M. Murzayev, 1962). In contrast to the eastern portion of China where the rivers flooded and drained into the ocean, the territory of Central Asia, as at present, did not have internal drainage and was characterized by the presence of a number of large undrained basins. The rivers flowing down from the mountains ended in enclosed bodies of water. Proof of a more abundant inundation than at present for these territories is found in the numerous presently dry river beds, the remains of ancient banks and terraces and in lacustrine deposits which lie at various altitudes far from present bodies of water. Virtually all researchers who have visited Central Asia have noted these particular features (see the work of N. M. Przheval'skiy, M. V. Pevtsov, Sven Hedin, E. M. Murzayev, N. A. Belyayevskiy, V. M. Sinitsyn, Ye. I. Selivanov, and others).

However, it would be mistaken to suppose that the existence of pluvial periods on the territory of Central Asia proves the replacing of former arid conditions with humid ones. On the contrary, as is correctly pointed out by N. T. Kuznetsov and E. M. Murzayev (1962) and even was previously pointed out for Central Asia by I. P. Gerasimov (1937), although during glaciation and the subsequent thawing of the glaciers the climatic situation was somewhat different, nevertheless it remained arid although more moist. At present, many researchers are inclined to feel that during the Pliocene-Quaternary Age on this territory there occurred an alteration of more moist periods, with glaciation in the mountains and the development of lakes on the plains,

with drier periods, when the areas of the lakes were greatly
reduced and enormous sandy deserts were formed. For the
western part of Central Asia, and more precisely for the
Tarim Depression, there has been an attempt to date these
periods. Thus, by geographic and geological research in
recent years carried out by Sino-Soviet expeditions, it has
been established that the more moist climate was confined
here to the Upper Pliocene, Lower Quaternary and Middle
Quaternary times (Ye. I. Selivanov, 1959b).

Thus, the numerous data show that in the Quaternary
Age the Central Asiatic part of China had a well-developed
lacustrine-fluvial network, and the areas of the lakes were
incomparably greater than at present, and the levels were
significantly higher. N. T. Kuznetsov and E. M. Murzayev
have noted that, regardless of the great dimensions of the
lakes, they were not deep and the plain lakes usually were
not more than 20-30 meters deep, and only as an exception
exceeded 100 meters. The designated researchers have
pointed out that virtually all of the large bodies of water
were confined to the tectonic depressions, although there
were those which occupied the broad river valleys. Here
many of the plain lakes of Central Asia occupied the same
depressions as in the Tertiary, i.e., to a significant degree
they were inherited. The mountain lakes usually had either
a glacial or caving origin, and consequently they developed
later, usually in the Quaternary time. Subsequently the
majority of the mountain lakes, due to the intensified erosion activity of the rivers, were emptied. On the plains,
conversely, many ancient bodies of water exist even now
(Lobnor, Ebi-Nur, Ikhekak, etc.), although their dimensions have been greatly reduced, and the depths have dropped
even more.

N. T. Kuznetsov and E. M. Murzayev suppose that
the dying-out of the ancient lakes in Central Asia has been
due to the termination of the Ice Age and to the establishing
of a climatic regime close to the modern, but this, however,
in their opinion, does not exclude in addition the influence of
the cyclical and episodic changes in the precipitation regime.
The latter has been clearly established in the frequent fluctuations of the shore lines of the ancient lakes.

Observations have established that the greatest amount of Quaternary lakes, and the particularly large ones, was confined to the western part of Central Asia, and this can be explained chiefly by the orographic features of this territory. As has already been mentioned, at that time, as at present, here were located the largest mountain systems; numerous rivers flowed off them and these fed the lakes lying in the submontane plains.

In the eastern part of China, under the conditions of a humid climate, the lakes did not last for long and they, as a rule, disappeared, either being emptied by the rivers or being filled up with detritus. Thus, for example, at present along the middle course of the Hwang Ho one will widely find relatively small flat plains composed of a thick bed of Neogene and Quaternary lacustrine-alluvial deposits. On the basis of this it has been established that in the Miocene-Pliocene here was located a chain of depressions filled with flowing lakes. In the Early Quaternary Age, in line with the intensification in tectonic activity, the processes of deep erosion revived and this led to an intensified incutting of the rivers and to the formation of gorges such as the Sanmenhsia, etc., and subsequently to the emptying of the lakes (V. G. Lebedev, 1961).

Analogous data exist for the river basins of Northeastern China. The existing materials make it possible to suppose that the Neogene-Quaternary lakes in Eastern China were evidently significantly smaller than the Central Asiatic, and the number of them was not nearly as great as there.

In the pluvial phases of the Quaternary Period, when erosion activity of the rivers intensified sharply in the mountains, within the intermontane and submontane depressions there was intensive sedimentation of the friable material and extensive aggradation plans were formed. As has been noted, this process of the accumulation of thick chiefly alluvial beds was further intensified due to the activization of tectonic movements in the Pliocene-Quaternary Age which in various areas of the territory of China had differing force and intensity.

Above it was pointed out that the maritime parts of
China at this time experienced an absolute subsidence; the
large plains in the western part of China although they were
uplifted, were in the speed of their uplift so behind the
speed in the uplift of the surrounding mountains that they
have been bordered by deep depressions.

As a result within China there have developed those
extensive alluvial plains as the Tarim, Dzungar, North
China, Northeastern, etc., which at present are extremely
characteristic relief elements of this land.

The sharp intensification in the orographic contrasts
which occurred in the Pliocene-Quaternary Age naturally
should have influenced the increase in the aridness of the
climate in Central Asia, the isolation of which from the
oceanic influence was increased by the uplifting of the surrounding mountains. At the same time, the climate of the
eastern maritime part of the land became more humid. All
of this, of course, brought about significant changes both in
the character of the exogenic relief-forming processes and
in the entire appearance of the landscapes.

Thus, it was precisely in the last period in the geological history that there occurred that very sharp division of
the territory of China into two basic major parts: the western elevated arid part and the eastern lower humid part
which is so characteristic for the modern period.

Above it was pointed out that in the northwestern part
of China there lie thick beds of loess deposits. In general,
the loess and chiefly loess-like deposits are found rather
widely in China, being encountered over an extensive area
from Inner Mongolia in the north to the southern slopes of
the Ch'inling Range in the south and from the seacoast in
the east to the foothills of the Kunlun in the west. They are
encountered in depressions, high plains and even in mountains, filling in the intermontane valleys and synclines. However, the loess deposits have gained particular development
in the middle course of the Hwang Ho in the provinces of
Kansu, Shansi, Shensi and Honan.

The Chinese loess has long attracted the attention of
researchers. Even at the end of the last century it was

studied by F. Richthofen (Richthofen, 1877 and 1882) and
Pumpelli (Pumpelli, 1879) and a very detailed study was
made by V. A. Obruchev (1900, 1951a, e, 1959), and many
foreign scientists working in China have written about it
(Loczy, 1893; Willis, 1907; Tafel, 1914; Anderson, 1923,
and others); subsequently a detailed study was made by Chinese researchers (Ma Yung-chih, 1944; Li Ssu-kuang, 1952;
Huang Ping-wei, 1954). The hypotheses on the origin of
these specific deposits, as is known, are extremely diverse
and, regardless of the rather numerous research, there is
still no unanimous viewpoint on the origin of the loess, even
among the Chinese.

In recent years, in China, they have begun a special
study on the loess deposits and this has made it possible to
collect a large amount of new factual data related to this
problem. The materials of these studies have been brought
together in a special collection and published in Trudy
komissii po izucheniyu chetvertichnogo perioda (Transactions of the Commission to Study the Quaternary Period,
1959).

As has already been noted, research has established
that the deposits of a loess character were noted in China
beginning with the Lower Pliocene. The red clays with Pliocene fauna underlie red loams ("red loess") with intercalations of buried soils and Lower Quaternary fauna (the
Sanmen suite) above which lies the "yellow loess" with
fauna of the Middle and Upper Quaternary Age (the Huangt'u
suite). It is rather difficult to distinguish the loess-like
deposits of the different ages from one another (if they do
not lie all together), and this is possibly why there is such
a diversity in the ideas of scientists on the origin of the
loess.

A detailed study of such a complex question as the origin of the Chinese loess is not a task for the present work.
A whole series of special articles has been devoted to this
question, and here we will merely briefly list the main existing hypotheses.

One of the first researchers of the Chinese loess was
F. Richthofen and he advanced the proposal that loess is
produced from the weathering of rock from the undrained

areas with a dry climate. He supposed that the loess was
formed in Central Asia where the fine dusty material was
carried down the slopes of the mountains by the wind and the
water and accumulated in situ in the intermontane steppe depressions. Thus, according to the theory of Richthofen, the
loess was formed in situ by a water-aeolian means.

Later V. A. Obruchev rejected the viewpoint of Richthofen concerning the means for the accumulation of loess
beds, and created his famous aeolian hypothesis on the origin
of the Chinese loess. This scientist felt that the dust particles which were formed by the weathering and winnowing of
the Central Asiatic deserts were not deposited here (since
he did not discover depressions filled with loess in Central
Asia), but rather carried by the wind over great distances
and deposited along the edges of the deserts beneath the
protection of the steppe vegetation. Here the beds of this
dust gradually grew, they were held down by the rain and due
to the soil-forming processes were changed into loess. Such
loess having an exclusively aeolian origin (i.e., formed from
the dust of the desert), was called by V. A. Obruchev typical or primary loess, in contradistinction to the secondary
loess, or more precisely, the loess-like rock which has a
different origin and has received some (but not all) properties of the loess in line with the processes of soil formation
(V. A. Obruchev, 1951). V. A. Obruchev felt the middle
of the Ice Age to be the time of the most intensive loess formation as this age was marked by a dry climate and had an
anticyclonic wind regime.

The aeolian hypothesis of V. A. Obruchev, although
frequently in a significantly altered form, at one time was
widely supported by a number of European and Chinese
scientists. At present, as has been correctly noted by V.N.
Pavlinov (1959), the aeolian hypothesis on the origin of the
Chinese loess (with the different variations), it would seem,
is most widely accepted in China. It is defended by such
scientists as Yang Chung-chien, Sun Meng-ling (1959) and
certain other Chinese researchers, and of the Soviet spe-
cialists studying the Chinese loess, by A. S. Kes' (1959a)
and V. G. Lebedev.

At the same time, at present, there are other view-
points on the formation of the Chinese loess. Thus for

example, I. P. Gerasimov who has visited the Loess Province
of Northern China, feels that the thick beds of loess deposits
in China are a complex of sediments of differing genesis,
chiefly water, which have accumulated in the intermontane
depressions and river valleys by the carrying-off of material
from surrounding elevations by surface waters. This researcher does not also deny a certain participation of sedimentation of aeolian material brought here from Central Asia.
However, I. P. Gerasimov stresses that these genetically
different deposits acquire typical loess properties only under
the influence of the weathering and soil formation processes
which thus have a leading role in the formation of the Chinese
loess, i. e., he supports the soil or eluvial hypothesis advanced by L. S. Berg (I. P. Gerasimov, 1955). V. N. Pavlinov (1959) has advanced a viewpoint close to this.

Yang Chung-chien in the above cited article "The Loess
of China" (1957) has compared the views of various scientists
on the classification and origin of the most important deposits
of the Lower Cenozoic. As a result he has come to the conclusion that one cannot speak about the properties and origin
of loess, without having differentiated the very concept of
"loess." He writes: "If we call the red loess-like deposits
loess, then no one would deny that a large portion of these deposits is formed in situ by water. But if we speak about the
Malan loess, i. e., about loess in the narrow sense of the
word, then in this case only the gravel and sands at its base
have a water origin" (Yang Chung-chien, 1957, page 66). In
the opinion of the author, the Malan loess (yellow loess)
evidently was formed by wind to a significant degree.

Thus, we see that although up to now rather a large
amount of factual data has been accumulated on the loess of
China, the question of the origin of loess and chiefly the question on the ways the loess beds have accumulated in China remain disputed and require additional research.

RECENT RELIEF-FORMING PROCESSES

The recent soil-forming processes, like the processes
of the past, within China are marked by a great diversity and
yet have their own specific features. Their inherited features from the recent processes of the Neogene and Quaternary Age differ. This inheritance can be seen most clearly

in the manifestation of endogenic processes, in particular,
in the features of the tectonic movements and volcanic phenomena. The modern tectonic movements, like the movements of the recent time, have a differential character and
on the whole have the same direction. The inner areas have
experienced a general uplift, and the maritime areas a general subsidence which is clear from a number of the geological and geomorphological features. Thus, the uplift process has been clearly established in the features of the long
profile rivers, beginning with the antecedent areas, in the
intense incutting of the rivers, in the beheading phenomena,
the sharp turns and bends. The latter is particularly characteristic for the rivers in Southwest China where we know
a number of major beheadings, for example, the beheadings
of the Shihku in the upper reaches of the Yangtze.

        V. G. Lebedev (1959b), in using materials of Chinese
researchers, computed that the subsidence rate of the North
China Depression over the Quaternary Age was not less than
1 mm. per year. According to Belousov (1956), the area of
this region of downwarping gradually increased due to the in-
volvement of new areas in the subsidence. Thus, in particular, areas of recent subsidences are the lacustrine plains
lying in the middle reaches of the Yangtze. According to the
observations of a number of researchers (V. V. Belousov,
V. M. Sinitsyn, V. G. Lebedev and others), the subsidence
process at present is not limited to merely the plain territories, but also covers the mountainous part of Southeastern
China. This is clear both from the features of the mountain
relief and from the character of the seacoasts. The rate of
the tectonic movements, and also the character of their manifestation within the smaller regions were not and at present
are not constant.

        The character of the modern tectonic movements in
China is studied best of all for the maritime areas of the
land where they have established concrete areas of uplifts
and subsidences of the coast. The character of the coasts
in China is heterogeneous. The sharpest difference is noted
between the coasts of the East China and the South China
seas, on the one hand, and the coast of the Yellow Sea, on
the other. The coasts of the East China and South China
seas are predominantly rocky, precipitous and very rugged
with numerous bays, gulfs, inundated river mouths,

peninsulas and islands, and this clearly shows the general
subsidence of the dry land. Long ago, as early as the research done by Richthofen in 1868-72, these shores were
considered as subsiding. The shore of the Yellow Sea, on
the contrary, over the larger part is sandy, even, slightly
broken up and at first glance looks like an uplifting marine
bottom. Richthofen made such a mistake, considering it
among the type of uplifting shores. However, subsequently
it was shown that this even sandy shore with relatively simple reliefs was formed as a result of the aggradation activity of the Hwang Ho and Yangtze rivers, and also is related
to the subsidence shores. This can be seen from a whole
series of features, and, in particular, the presence of littoral deposits buried at a significant depth in a number of
places of the coast. These littoral deposits composed of
sands and clays containing remains of freshwater mollusks
were discovered by drilling in the region of T'ienchin at a
depth of almost 155 meters below the marine deposits located on the surface (Li Ssu-kuang, 1952).

At the same time, in a number of areas of the coast,
there have also been uplifts. The proof of the uplifting in
certain areas of the coast of the East China and South China
seas is the presence among the incised banks with filled
river mouths of narrow and long coastal plains composed of
marine deposits from 3 to 20 km. wide and marked by an
exceptionally even and slightly inclined surface towards the
sea; the rock benches and aggradation terraces predominantly up to 20 meters high above sea level and in places
40-50 meters; levelled coral islands at approximately the
same heights in places connected to the shore by uplifted
shoals, etc.

Research on the deposits of the aggradation terraces
discovered in the mouths of the Ch'ient'angkiang, Minkiang,
Chukiang (Pearl River) and other rivers has established that
the uplifting of these portions of the coast occurred evidently
in the Upper Pliocene, since the gravel of these terraces
corresponds to the "Hsiashu clays" of the Upper Pliocene
Age (Ch'en Ko-ta, 1950). The mouths of the listed rivers
are drowned valleys and this shows the previous subsidence
of these portions of the coast while now these are elevated
terraces.

The traces of the uplifts along the shore of the Yellow Sea can be noted chiefly within the limits of the Shantung and Liaotung peninsulas where they have found rock benches and aggradation marine terraces, sandy coastal plains sloping gently to the sea which are clearly an uplifted shoal, fluvial terraces cut by narrow deep valleys of modern streams, islands articulated with the continent, etc. On the basis of this Chinese scientists suppose that the shore line of the Liaotung and Shantung peninsulas which was formed as a result of the subsidence of dry land at present is undergoing an uplift. It should be noted that Liu Ko-ch'eng feels that in general the larger portion of the coast along the continental part of China is basically uplifting slowly.

On the Island of Taiwan, judging from the geomorphological data, there has been a gradual uplift along the western coast of the island and a subsidence along the fault line of its eastern coast (Ch'en Ko-ta, 1950, and others). Here if one considers that on the slopes of the Tat'ungshan Volcano which lies in the northern part of the island and is composed of Upper Tertiary lava there is a series of abrasion surfaces, the highest reaching 800 meters above sea level, it may be considered that the rate of uplift of Taiwan after the formation of the volcano, i.e., during the Quaternary Period, was 800 meters.

Evidence of recent tectonic activity in China exists in the frequent earthquakes and the manifestations of volcanic activity. According to seismic data, the predominant number of earthquake epicenters is confined to the mountains of the western half of China and to the Island of Taiwan. In the eastern half of continental China there are few epicenters. There are virtually none within the Tarim, Dzungar and Tsaidam depressions, and also on the plains of the Chinese portion of the Gobi and the northeast. Seismologists have noted that in the predominant majority of cases it turns out that the areas of intensive differential movements are areas of high seismic activity (G. P. Gorshkov, 1960). Analysis of the seismic zoning map for China given in the work of G. P. Gorshkov indicates that the highest seismic activeness (more than 8 points) has been noted in the mountainous regions of Inner Asia, the Island of Taiwan, and also certain areas of the Ch'inling, Yinshan, Shantung, and the mountains of Shansi and Shensi provinces. Here recent and modern

tectonic movements were particularly strong and had a differential character. Here the highest seismic activity where
earthquakes reach and exceed 9 points is found in the Himalayas, the Karakorum, the Kantissushan, the Kunlun, the
Eastern Tien Shan and the Island of Taiwan; within the limits
of them the juvenile tectonic movements reach extreme intensity. Within the same mountain systems one will also encounter areas which are seismically less active (6-7 points),
for example, the alpine plains of the Changtan, the Tsaidam
Kokonor (Tsinghai); tectonic movements here were not differentiated although they had a great intensity. Much weaker
seismic activity is noted in the eastern half of China which,
with the exception of individual areas, is related to the 5-6
point zone. The virtually complete absence of local earthquake foci is characteristic, as has been noted, of the northeast plain and the Gobi Plain; on the map of G. P. Gorshkov
these areas are considered in the 4-point zone.

The volcanic phenomena of recent times, including the
modern ones, which, as we have noted, are confined, as a
rule, to the same regions, are known in a number of areas
of China. They have been best studied in the northeast
where one can observe well-preserved volcanic reliefs. The
last established eruptions of the volcanos occurred here in
the 16th and 18th centuries. Thus, in 1597-1702 there was
an eruption of the Pait'oushan Volcano which lay, as has
been noted, on the Chinese-Korean border in the mountains
of the Ch'angpaishan (Jen Mei-e, 1953). Mount Pait'oushan
has the form of a cone and is composed predominantly of
andesite. In 1720-21 the volcanos in the northern part of
Manchuria erupted, in the region of the town of Mergen. The
volcanic reliefs here are extremely diverse and are represented by individual volcanic peaks of differing structure and
outline, by volcanic groups and basalt plateaus and plains.
The volcanic cones lie basically linearly and this is clearly
related to the direction of the tectonic dislocations.

Chinese researchers have divided the volcanos into
five types: volcanos in the form of truncated cone with an
open crater at the top; volcanos with a horseshoe top formed
as a result of protracted erosion; shield volcanos with very
gentle slopes and a well-preserved vent funnel; rock piles
either in the shape of a pyramid or in the form of several
connected mud volcanos (for the volcanos of this type the

crater is poorly shown); necks or sharp-pointed peaks. Researchers have come to the conclusion that the eruptions
here were of a differing type: strong eruptions with explo-
sions when volcanic ash and slag were thrown up; peaceful
when basalt lava was discharged, and mixed when initially
there was an explosion and then lava poured out which melted
the walls of the crater. The majority of the volcanos in this
area belong to the latter type (Chang Wen-t'ang, 1954).

In the Chinese portion of the Lesser Khingan and in the
east of the Greater Khingan, large territories have been covered by basalt lava. Studies of this basalt mantle and its
stratigraphic position have made it possible for Chinese researchers to establish the more or less precise time the
volcanos were active. The latter occurred evidently subsequent to the uplift of the Lesser Khingan which occurred at
the end of the Tertiary and the beginning of the Quaternary
Period and continued up to the recent past. The fact that
these volcanos erupted in the 18th century shows processes
of tectonic pressures continuing even now in this area.

The volcanic reliefs of recent eruptions are also
widely found within Inner Mongolia. Here in the area of Dar-
igangi hundreds of conical volcanos have remained, and in
places one can clearly see streams of block lava still un-
touched by the soil formation processes.

According to Chinese statements recently they have
discovered an active volcano in the western part of China in
the Kunlun Mountains (V. M. Sinitsyn, 1954). This discovery is undoubtedly of great interest since up to now active
volcanos in the central areas of the continents have been
virtually unknown. It should be remembered that traces of
recent volcanic activity, in the form of fresh volcanic cra-
ters, and juvenile flows of eruptions have been noticed in the
Kunlun by earlier researchers. The numerous volcanic reliefs show that Northern Tibet and the central portion of the
Kunlun even in the postglacial age were areas of active volcanic activity. At present here there are numerous geysers
and thermal springs; in addition, as has already been noted,
the area of Tibet and, in particular, the area of Sino-
Tibetan mountains, has been subject to strong earthquakes.
The latter shows the tectonic activeness of this area.

There are also numerous volcanic reliefs on the Island
of Taiwan, particularly in the northern part. The volcanos
of Taiwan are an extension of the chain of volcanos from the
Japanese islands. They have been quiet for many years, but
the presence of hot springs and active mud volcanos shows a
potential volcanic activeness in this territory. Basalt lava
has also covered the northern part of Hainan Island, a number of sections of the Hanchouwan Peninsula and the southern coast, and it forms the Pescadores Islands.

From the above-given data it follows that the earthquakes, volcanism and consequently also the recent and modern high-intensity movements have appeared in a number of
regions of China, but in general rather independently of the
age of the tectonic structures. This is also pointed to by a
number of geomorphological features, and the clearest expression is the distribution of the high-mountain relief. The
recent and in part the modern movements here covered both
the ancient crystalline rock masses and the folded zones of
various ages--Caledonian, Hercynian, Yenshan and particularly the Himalayas. G. P. Gorshkov feels that this is a
basic feature of neotectonics in China and gives a very in-
structive scheme on the relationships between the ancient
folded zones and the areas for the appearance of modern tectonic movements.

The analysis of the entire complex of geological and
geomorphological data has made it possible for us to divide
the territory of China into the following major areas, with a
differing direction and intensity of recent movements: I--the
area of predominant intensive uplifts; II--the area of predominant less-intensive uplifts; III--the area of predominant
weak uplifts; Iv--the area of predominant subsidences. Within the designated areas, in turn, one can establish areas with
a differing character caused by the recent movements. Thus,
in the uplift area we have established the following sections:
differentiated movements, slightly differentiated movements,
relative subsidences and absolute subsidences. In the subsidence area, there are the following sections: the greatest
subsidences, weak subsidences, weak uplifts with a non-
differentiated character in the movements and uplifts with a
differentiated character of the movements.

The area of the most intense recent uplifts includes
the Chinese slopes of the Himalayas and the Karakorum, the
mountain systems of Tibet, the Kunlun, a significant portion
of the Nanshan, the western and in places the eastern portion of the Eastern Tien Shan, and also the mountains of
Taiwan over a larger area of which there have predominated
movements of a sharply differentiated character and a high-
mountain relief has been formed. However, rather good-
sized areas are also occupied here by sections where the recent movements, in possessing a positive sign and sufficient
intensity, have not been differentiated and this has led to the
formation of upland plains lying at a very high absolute altitude. Such are the upland plains of the Changtan, the Kul'tal
and other smaller ones.

The described area is abutted by the area of less intense uplifts which includes the entire Central Asiatic part
of China and the mountains bordering it of the Greater Khingan, the T'aihangshan, Ch'inling, the western part of the
Yunnan Uplands, and also the Eastern Manchurian Mountains. Here approximately level areas occupy territories of
rather intense but virtually undifferentiated movements and
territories with a differentiated character of the recent movements. In accordance with this, in the relief there predominate both plains lying at a high hypsometric level, and
medium-altitude and more rarely high mountains. Within
this area they have also noted subsidence sections which include the piedmont plains. The intensity of these subsidences differs. Thus, the greatest intensity of the subsidences
has been noted in the Yarkend, Kuchar, Manass, Suichow
and particularly the Turfan-Hami plains, and also the grabens of the Weiho and Fenho which are areas of absolute subsidences. At the same time, the subsidence rate of the other
areas, for example, the Hot'ao Plain, is much less or more
accurately, this is only a relative subsidence in terms of the
uplifting neighboring mountains.

The area of weak uplifts includes the mountains of the
eastern part of China--the Jehol, the Tapashan, the eastern
part of the Yunnan Uplands which in the modern relief are
basically low-mountain areas or more rarely medium-
mountain areas. The least differentiated movements are
noted in the Szechwan Depression where plains predominate

and the northern portion of the Greater Khingan and partially the territory of Kweichow Province which are high plateaus.

The subsidence area covers, as has already been mentioned, the border area of the continent including the San-kiang, Northeastern and North China plains, the plains of the middle and lower reaches of the Yangtze and other smaller plains, and, in addition, the mountains of Southeastern China. The latter must be particularly emphasized, since this is one of the characteristic and very basic features in the modern relief of China. At present a large portion of the plain territory lies at a very low hypsometric level, below 100 meters, being typical depressions. Against the background of this general subsidence, the piedmont areas of the plains, and also the divides of the Sungari-Liaoho rivers have experienced a weak uplift. Here the movements had a non-differentiated character, and in the relief there were formed plains with higher absolute altitudes--approximately 200 meters above sea level. The stronger uplifts, and chiefly those marked by a differentiated character of the movements, are typical for the Shantung and Liaotung peninsulas and also for the Huayenshan Mountains; in the relief low- and medium-altitude mountains predominate.

The mountains of the southeast which have undergone subsidence have very low absolute altitudes, averaging on the order of 600 meters above sea level, generally insignificant elevations of the watershed areas above the surface of the submontane plains and, what is particularly typical, thick beds of friable alluvial deposits covering the lower and frequently even the middle portions of the mountain slopes. Where the mountains extend into the sea, in many areas they drop steeply into the water, without any features of marine terraces.

Thus, the differing character of the recent tectonic movements, their rates and force have had an extremely great influence upon the formation of various structural forms in the modern relief of China and their distribution over the territory of the land. At the same time, the placement of the basic structural (orographic) units in the various climatic belts, their orientation in terms of the dominating air currents and also the absolute altitude of the locale play, as is known, a very great role in the appearance of the modern physical geographic and, in particular, climatic processes under the effect of which the exogenic relief is formed.

Above it was pointed out that in the modern relief of China one can clearly distinguish two basic parts: the western very high, where are concentrated all of the highest mountain systems of the land and also extensive greatly uplifted plains; and the eastern part which is less elevated, where medium and low-mountain reliefs alternate with major depressions. Such a sharp contrast in the relief of Western and Eastern China influences the great difference in the climate of these territories, as can be clearly traced in the character of the temperature regime and the degree of wetness.

The specifics of the relief and climate in the various parts of China naturally bring about a uniqueness in the hydrological conditions, the soil-vegetation cover and in general all the components of the physical geographic environment, including the exogenic relief-forming processes.

In order to gain a better idea of the particular features in the course of the exogenic processes on the territory of China which have transformed the endogenic relief, let us review step by step all of the basic stages in their development, i.e., the processes of weathering, denudation and accumulation.

The analysis of climatic materials, * and in particular, the data on the amplitude in the fluctuations of the average daily temperatures, the degree of cloudiness and the rarity of the atmosphere, the frequency of temperature changes over 0° and the distribution of the snow cover and its thickness will help to form a rather clear picture on the intensity of the processes in physical (thermal and frost) weathering on the territory of China.

---

*Here and below we have extensively used the work of Ch'eng Shih-hsun, 1959, 1961; Klimaticheskiy atlas Kitaya (A Climatic Atlas of China), 1953, and certain other Chinese sources.

The degree of intensity in thermal weathering observed during all seasons of the year and in all of the altitude belts of China rises from south to north and particularly from east to west, and also with an increase in the absolute altitude of the locality.

The processes of frost weathering have developed ubiquitously only in the western and northern regions of China. In many areas of China where there is no solid snow cover, the frost weathering is episodic only during the thawing of this thin layer of snow which, in falling rather frequently, lasts only several days or even hours.

As a whole the processes of physical weathering are marked by the greatest intensity under the conditions of the sharply continental arid climate of the deserts and semi-deserts of Central Asia and the high-mountain Tibetan Uplands. Here they play an important role in the formation of the relief, creating rock streams which cover extensive expanses of the mountains and plains. Physical weathering processes also occur in the mountains of Northeastern China, although the scale is completely incomparable with the western part of China. While there (the west) the intensity of these processes is such that they hold one of the leading places in the working of the exogenic relief in the northeast they play a secondary role.

On the contrary, the processes of biochemical weathering have developed most on the territory of Southeastern China, to the south of the Yangtze River, where temperatures year-round are positive and only during two or three months of the year does one note a lack of moisture. Particularly favorable conditions for the development of these processes occur evidently in a portion of the hill region, the mouth of the Ch'ient'angkiang River, the northeastern part of Taiwan and Hainan where a lack of wetness in general is not observed (Ying Tsung-chang, 1959). As a result here there has formed a laterite weathering crust which reaches 20 meters in thickness and in places even 60-70 meters (Shu Chun-ming, 1957).

In other regions, for example, in areas in the north and northeast of China, the processes of biochemical weathering can occur more or less actively only during the

two summer months, but on the predominant area of China,
and more precisely in the steppe, semidesert and desert
regions of the northern and western parts of China which are
characterized by a constant lack of moisture over the year,
these weathering processes have virtually no significance in
forming the relief.

Denudation and aggradation of weathering products in
the various parts of China have created very diverse complexes of exogenic landforms. Thus, in the east of the nation
one will find particularly widely landforms which were created by the erosion and aggradation activity of rivers; in the
Central Asiatic plains there are paleoalluvial and aeolian
landforms; in the Tibetan Uplands there are landforms
formed under the influence of plane denudation processes
and also nival and glacial. Of course, one should keep in
mind that aside from the exogenic processes which have created the listed landforms--and are the main ones--since in
individual areas of the nation they play a leading role, there
is, in addition, a whole series of factors which either weak-
en or strengthen the intensity of the leading processes and,
consequently, to one degree or another influence the formation of the present relief features. However, if we view the
nation as a whole, their role in itself is already secondary,
and therefore in this discussion we will not dwell upon them
further.

As has already been noticed, at present running water
has most actively influenced the working of the landforms
within the limits of Eastern China. According to the hydrological data, Chinese rivers here are basically fed by
surface waters, and underground waters have a subordinate
significance. Therefore, it is clear that the intensity of the
erosion processes to a significant degree depends upon the
amount of atmospheric precipitation and its distribution over
the seasons of the year. The average annual amount of atmospheric precipitation in Eastern China fluctuates from
400 mm. in the north to 2, 000 mm., and in places even more
(in the south). The river network is dense and developed,
and many rivers are very long and carry a great deal of water. All of this leads to the intensified working of the rivers
in the mountains and to the aggradation of alluvial deposits
in the depressions. However, although the processes of
river erosion and aggradation are active everywhere in

Eastern China, the intensity of them and the duration over
the year are not the same in the various sections of this extensive territory. This can be explained by various factors,
in particular, by the differing regime of the rivers, the altitude of the mountains, the character and force of the present
tectonic movements, the lithology of the eroded rock, etc.
In line with this the relief-forming significance for the activity of flowing water will differ in the various areas of Eastern China.

In terms of the character and the intensity of the erosion processes, the territory of Eastern China can be divided into two basic and rather sharply differing parts: the
northern which lies under conditions of moderate wetting and
the southern which is under conditions of increased wetting.
The boundary between them passes approximately along the
Ch'inling--Huayenshan line.

All the rivers in the northern portion of Eastern China,
with the exception of the rivers flowing to the south of the
Great China Plain are fed by snow and rain. Their regime
is almost everywhere characterized by two flooding periods:
the spring flooding connected to the thawing of the snow in
the mountains and ice on the rivers, and the summer-autumn
which is confined to the maximum rainfall (Shih Ch'eng-hsi,
1959). At this time there is a sharp rise in the discharge of
water in the rivers and in the load, and thereby the eroding activity of the rivers; during the low-water period this activity
is greatly weakened, and in individual instances virtually
dies out. And here naturally under the various natural conditions one can observe certain particular features. Thus,
in the extreme north, where the annual amount of precipitation is in general slight (on the order of 300-600 mm. and
only in the south of the Eastern Manchurian Mountains somewhat above 1,000 mm.) but the climate is rather cold and
therefore evaporation is not so significant, the water discharge is great. In the mouth of the Sungari, for example,
the average annual discharge is 2,350 cubic meters per
second.* However, for five or six months of the year the

---

*Here and below the indices for the discharge have
been taken from the work of Ko Ching-hoi, 1957.

rivers are blocked with ice, and small rivers freeze down
to the bottom; floods, with the exception of very rainy years,
are not particularly heavy. Consequently, the activity of
the erosion processes has a seasonal character here, in being limited for all intents and purposes to half the year.
The morphology of the mountains (except the Eastern Manchurian) which is marked by a levelling of the watershed
areas and in general by little steepness particularly in the
upper portions, also does not help in the intensity of the erosion processes. It has been pointed out that the latter intensify only in those areas where the slopes exceed 15° and
there is no vegetation, and also on the lower steeper mountain slopes.

As one moves to the south, the winter becomes shorter
and the ice period on the rivers is significantly reduced (in
the lower reaches of the Hwang Ho it is down to 30 days),
although the amount of atmospheric precipitation as before
remains slight while evaporation increases, and this leads
to a drop in the discharge of the water (for example, the average annual discharge of the Hwang Ho is already 1, 545
cubic meters per second). In contrast to the northeast, the
spring flood season here is weaker and shorter in terms of
time and on individual rivers is even absent, since the snow
cover is extremely thin, but on the other hand, the summer
rain floods (July-September) are much more intensive. They
reach a particularly great force in August, when the discharge of the water increases significantly (up to 20, 000
cubic meters per second and more), and within the North
China Plain this frequently leads to flooding, sometimes of
a catastrophic character.

A distinguishing feature in the river regime of this portion of China is the very great load. In terms of the load,
the Hwang Ho--Liaoho region holds first place in the nation.
The load of those rivers flowing through areas composed of
loess deposits is particularly great; for example, the load of
the Hwang Ho in cutting across the Loess Province reaches
the enormous figure of 1 billion 360 million tons.

Thus, the intensity of the erosion processes here
should be much greater than in the northeast, and this is due
chiefly to the lithological features of the eroded rock, but
the duration of the activity of these processes is less.

The activeness of erosion washout also causes the great intensity in the aggradation process of friable material within the maritime plains, particularly in the North China Plain. Here the process of depositing alluvium is so great that it has predominated even over the subsidence of the dry land, which, as has already been noted, occurs in this part of the continent (V. G. Lebedev, 1959b). The deposits from the rivers Hwang Ho, Huai Ho and Yangtze have covered the marine sediment with a thick layer, and have here created a unique source of lowland gentle coast and, in addition, they have covered a significant part of the submerged shelf plains, and due to this the coastline has constantly moved into the sea, particularly in the delta regions. It has been computed, for example, that the delta of the Hwang Ho River in five years (1947-52) advanced 25 kilometers into the sea (A. P. Muranov, 1957).

According to the materials of Chinese hydrologists, all the rivers in the southern part of Eastern China are fed by rain (Shih Ch'eng-hsi, 1959). The regime of the rivers flowing between the ranges of the Ch'inling and Nanling, but which in terms of territory are relatively remote from the sea, is characterized by a single protracted flood which begins in April and terminates in October. Maximum drainage here occurs over the summer, but on various rivers is confined to the different months depending upon the character of the rainfall. The low-water period lasts, thus, about five months, and the water discharge over this time significantly drops.

In considering that the rivers lying to the south of the Hwang Ho do not freeze and that the amount of atmospheric precipitation here is significantly greater than in the north (on the order of 750-2,000 mm. per year) and the water discharge is extremely great (for example, the average annual discharge of the rivers in the Yangtze Basin is 32,620 cubic meters per second), it may be supposed that the erosion processes occur here over the entire year, but their greatest activeness over the major portion of the territory is confined to the warmer seasons. Thus, the southern part of Eastern China which is under conditions of an increased and in places abundant moisture, has an increased intensity in the processes of erosion relief formation. The latter is also aided by the steep-slope relief, and in the southwest of China and

on the Island of Taiwan there is also the high absolute altitude of the mountains. As a result here predominate processes of deep erosion.

In addition to the processes which are directly related
to the activity of the flowing water, within the extreme northeast the frost phenomena related to the extensive development of seasonal and in certain places perennial frosts are of
great relief-forming significance, and in South China there
is the karst process.

The existence of frost is related both to the modern
climatic conditions with the deep-freezing of the soil in line
with the low winter temperatures and the shallowness of the
snow cover, and also to the climate of the past, being to a
certain degree an inheritance of the Ice Age. Perennial
frost here has an insular distribution, but nevertheless
masses of it in places occupy a rather extensive area. According to Chinese data, the southern boundary for perennial
frost corresponds to the annual isotherm of 0° and the January isotherm of -24°. Thus, frost has developed in the
northern mountainous portion of Northeastern China (Hsin
K'uei-te, Jen Ch'i-chia, 1956). The stratification depth of
the frozen ground fluctuates from 0.5 to 3 meters depending
upon the composition of the earth and the exposure of the
slopes. Thus, for example, it has been noted that in the region of the Greater Khingan on areas composed of sands,
perennial frost lies at a depth of 2.5-3 meters, and in places
composed of clays at a depth of 1.5-2.5 meters, beneath
peat bogs at a depth of 0.5-1 meter. On the shadowy slopes,
the frozen ground is found approximately 1.5 meters beneath
the surface, and on sunny slopes the depth increases to 2.5
meters. The thickness of the perennial frost fluctuates
from 2 to 20 meters, however, in areas one can note layers
up to 40 meters and more. In the Greater Khingan the thickness of the perennial frost is usually approximately 10 meters.

Seasonal frost extends significantly more to the south
than does the perennial and therefore covers an even greater
area; it lies in a solid layer. The seasonal frost thaws completely only in the second half of the summer (July-August),
thereby existing most of the year.

The presence of a frozen watertight layer impedes the penetration of water into the soil, and this weakens the river-bed washout and helps to increase the development of lateral erosion processes and also the swamping processes. The predominance of lateral erosion processes over a river-bed in turn leads to the formation of wide valleys with meanders, channels and mort-lakes. The presence of frost is also involved in the phenomena of solifluction which develop on the treeless sunny areas of peaks and slopes and create specific forms of the micro-relief. All of this is very typical for the territory of the extreme northeast.

The karst relief in the south of China has developed over such extensive areas that this territory has rightly been considered the most extensive karst area in the world. In addition, the karst relief here is exceptionally diverse and, most importantly, unique. Aside from the ordinary karst-hole forms, here one will widely find stone outliers which in Chinese literature have been given the term "shihling" ("stone forest") which very aptly describes the specific features of the karst relief in many regions of Southern China. There is the opinion that these outliers were formed as a result of the combination of an intense karst process occurring through the entire bed of limestones which are one of the basic rocks forming the surface of Southern China, by the energetic activity of running water. The running water simultaneously washes out the rock and dissolves it, and thus on elevated areas there predominates a vertical articulation owing to the activity of surface currents; on depressed areas there are the processes of interior corrosion (V. G. Lebedev, 1959a).

The action of running water is, of course, manifested not only in the eastern half of China. To a certain degree it also occurs in the west; however, the rivers are confined here basically to mountains and the predominant portion of the plains in Central Asia and the Tibetan Uplands at present do not have permanent streams (in the past, particularly during the period of the thawing of the glaciers, the picture, as has been noted, was different). The discharges of river water in the western part of China are in general small. According to the Chinese hydrological data, the annual discharge of all the rivers in the northern foot of the Kunlun is 921 cubic meters per second, and if one adds the annual discharge of rivers flowing on to the Central Asian plains, then it is 3,120 cubic meters per second, i.e., approximately ten times less than the annual discharge of the rivers in the Yangtze Basin. The distribution of the runoff over the seasons of the year is extremely uneven. During the winter the discharge of the rivers is extremely insignificant, during the spring and autumn the runoff increases somewhat, but the basic flood season is confined to the summer months, when there is the intensive thawing of the snow in the mountains coinciding with the falling of rain. In certain years when heavy torrential rains fall in the lower parts of the mountains, the summer floods increase even more and flowing in the form of a mud stream assumes a catastrophic character.

Thus, the rivers flowing off the high steep mountains surrounding the Central Asian plains have relatively great discharges of water and of load only during the summer season when they carry out significant erosion work. As a result on the slopes of the mountains deep valleys are formed and in the intermontane tectonic depressions extensive aggradation plains are formed.

The thickness of these friable deposits carried down by the water are particularly great along the foot of the Kunlun where, according to the materials of the Sinkiang Expedition, the width of the piedmont proluvial-alluvial trains is usually 15-20 kilometers, and in places even approaches 70 kilometers, and the amplitude in their altitude reaches 1,600 meters (V. A. Fedorovich, 1961). However, we must stress once again that the predominant portion of this territory does not have permanent streams. Only after heavy torrential rains which fall very rarely in the dry channels does water appear for several hours, and although at this time the eroding force of the water stream is very intense, it is also extremely brief.

Wind as a relief-forming factor acquires exceptionally great significance within the slightly watered desert plains of Central Asia, and also in the interior areas of the Tibetan Uplands.

According to the data of Chinese researchers, the average annual wind velocity here is not particularly great,

and in any event much less than in the maritime portion of
the nation, but there are many days with storms and they are
confined basically to the spring. However, regardless of the
generally seasonal character of the winds, the relief-forming
role of the wind is very great, and it not only winnows sand
and blows the silt from the hammadas, but also directly
works on the bedrock as a result of which sheep-back rock,
deflation grooves and other specific reliefs are formed which
are particularly typical for the Gobi deserts. In places of
sand accumulation there have formed diverse types of sand
relief.

The sand masses occupy enormous areas within the
Tarim, Tsaidam and Dzungar depressions, and also on the
plains of the Ordos, Alashan and Inner Mongolia. Here barren sands and the barkhan topography are very widely found.
These sands have developed particularly within the Tarim
Basin where they form the enormous sand desert of the
Takla-Makan. According to observations of recent years,
the predominant area of this desert is composed by loose
sand beds. The presence of them, combined with the sharp
desert climate, has been the cause of the fact that the chief
relief-forming factor here has been the transporting force
of the wind. The virtually complete absence of precipitation, the extreme dryness of the air, the hurricane winds in
the spring and the absence of a vegetation cover have helped
to form here the diverse reliefs of barren sands (B. A.
Fedorovich, 1961).

Thus, where somewhat more precipitation falls or the
ground water lies closer to the surface, the sands are partially held in place by vegetation and here other types of a
sandy relief are formed--ridgy, alveolar, piled, socket,
pyramid, etc. (B. A. Fedorovich, 1948). These sands are
found on the plains of Inner Mongolia, partially in the Ordos,
Alashan and on certain areas of the deserts in the extreme
west.

Wind activity, of course, is observed not only within
Central Asia but also in other regions of China, and particularly on the aggradation plains in the western part of the
nation--Northeastern, North China, etc. However, the
relief-forming role of the wind has secondary significance
here.

The processes of plane denudation, i.e., the ablation
of weathering products under the effect of the force of gravity, rainfall and a number of other factors, as is known, are
possible anywhere where the grade of the locality exceeds
3-5°, and this leads to the levelling out of the slopes and
thus to a smoothing of the relief. Naturally, the greater the
angle, the more active the processes of plane denudation.
In China these processes acquire the greatest relief-forming
significance in the upland regions in the west where the shift
of weathering products over the slopes has occurred very
energetically, and the other denudation processes, in particular erosion, due to the small amount of atmospheric precipitation, the great rarity of the air and the dryness of the
climate, are extremely weak. Here under the influence of
the force of gravity and in part the thaw and rain waters,
enormous amounts of fragmentary material have slid down
the slopes and either reached the submontane plains or have
been deposited in the intermontane depressions and low areas.
The latter is particularly typical for the area of the Tibetan
Uplands where the rock weathering products have so filled
the previously deep valleys and synclines and thereby levelled
off the relief that the relative altitudes of the highest mountains, in terms of their absolute altitude, have become very
insignificant. Here the surface of the mountains is scattered
with rock trains and talus.

Plane denudation is widely developed also in the southeast of China, where under the conditions of abundant moisture and intensive biochemical weathering the processes of
plane washout and soil pulverization (the so-called tropical
solifluction) acquire great relief-forming significance.

The relief-forming role of modern glaciers, in contradistinction to the above listed exogenic processes, on the
scale of the nation is very small and limited only to the highest regions in the western part of China. This is due to the
extremely insignificant scale of modern glaciation which, as
we have already noted, in no way corresponds here to the
enormous altitude of the mountains, where conditions are
completely favorable for the conservation of snow and ice.
The very small dimensions of glaciation on these highest
mountains in the world have been caused by the extreme dryness of the climate, and even at the highest altitudes, where

the amount of atmospheric precipitation is greater than on the plains, it is still insignificantly small.

For describing the scale of modern glaciation in the mountains of China, one can give the following general data. The greatest glaciation occurs in the Karakorum, and particularly the south slope of this mountain system which is not related to China but which has been subjected to the wetting influence of the Indian monsoon. Here lie enormous glaciers which are up to 60-70 kilometers long (the glaciers of Siachen, Hispar, Biafo, etc.), and they descend to a level of 3,000 meters above sea level and below. As G. K. Sobolevskiy wrote (1918), many glaciers occupy here not only the valleys but also the divides, due to which the total area occupied by the glaciers and eternal snows on the southern slope of the Karakorum is enormous. On the northern slope of this mountain system, glaciation is much weaker, and the snow line is more than 1,000 meters higher, and the dimensions of the glaciers are correspondingly reduced.

In the second place in terms of the scale of glaciation stand the Himalayas. The number of glaciers here is also very great, but their dimensions are significantly smaller than in the Karakorum; the largest glaciers in the region of Chomolungma do not exceed 26 kilometers. As in the Karakorum, on the southern slope of the Himalayas, the eternal snows and glaciers occupy a much larger area than in the Chinese north.

In the Kunlun and particularly in the Tibetan Uplands, glaciation is very small and covers only the highest parts of the ranges. The western portion of the Kunlun has been best studied. Here there are numerous individual glaciers, but all of them, as a rule, are not more than 10 kilometers long, and only in rare instances exceed this figure; the largest of the presently known glaciers reaches 21 kilometers, according to the data of Ye. A. Beletskiy (1958). The degree of mountain glaciation in this part of the Kunlun drops sharply from west to east.

In the Tien Shan, the scale of modern glaciation is greater than in the Kunlun. In the Eastern Tien Shan, glaciation covers basically only the western portion; in the east the glaciers can be observed only on the highest mountain areas.

In general the greatest glaciation is confined at present to mountains of more than 5,000 meters absolute altitude, basically to the mountain areas lying on the border with the Soviet Union, the Iren-Khabirga and Bogdo-Ula Mountains. These high-mountain territories are characterized by the presence of relatively large firn fields which feed a large number of glaciers which reach maximum dimensions for the mountains of the Eastern Tien Shan. For the ranges with altitudes of 4,000-5,000 meters above sea level and which have sharply articulated narrow ridges such as the Borokhoro Range, etc., glaciation of the alpine type is characteristic; the firn fields here are relatively small, scattered, and the glaciers are numerous. Ranges with an extensive development of ancient levelling planes such as the Saarmin, Khalyktau and certain others, carry glaciers of the mantle type (B. A. Fedorovich and Yang T'ing-hsiang, 1961).

For the mountains of the Eastern Tien Shan as a whole, like the Kunlun, there are characteristically greater scales of glaciation on their southern chains in comparison with the northern, although in the Eastern Tien Shan, in contradistinction to the mentioned mountains, the northern chains receive more atmospheric precipitation than the southern. According to the data of V. M. Sinitsyn (1959), on the southern slopes of the Eastern Tien Shan one can count about 200 glaciers, and certain of them reach 30-35 kilometers in length and descend to an altitude of 3,000 meters and even somewhat below. At the same time, in the northern part of the mountains, the total number of glaciers is less than 100 and the length of the largest of them does not exceed 12 kilometers.

In the Nanshan the scale of modern glaciation is less than in the Eastern Tien Shan and it is concentrated almost exclusively in the highest western and central parts of this mountain system. In the eastern part of the Nanshan where the ranges are lower there are very few glaciers, regardless of the fact that the amount of atmospheric precipitation is greater here than in the west. The sole large glacial region of the Eastern Nanshan is the Malingshan Range (Lungtungling), reaching an altitude of 4,800 meters.

At present the information on glaciation in the Nanshan is relatively complete, since in 1958-59, the Chinese

Academy of Sciences organized a special expedition to study
the alpine snows and glaciers of this mountain system.

According to the data of this expedition (see L. D.
Dolgushin, 1959; Shih Ya-feng, Wang Tsung-t'ai, 1959) the
glaciers lie in the high-mountain ranges of the Nanshan
rather extensively, but they are comparatively small (on the
average of 1-2 kilometers, maximum about 10 kilometers)
and rarely form large solid masses. Typical is the rise in
the snow boundary and the ends of the glaciers from east to
west which is due to the increase in climate aridness in this
direction, and also in the lower position of the snow line on
the slopes with a northern exposure in comparison with the
slopes with a southern exposure. The latter is due basically
to the greater amount of atmospheric precipitation falling on
the northern slopes brought in by the predominating northwestern winds. Correspondingly the degree of glaciation on
the northern mountain slopes is much more significant than
on the southern; of the 965 glaciers in the Nanshan, about 80
per cent lie on the northern mountain slopes (L. D. Dolgushin, 1959).

In the Chinese part of the Mongolian Altai, modern glaciation is even weaker, and it covers only the highest parts
of the mountains lying on the border with the Soviet Union and
the Mongolian People's Republic. In terms of the general
character of the glaciation, these mountains virtually do not
differ from the mountain area of the Munkh-Khayrkhan-Ula
which is located on the territory of the Mongolian People's
Republic. The glaciers, as a rule, are short, 3-5 kilometers, and only one of them, the Potanin Glacier, reaches 20
kilometers (E. M. Murzayev, 1952).

Modern glaciation in the mountains of the northwest of
Dzungaria is also small, and only the highest parts of the
ranges rise somewhat above the snow line and have glaciers.
These glaciers are small in area and there are few which
form large solid areas and in most parts are confined to the
slopes with a northern exposure.

Thus, all of the highest mountains in the interior part
of Asia are covered by glaciation. But the scale of it in comparison with the absolute altitude of the mountains is small.
The degree of glaciation on all of the mountain systems, with

the exception of the Nanshan, falls sharply from west to east.
The influence of the exposure is different for the various
mountains, in the Eastern Tien Shan the greatest glaciation
is found on the southern slopes, and in the Nanshan and Dzungar Alatau on the northern. Among the glaciers one will
most frequently find corrie, corrie-valley and valley. Judging from the existing data, modern glaciers at present have
somewhat receded. We might recall that similar periods of
recession and advancement of the glaciers occurred over the
Upper Quaternary Period more than once and were a regular consequence in the periodic changes of the world's climate.

        The relief-forming significance of snows and glaciers
in the development of the present relief differs for the various mountain systems of China. In the upper parts of the
highest mountains there occurred processes of glacial exaration, and as a result of this there developed specific glacial reliefs--cirques, corries, sharp ridges, trough valleys,
and lower along the slopes, morainic accumulations and other
forms of glacial accretion. In the western parts of the mountains, where the climate was somewhat moister, the scale
of glaciation was greater and large rivers developed, the
relief-forming role of the snows and glaciers was also real-
ized through the force of the thaw waters which were the
main source of the feeding of the rivers beginning in the upper parts of the mountains. This led to the intensifying erosion work of the rivers in the mountains and to the aggradation on the submontane plains, as was mentioned above.

        The given material shows that on the territory of China
one can observe a number of particular features in the manifestation of the modern exogenic relief-forming processes
caused by the physical geographic factors. First of all there
is the sharp contrast in the structural relief typical for China
which leads to a situation where the exogenic relief-forming
processes have not so much a zonal manifestation as a
sharply expressed provinciality. The latter, from our view,
is the chief and most characteristic feature in the relief of
China.

        In line with the particular features of orography--the
placement of the major mountain systems, their orientation
and absolute altitude--the phenomena of geographic zonality,

including the zonality of the exogenic relief, are marked by a
much greater complexity than, for example, in neighboring
Mongolia or the USSR. In China, under the influence of the
relief and the eastern seas, the boundaries of the individual
zones are so greatly extended in the most diverse directions
that it seems to us more correct to speak not about the zonality of the relief of China as a whole, but rather about the
zonality of the relief within the limits of its individual provinces.

It is possible to establish in essence three such provinces which are marked by a very specific complex of exogenic processes and which have their own and only their own
particular features and patterns of the exogenic relief.
These are the Tibetan-Tien Shan province, the Central
Asiatic province and the province of Eastern and Southeastern China. Over the predominant area of the Tibetan-Tien
Shan province marked by the exceptionally high-mountain relief, there predominate processes of thermal and frost
weathering plane and arid denudation and also nival and glacial denudation. The manifestation of these processes is
subordinate here chiefly to the laws of vertical zonality, although it is expressed not as strongly as might be expected
for such an alpine territory as the Tibetan Uplands. The
manifestations of latitudinal and meridional zonality, regardless of the extensive area of this province, are here very
weak. All of this can be explained by the rather even, very
dry and cold climate of this territory which is virtually un-
effected by outside influence.

In the upper belt of the mountains, and in many places
even lower, there predominate processes of mechanical
rock destruction, the mass development of gravitational
creep, and nival and glacial processes. As a result here
there are numerous rock trains, talus, cirques, corries,
troughs, morainic accumulations, deep nival ravines and
other exogenic reliefs typical for these conditions. On individual somewhat better watered areas of this province (in
the western part of the Kunlun and in the Eastern Tien Shan),
in the upper and middle belts of the mountains the processes
of river erosion have developed due to which one will encounter deep valleys here. In the lower desert strip of the
mountains there once again predominate processes of the
physical weathering and arid denudation.

Another picture may be observed in the eastern part of the Nanshan, and particularly in the southeastern mountains of the Tibetan Uplands, where the climate is much moister and where the predominating role in the formation of the exogenic relief is played by erosion processes, basically river-bed. Due to these features, the entire eastern part of the Tibetan Uplands and the Nanshan would more correctly be considered in the eastern province.

Within the Central Asiatic province there predominate processes of thermal and frost weathering, deflation and aggradation. Regardless of the fact that this province is extremely extended along the latitude (more than three times greater than along the longitude), of predominant significance here are phenomena not of a meridional but rather a latitudinal zonality for the exogenic relief-forming processes. This is due to the intracontinental placement of this territory, its closing off on three sides by mountains (which has led to isolation from the influence of oceanic air masses), and also the predominance of the levelled relief. In truth, the latitudinal zonality of the relief is expressed here not particularly clearly, and this may be explained by the relative monotony of the climatic situation (and more precisely by the greater degree of aridness in the territory) and by the features of the endogenic relief. The latitudinal zonality in the relief can be traced best of all along the borders of the province, particularly in the east, where one can even observe a gradual transition from the erosion reliefs, and consequently from the processes forming them, to typical desert relief. The influence of the structural relief, and more precisely the combination of exposed outwashes and relatively low elevations with deep intermontane aggradation plains (depressions), also tell upon the distribution of the exogenic processes. In particular, within the aggradation plains composed basically of sandy deposits, the dominating role belongs to the processes of deflation and aeolian accumulation; within the limits of the washouts and the elevations, to the processes of physical weathering and corrasion.

The province of Eastern and Southeastern China, lying virtually entirely on the border of the continent, in contradistinction to the above described intracontinental provinces, to a significant degree has been subjected to the oceanic influences, and this is expressed, in particular, in the

abundant amount of atmospheric precipitation falling here.
This in its turn has caused a sharp activization in the processes of river erosion and aggradation which are dominant
for this part of China. Due to the fact that this province has
been greatly extended both along the longitude and latitude
and there are no very high mountains in the interior, the
manifestation of the exogenic processes has been here sub-
ordinated to the laws of both meridional and longitudinal
zonality. In line with the presence of a mountain relief here,
vertical zonality also has a certain significance.

The zonality of the relief-forming processes is expressed here, as has been noted, in the increase in the intensity of the erosion process from north to south and from
west to east, and in the development of frost processes in
the extreme north and by the biochemical weathering and
karst processes in the south.

BASIC FEATURES IN THE
PRESENT TOPOGRAPHY

The extreme diversity in the present topography has
been a consequence of the appearance on the territory of
China of the complex of above described ancient and modern
endogenic and exogenic relief-forming processes. The topography, as has been pointed out, here differs strongly both
in terms of the altitude and external appearance, and also in
terms of the origin, structure and age.

In summing up what has been stated above, one can
once again stress that in the major relief forms of China one
can clearly see the influence of tectonics. The general orographic map of China has been predetermined by the entire
course of the geological history, and the modern topography
in its main outlines was inherited from the Mesozoic, and in
the topography one can trace an even closer and frequent
direct relationship with the structures of the Cenozoic Age.

The influence of tectonics is seen particularly clearly
in the location of the mountain and plain territories, and also
in the strike of the basic orographic lines. Thus, the major
plains of China lie either within fixed platform areas, the
geotectonic regime of which is marked by relative stability

over many geological eras, or in the depressed areas of former geosynclinal areas.

The mountains of China lie either within the limits of
ancient mountain areas and the most shifting areas of the
platform bordering its stable parts, or within geosynclinal
areas involved in orogenic movements of various cycles.
The character of the tectonic movements and the direction
of the folding have determined the general structure and the
strike of the basic mountain structures of China. On areas
of ancient pre-Paleozoic dry land, these are isolated mountain areas without a definite orientation composed predominantly of ancient crystalline rock. Mountains lying in the
area of the Paleozoic (Hercynian) folding have in the majority of instances a strike which is close to longitudinal or in
individual cases almost meridional, and this was caused by
the contours of the Chinese Platform which existed even
then. In the area of the platform involved in the Mesozoic
(Yenshan) folding, there were formed intra-platform mountain structures usually with a northeastern strike. The
mountains lying in the area of the alpine (Himalayan) folding have in the zone of the Himalayas a latitudinal strike
caused by the contours of the Tibetan median mass, and on
islands a north-northeast strike caused by the direction of
the island arcs.

To a significant degree the morphological features of
the relief have also been caused by tectonics (ancient and
young), and this is expressed, for example, in the types of
mountains--block, folded-block, block-folded, folded,
faulted, monoclinal, etc. If one tries to trace the spatial
distribution of the basic structural types of mountains over
the territory of the nation, then the following general patterns emerge.

Mountains with a block structure are spread, as a rule,
on the platform within the limits of the shield and are confined to those areas of it which were involved in the Meso-
Cenozoic and recent faults. These are the Shantung Mountains, the Huayenshan, Yinshan, Peishan, Altyntag,
Chimentag, Kuruktag and Kil'pin ridges. The folded-block
mountains are found more widely in China. Above all this
structure is characteristic for the mountains lying in that
portion of the Chinese Platform which was touched by the

Yenshan folding and where rock from the Precambrian crystalline basement lies close to the surface. The latter, and
also the extensive distribution of granite intrusive bodies and
effusive formations have caused here a great intensity of
block tectonics, along with the folding, and this frequently
has determined the direction of the ranges. Thus, a folded-
block structure is found for all mountains lying in the northern part of the platform within the limits of the shield, i.e.,
the Eastern Manchurian Mountains, the Shansi Mountains,
the Jehol Upland, and the Alashan Range. The folded-block
structure is also characteristic for mountains lying in the
area of the Paleozoic folding--the Kunlun, the Eastern Tien
Shan, the Nanshan, Ch'inling and the Greater Khingan. For
them there is a typical alternation and a clearly expressed
linear strike to the mountain ranges and intermontane depressions linked to the direction of the large plicated structures (anticlines and synclines) caused by faults and shifts.

The block-folded mountains lie within the platform of
the Chinese Platform the thick sedimentary mantle of which
was touched by the Yenshan folding; here linear structures
predominate such as anticlinoria and synclinoria expressed
in the topography as ranges and depressions complicated by
faults. The folded and block-folded structure is characteristic for the youngest mountains formed in the period of the
Cenozoic folding. These are mountains which lie basically
within the alpine folded belt in the south of the Tibetan Uplands, and also the mountains on Taiwan which are related to
the Pacific Ocean folded belt.

The formation of the plains with varying genesis is
also closely related to tectonics. Analysis of the materials
has shown that, for example, the aggradation plains of
China occupy the greatest areas within the platform and are
confined to the sites of their recent absolute and relative
subsidences. These are the North China, the Northeastern,
the plains of the middle reaches of the Yangtse, the Tarim
Plain and other smaller ones. Moreover, the aggradation
plains, but of smaller area, have also developed in all of the
folded areas and on the juncture of them with the platform
structures. They have been confined here to areas of young
subsidences and to the foredeeps which have undergone intensive recent subsidences. Among the former are, for example, the Turfan-Hami, Dzungar and Sankiang plains lying

in the intermontane depressions; among the latter are the
piedmont plains of the Kunlun, the Eastern Tien Shan, Nanshan, etc.   The aggradation plains are composed of thick
beds of Neogene and Quaternary deposits of varying genesis.

The denudation plains, on the contrary, are found
within the more stable areas of the platform and on the levelled areas of the folded regions which have not been recently
subjected to differentiated movements.   Here the plains
which have been cut into the socle (denudation socle-plains)
are confined, as a rule, either to areas of the shields or to
the outcroppings of the crystalline basement in the area of
the ancient Paleozoic foldings which have been subjected to
uplifting and denudation in the Mesozoic and Cenozoic.   The
surface of the plains which have been cut into the socle is
either completely devoid of friable deposits or the mantle is
shallow.   An example of the socle plains of the first type is
the Kashun Gobi, and an example of the plains of the second
type, the southern part of the Alashan Plain.   Plains cut into
bedded rock (denudation-bedded plains) are more widely
found.   They are confined to the areas of the platforms, to
subsided areas of the folded Paleozoic and Mesozoic basement, and to the median masses in the area of the Cenozoic
folding.   The bedded plains are composed chiefly of pre-
Neogene sedimentary strata and, like the socle, in places
are over-covered by a shallow mantle of recent deposits, and
subsequently, during the Neogene they were, as a rule, uplifted and subjected to denudation.   The plains cut into bedded
rock in China are the Ordos, the Eastern Gobi, the northern
parts of the Dzungar and Alashan plains, the Szechwan Plain,
and portions of the Changtan and Tsaidam.

The volcanogenic types of relief are also related to the
tectonic disturbances of the various ages, and among these
landforms in China one can establish two basic groups--the
volcanic mountains of the pre-Quaternary (Late Mesozoic)
eruptions and the juvenile volcanic mountains, the lava
plains and plateaus of the Quaternary and recent eruptions.
The first are concentrated within the platform of the Chinese
Platform and are confined to the Cathayan-Asian geosyncline,
the Precambrian crystalline rock of which lies close to the
surface and during the Mesozoic has been subjected to faulting, along which there were heavy eruptions of rhyolite lava.
The second group is encountered in a number of areas of

China and is confined to the tectonic structures which are extremely diverse in terms of type and age and which were involved in the faulting of recent times. The areas of distribution for the juvenile volcanic relief was indicated by us above.

Along with the described types of endogenic relief in China, one will also encounter those which do not have a direct link with the ancient structures. These are above all the uplands and highlands which, proceeding from the very nature of these terms, are usually difficult to compare with any definite types of tectonic structures. The uplands which are significant in area are distributed in the northeast and in the Kweichow Mountains, and the highlands in Tibet and in the south of the nation along the border with Vietnam and Burma.

The altitudes of all these mountain and plain territories of China, as we have already noted, are extremely diverse and this is caused, in the first place, by the character of the recent movements which appeared within the tectonic structures of the various ages.

The endogenic relief of China with the passage of time underwent significant transformations under the influence of a general and repeatedly changing climatic situation and this, in turn, caused a number of its specific features. The processes of erosion and aggradation, weathering, wind activity, snow and ice, and a number of other factors here created that diversity of exogenic landforms which is so typical for the topography of this land. One of the particular features in the territorial distribution of exogenic landforms is the strict confinement of them to definite parts of China. Thus, the wide development of fluvial landforms, i.e., forms created by the activity of running water, comprises a specific feature of the eastern wetter part of the land, and the aeolian landforms, of the arid territories of the northwest, and the glacial landforms, the alpine regions, etc.

The basic genetic groups of exogenic forms are within China the fluvial, aeolian, arid-denudation, cryogenic and karst. All of these groups contain a greater or lesser number of landforms and their complexes of both recent and ancient (relic) relief formation.

In China the fluvial landforms are marked by particular diversity. Among them one can clearly differentiate the
erosion landforms of permanent channels, valleys, which
are particularly widely found in the eastern part of China;
erosion forms of temporary torrential channels confined to
the western part of the land; erosion-mesa landforms which
are well developed in the Szechwan Plain composed of friable Meso-Cenozoic deposits; the ravine-gully landforms
which have developed in the loess; the hummocky landforms
of the arid areas, and, finally the ancient erosion landforms-
arroyos--traces of pluvial periods which have been well preserved under the arid conditions of the western, Central
Asiatic part of China. As has already been pointed out, the
morphology of the valleys and the density of their location in
the various parts of the nation differ and this frequently depends upon the influence of other exogenic processes working on these reliefs. Thus, for example, the erosion landforms which are widely found in Northeastern China, i.e.,
under the conditions of moderate wetting, and the development of frozen ground, are represented by broad flat-
bottomed usually boggy valleys; the erosion landforms of
Southeastern China which are located under conditions of increased wetting are narrow, deeply incised, frequently rapidy valleys, etc. On the plains of China there have widely
developed aggradation fluvial landforms, both purely alluvial and mixed genesis such as lacustrine-alluvial, alluvial-
marine, etc.

From the reliefs specific for the arid conditions, i.e.,
for the entire Central Asiatic part of China, aside from
those already designated, one should note the extensive development of the aeolian accumulative-deflation landforms
(barkhans, ridges, hillocks, etc.) which are characteristic
for all of the sandy deserts and semideserts, and also the
denudation-deflation and arid-denudation forms created by
the joint action of physical weathering and wind erosion processes, i.e., deflation, and typical for the gravel-rock deserts (hammadas).

The cryogenic and glacial forms of the relief which,
as has been noted, are distributed in China basically in the
alpine regions of the west, include a complex of nival, solifluction and permafrost landforms, recent glaciers, paleo-
glacial, exaration and accretion landforms, and also the

lacustrine-fluvial glacial plains which have extensively developed in Tibet. The karst landforms are confined to the southeastern part of China and are extremely unique. The particular feature of the karst topography of China is the predominance of outlier landforms.

In summing up all that has been said, let us list the
basic major types of relief in China. Among the mountain
relief one can note the highest mountains (absolute altitude
of more than 5, 000 meters) which occupy an enormous area
in the southwest of China. These mountains are represented
by very high ranges of a folded and folded-block structure,
by areas of uplands and high upland plains. Among the latter
one will most frequently encounter aggradation plains composed of lacustrine-fluvial glacial deposits and plains cut
into bedded rock. An example of the highest mountains of
China is the Tibetan mountain plexus. The predominant portion of the mountains, particularly in the interior regions
of Tibet is characterized by significant smoothness due to
the abundance of rock trains. The highest section of the
ranges where there are numerous glaciers is marked by
sharp outlines, and the southeastern portion of the Tibetan
Mountains which are exposed to the sea has been greatly
disjointed and has a typical alpine appearance.

The uplands (absolute altitude 2, 500-5, 000 meters)
occupy a relatively small area in China. They are distributed in the northwest, southeast and in the central part of
Taiwan and are represented by ranges predominantly of a
folded-block structure with a predominance of glacial and
frost-nival landforms (the western portions of the Eastern
Tien Shan), by high rugged uplands (for example, the Yunnan), and by folded ranges with an alpine complex of landforms (the Taiwan Ranges).

The medium-altitude mountains and low mountain
areas are very widely found in China. The medium-altitude
mountains (absolute altitude 1, 000-2, 500 meters) are most
encountered in the north of China. They are represented by
the medium-altitude ranges of a folded-block structure with
aeolian reliefs (the Greater Khingan, the T'aihangshan,
Ch'inling, etc.), by the block mountains and uplands with
extensive development of landforms caused by the disjunctive

dislocations (the mountains of the Yinshan, Huaiyenshan, the Peishan Uplands) and by young volcanic massifs.

The low mountain relief (absolute altitude less than 1,000 meters) occupies in essence the entire southeastern continental part of China where these areas are a combination of short ranges of a predominantly block-folded structure, individual massifs and peaks which are frequently granite intrusives prepared by denudation. The low mountain reliefs are rather widely found in the northeast as well, but here these are usually foothill ranges of the basic mountain systems. Here isolated low mountain areas are encountered more rarely. As an example one might cite the Shantung block mountains composed of crystalline rock.

The paleovolcanic mountains and the loess topography in the bend of the Hwang Ho are unique reliefs in China. Mountains composed of volcanic rock from the Mesozoic which completely blanketed the earlier relief occupy the maritime part of Southeastern China, they have differing altitudes (but not more than 1,800 meters) and are marked by extreme ruggedness. The loess relief is a typical erosion relief created by the energetic washout of the loose loess beds. As a result there developed a very unique combination of loess hills, ravines and ridges with varying forms and outlines with areas of rugged loess plateaus. The relative altitude of the hills is generally 100-150 meters, and rarely above 200 meters. Among them two types are most widely found-- the extended ridges (according to the Chinese terminology "liang") which are the interfluve of ravines, and isolated hills with a rounded form ("mao").

The plains of China which occupy also a basically small area can be divided into the lowland plains (absolute altitude less than 200 meters), plains (absolute altitude 200-500 meters) and high plains (absolute altitude more than 500 meters) of varying genesis. The lowland plains are found chiefly in the maritime areas and are predominantly aggradation--alluvial (for example, the North China), lacustrine-alluvial (for example, the Northeastern), lacustrine-marine. The plains are found basically in the eastern half of China, in the foothills and in the intermontane depressions. They occupy a relatively modest area, and the largest is the

Szechwan Plain cut into bedded rock. The high plains are
confined to the Central Asiatic part of China; the area of
them, as has been noted, is extremely great and the genesis
is diverse. Aggradation plains are also widely found here--
the paleoalluvial overwinnowed (for example, the Tarim),
alluvial-proluvial (the submontane plains of the Kunlun) and
also denudation--bedded (for example, the plains of Inner
Mongolia), socle (Kashun Gobi, etc.).

The territory of China which is so diverse in terms of
relief naturally can be divided into a number of geomorphological areas and regions.

The questions of the geomorphological zoning of China
have been the concern of Chinese scientists (Li Ssu-kuang,
Jen Mei-e, Hsu I-chao and certain others). The most recent
published scheme which we know is the scheme of geomorphological zoning compiled by Chou T'ing-ju, Shih Ya-feng and
Ch'en Shu-peng (1957). Having used as the basis of the zoning the morphogenetic principle, the authors divide the territory of China into three major geomorphological areas--
Eastern, Mongolo-Sinkiang, and Tsinghai-Tibetan. Each of
these is divided into regions which are combined into groups
of regions. Thus, the Eastern area includes 16 regions combined into four groups: the Mongolo-Sinkiang has six regions
(two groups); the Tsinghai-Tibetan has seven regions (three
groups).

In agreeing basically with the geomorphological zoning
compiled by the Chinese authors, we feel it in place to make
certain remarks. First of all we propose that it is not completely correct to consider Taiwan as one of the regions in
the Eastern area. In terms of the particular features of the
modern relief and in terms of the history of its geological
development, it differs sharply from the neighboring continental territories and, on the contrary, has a great deal in
common with the remaining islands of the eastern border of
the Asiatic continent. Therefore, in the zoning of China, one
should establish another geomorphological unit of the first
order, i.e., an area which would include Taiwan. The principle for establishing the regions is not always clear. In
certain instances, sections of the territory which clearly

differ in terms of genesis (and frequently even in morphology) are combined (for example, the Altyntag with the
Nanshan, the Tarim Depression with the Kashun Gobi and
the Peishan, the Shansi Mountains with the Loess Plateau);
in other instances, conversely, a single geomorphological
unit is divided into regions (for example, the Kunlun is divided into three parts and basically has vanished as a mountain system).

On the basis of analyzing the materials available, with
special emphasis on the work of Chinese researchers, and
also considering all of the particular features in the modern
relief and developmental conditions of each given territory
stated in the preceding sections of this chapter, we feel it
possible to introduce certain changes into the above-
designated scheme which at the same time has been used by
us as the basis. The largest geomorphological units--
geomorphological areas--in this case will be: I. The Eastern Chinese Area of medium-altitude and low mountains and
lowland plains; II. the Central Asiatic Area of high plains
and mountains; III. the Tibetan-Nanshan Area of highest
mountains and uplands; IV. the Eastern Asiatic Insular
Area.

Without being able to give in this work an exhaust-
tive description to the geomorphological areas, regions and
subregions of China, here we will point out only the chief
and most specific features in the designated geomorphological units.

The Eastern Chinese Area of Medium-Altitude and Low Mountains and Lowland Plains

The characteristic feature of the relief in this geomorphological area is the predominance of medium-altitude
rugged mountains and low mountain areas, and also the extensive development of accumulation depressions which lie
in the extensive intermontane and piedmont basins. In contradistinction to the other geomorphological areas of China,
the area occupied by depressions here is very great, and,
on the contrary, the area occupied by high mountains is
relatively small.

The heterogeneous history in the development of this territory, the very diverse lithological and age composition of the rock forming the various relief elements, the sharply different temperature conditions and moisture conditions, the differing and different character in the degree of ruggedness and certain other factors here have caused the great diversity in the relief. In line with this, the number of geomorphological regions here is very great, in any event much greater than in the other geomorphological areas of China.

From the materials of the preceding sections of this chapter, it follows that the greatest difference in the relief may be observed between the northern and southern parts of the Eastern Chinese Area and this is due to both the geological and the climatic conditions of this territory. First of all in the northern part there are the major depressions of the land--the North China and Northeastern--formed by a thick bed of friable deposits which are characterized by a flat relief and by the presence of a thick network of slightly incised river valleys. The latter are particularly numerous within the lowest and flat North China Plain.

For the mountains of this part of China, there is a very characteristic direct reflection in the relief of the disjunctive dislocations of recent times. The latter are frequently inherited and cause a number of important local relief features. Thus, for example, the sharp asymmetry in the slopes of the Greater Khingan, where the western slope is gentle and the eastern steep, has been caused by the presence of a major fault which passes in a meridional direction along the eastern slope of these mountains. The sharply asymmetrical slopes caused by disjunctive tectonics may also be found in the Ch'inling Range, and here the northern slopes are steep and descend along the fault line towards the graben of the Weiho River. The modern structural-orographic features in the Jehol Uplands are also due to the presence of major faults with a northeast strike.

The influence of block tectonics is even stronger in the relief of the Shantung and Huaiyenshan Mountains which lie on the site of the most ancient dry land masses and are composed in a significant amount, as has been noticed, by crystalline rock. This is manifested particularly clearly in the Shantung Mountains which are broken up by such a thick

network of faults that regardless of the small area of these
mountains, the relief is extremely heterogeneous. The latter is a combination of numerous but usually short mountain
ranges, frequently of an asymmetrical structure, massifs
and individual peaks.

The young volcanic relief is also very characteristic
for the northern part of this geomorphological area, and
this, in turn, expresses the activity of disjunctive tectonics.
The volcanic landforms here are represented by plains and
plateaus composed of basalt lava which in places completely
shields the ancient relief, and also by cone-shaped elevations. The landforms of the young volcanic relief are also
very widely found here in the Eastern Manchurian Mountains, in the northern part of the Shansi Mountains and in
certain other areas.

The morphological features of the relief caused by the
climatic factors are due, as we have noted, in Eastern China
chiefly to the activity of flowing water. Of particular interest in this regard is the above-mentioned erosion relief of
the loess region in the great bend of the Hwang Ho. In literature this region is known under the name of the Loess Plateau but, as research has shown in recent years, this in fact
is not a plateau, but rather a territory which has been exceptionally heavily and finely broken up by river valleys and ravines. Such a relief will be encountered nowhere else in
China.

In the southern part of the Eastern Chinese geomorphological area, there predominate mountainous territories,
and here, in contradistinction to the north, one will encounter an alpine relief. The morphostructural features of the
modern relief here to a significant degree have been caused
by neotectonics, but, in contradistinction to the northern
part of the area, where the mountains in general have undergone an uplift while the depressions have subsided, here this
pattern cannot be found. As we have already stated above,
large areas of this territory, including the mountainous ones,
at present are undergoing a subsidence and this is a specific
feature in the southern part of China, and cannot help but tell
on the character of its present relief. In this regard, there
is the very unique territory in Southeastern China, to the
east of the Yunnan Uplands and the Kweichow Mountains, a

predominant portion of which during the Neogene-Quaternary
Age underwent, as we have pointed out, and continues to
undergo a slow subsidence. Here the mountains are low,
greatly destroyed, and they usually include numerous but
very short ranges, individual elevations and relatively small
intermontane basins.

In contrast to the southeastern low-mountain subsiding
part of this geomorphological area, its southwestern part, including the Yunnan Uplands and the Kweichow Mountains
(usually called on the Russian maps the "plateaus" which is
not completely accurate), has undergone an uplift and in
places even has an alpine relief. In the relief of the designated mountains, one can clearly tell also the disjunctive
disturbances which have here made basic changes in the direction of the rivers. The latter can be clearly established
in the relief by the numerous beheadings of the rivers, by
their jointed structure which is very typical for this territory, etc. Chinese sources indicate, for example, a significant change in the course of the Yangtze which occurred
recently. The above-described volcanogenic relief in the
mountains of the southeastern coast is also unique within the
southern part of the Eastern Chinese Area. The lithological
composition of the rock which is marked by extreme diversity also tells upon the character of the relief in the southern
part of this geomorphological area. Here, as perhaps nowhere else in China, the relief is subordinate to the lithology.
The influence of the latter is so great that it is reflected not
only in the morphological features but also in the altitudes.
Thus, for example, the higher mountain ranges and peaks
are composed here usually of granites and quartzy sandstones
which are more resistant to weathering processes; the basins
and broad valleys have been formed in limestones and red
sandstones; the gorges in the less stable rock between the
basins.

A specific feature of this territory, particularly its
western part, is, in addition, the broad development of karst
topography, and also, typical for the entire southern part of
Eastern China, the presence of an extremely dense and
deeply-incised river network.

All of this leads to a situation whereby as a whole the
relief in the southern part of the Eastern Chinese

geomorphological area, regardless of the subsidence and
relatively low absolute altitudes which are to be found here,
is rather sharp. Individual peaks and mountains have an extremely diverse and fantastic outline, a large portion of the
mountains has been greatly disjointed, and the rivers flow in
all sorts of directions, and therefore the river network here
frequently has a reticular structure.

The Central Asiatic Area of
High Plains and Mountains

The characteristic feature in the relief of this geomorphological area is the combination of mountain systems
and broad plain area of varying genesis lying at a high altitude above sea level. In line with the isolation against ocean
influences, here there has been an exceptional development
of the physical weathering, deflation and accumulations. Only
the western, northwestern and northeastern borders of this
area which are reached by the humid sea winds and drained
to the ocean carry traces of the effect of recent fluvial erosion processes and in the upper parts of the mountains there
has also been frost weathering, nivation and glaciation.

It seems to us that as a whole the relief of the Central
Asiatic Area is much more homogeneous than the relief of
the above-described Eastern Chinese Area and this can be
explained by the significantly greater homogeneity in the geological and climatic situation of the given territory. Therefore, the number of geomorphological regions, regardless of
the enormous size of this area is relatively small.

A larger portion of this geomorphological area is plain;
such enormous-area plains as the Tarim, Dzungarian,
Kashun Gobi, the plains of Inner Mongolia, the Alashan and
Ordos, lie here. This has been caused by the particular features of the tectonics; since the Mesozoic the territory of the
present plains of Central Asia has occupied a relatively depressed position between the higher mountain structures and
was an area for the accumulation of continental deposits.

Characteristically, certain of these plains (the Tarim,
Dzungarian, and others), with a significant absolute altitude
(1, 000 meters and more) lie in deep intermontane depressions so that the relative altitudes of them reach several

thousand meters. The presence of such broad intermontane depressions, as we have noted, is a specific feature in the relief of Central Asia.

Another typical feature of the plains in this area is the heterogeneity of their genesis, and thereby, naturally, the morphology. The depression-plains are, as a rule, aggradation. They have been formed from the surface like the aggradation plains of East China, by alluvial deposits, but in contradistinction to the eastern plains, the alluvium here is ancient and was put down by large rivers of the past. At present there are extremely few active rivers here and they lie basically only in the submontane areas, but the interior parts of the plains are waterless. The Tarim Plain, for example, is crossed by only two rivers, the Tarim (Yarkend) and the Hotan, but there is abundant water in them only during the flooding. At present these are enormous sandy deserts, arenas for the active working of wind deflation and accumulation.

The plains of the Kashun Gobi, Inner Mongolia, the Alashan and Ordos over the predominant area, as we have noted, are denudation. The relief is a combination of broad gently undulating areas covered either by aeolian sands or by a rocky-gravel material, and low rocky elevations composed of rock more resistant to the denudation processes. Depending upon the geological structure within these plains one can establish areas of differing genesis. Thus, in the present relief of the Kashun Gobi composed of ancient rock there predominate plains cut into the socle. Their surface has been broken up by shallow but numerous broad gullies which in combination with the individual flat hills and rocky ridges confined to the outcroppings of the rock more resistant to denudation, form the unique relief of this territory.

The plains of Inner Mongolia composed by thick beds of Mesozoic and predominantly Cretaceous deposits, are basically bedded (or cut into bedded rock). An exception is the Talainor Plain which occupies the lowest depressed region and is aggradation. Within the Alashan and Ordos, one will find both the socle and bedded plains, and in areas of recent subsidences also aggradation plains.

A characteristic feature for the relief of the Central
Asiatic geomorphological area is also the presence of relatively low mountains rising amidst the plain expanses.
These interior mountains include the Peishan, Yinshan and
Alashan. Here, as within the plains, there prevail rocky
or sandy deserts. As has been noted, the sandy deserts--
the hammadas--are widely found in the Kashun Gobi, the
Peishan, Eastern Dzungaria, and are areas of intensive winnowing. Sandy deserts occupy enormous expanses within
the Tarim, Dzungarian and Alashan plains, and also in the
Ordos and on the plains of Inner Mongolia. In the Alashan
and over a larger part of the Tarim, there predominate
shifting sands and barkhans have formed; in the south of the
Tarim plains, in Dzungaria and the Ordos, there are more
semi-shifting sands, but nevertheless landforms of hummocky ridgy sands have developed. Within the sandy deserts
frequently there are also outlier-deflation landforms which
developed as a result of the winnowing of horizontally strat-
ified ancient deposits. Such reliefs, the yardangi, are composed of Early Quaternary lacustrine-delta deposits of the
Tarim-Lobnor and are typical of the eastern part of the
Tarim plains.

In the interior portion of this geomorphological area,
aside from the purely arid reliefs, one will also find such
erosion landforms as hummocky topography and dry beds of
temporary streams. The hummocky landforms are particularly characteristic for the northern part of the Gobi plains,
while the dry channels are encountered everywhere--in the
flat alluvial plains, on the sloping piedmont plains, the denudation plains and plateaus and even in the mountains. Here,
regardless of the extremely dry climate in this territory,
the valleys of the temporary streams are usually deeply incised and are frequently whole branched systems--traces of
a previous hydrographic network. At present, as has already been pointed out, the water in the gullies can be found
only during the heavy torrential rains and their incutting has
basically stopped. Such dead channels and in places even
well-expressed terraced valleys show the energetic erosion
activity of the ancient rivers within the confines of these
present desert territories. The dead valleys are an extremely characteristic and unique element of the morphology in Central Asia.

The highest mountain structures of the Central Asiatic geomorphological area, the Eastern Tien Shan, like the medium-altitude mountains of Border Dzungaria which lie more to the north, are border and therefore less arid mountains of the area. Everything taken together has led to the development of unique relief complexes distinct from those which predominate within the confines, described above, of the lower interior mountain and plain regions. For them above all there is a characteristic rather sharp vertical zoning of the relief. Thus, in the highest parts of the mountains covered by glaciation, there predominate glacial and frost-nival processes. Below the zone of eternal snows, of predominant significance are the processes of fluvial erosion which are particularly intense in the western more moist regions of these mountains. But in the lower belt, and in the eastern parts of the mountains, and in the south of the Eastern Tien Shan and even higher, there predominate, as in the nearby plains, physical weathering, deflation and other processes of an arid climate.

The Tibetan-Nanshan Area of Very High Mountains and Uplands

This geomorphological area, located in the central part of the Asiatic continent, is sharply differentiated among the surrounding territories by its enormous absolute altitudes and the unique placement of the orographic units. In the center lie the Tibetan Uplands including the extensive plain expanses crosscut by ranges. The uplands are bordered by belts of even higher mountain chains--the Himalayas, Kunlun and Karakorum. For all of these chains there is a characteristic asymmetrical structure--their interior slopes, i.e., those turned towards the uplands are gently sloping, the exceeding of the ranges above the general surface of the uplands is relatively low, the exterior slopes are steep and the relative altitudes of the mountains above the nearby plains are enormous. The Nanshan which abut in the northeast to the Kunlun are also marked by very great altitudes, and the structure of them is analogous to the structure of the border ranges of the Tibetan Uplands.

In structural terms, this geomorphological area is extremely complex and heterogeneous. As a whole the Tibetan Uplands with the mountains bordering them belong to the

Mediterranean mobile zone. In the center lies the Tibetan median mass with a thin and gently sloping dislocated sedimentary mantle composed of Cretaceous deposits. On the north it is bordered by the folded structure of the Kunlun, the basement of which was created during the period of the Paleozoic folding; on the south by the Karakorum and Kantissushan which were marked by great mobility during the Mesozoic; the southern boundary of the Tibetan Uplands, the Himalayas, began to uplift from the Tertiary times. The uplift of the Tibetan Uplands themselves began after the Cretaceous Age. The joining of these territories which are so different in terms of the tectonic structure and age occurred recently as a result of very intensive recent uplifts. As has already been noted, the uplift rate of this entire territory over the Neogene-Quaternary Age was enormous. At present, this geomorphological area is the world's greatest young uplift, the active growth of which began in the Oligocene and has continued up to the present.

Inheritance from the ancient tectonics has basically manifested itself here in the spatial location and strike of the basic orographic units and in the difference in the amplitudes of their recent movements. The latter have been marked by the greatest scope and differentiation within the more mobile folded zones, particularly in the zone of the Cenozoic folding. Here there has formed a complex of linearly extended mountain ranges and intermontane depressions bordered by aggradation plains which are tectonically confined to the foredeeps and therefore show a very great thickness of the friable strata. Relatively smaller but generally more even uplifts occurred in the median masses and platform areas where plains basically were formed. Depending upon the direction and intensity in the ancient and young tectonic movements, these plains have a differing genesis. Thus, plains cut into socle predominate on areas composed of Paleozoic rock which, basically, underwent uplifting. On areas composed of friable deposits of the Mesozoic which prior to the Paleogene were interior basins, one will find a predominance of the plains cut into bedded rock. The lowest areas of the enclosed basins composed of Cenozoic deposits are aggradation plains.

The enormous absolute altitude of the Tibetan-Nanshan Area and its virtually complete isolation against exterior climatic influences have caused the unique course and relative homogeneity in the exogenic processes occurring on this territory. In the interior undrained and to a significant degree levelled areas of the uplands, a predominant role has been played by the frost weathering, by surface denudation and wind activity. In the peripheral regions with a steeper relief and moist climate, the erosion processes acquire greater significance.

Thus, for the relief of this geomorphological area there is a characteristic presence of broad interior plains of differing genesis lying at an altitude of about 5,000 meters, interior ranges which are relatively low and level, but which in terms of absolute altitude are enormous (5,500-6,000 meters) crossing these plains, and border mountains which are colossal in altitude and with steep alpine deeply disjointed exterior slopes and gently sloping interior ones.

The Eastern Asiatic Insular Area

This geomorphological area covers in essence all of the islands and certain of the peninsulas in the eastern border of the Asiatic continent. Within China, this includes the Island of Taiwan, the Pescadores and the smaller islands. The topography of it, in comparison with the other geomorphological areas of China, is very young. Territorially this area lies within the Pacific Ocean stage of the Cenozoic folding where the mountain-making processes have not stopped even now. The Island of Taiwan must be considered as one of the regions of this area.

Structurally, Taiwan is part of the Ryukyu-Korean island arc. The shape of the island is extended in a meridional direction virtually parallel to the eastern edge of the Asiatic continent, and the analogous orientation of its basic mountain ranges has been caused by the strike of the tectonic lines of this arc. The rock strata comprising the island are extended in the same direction. The oldest of this rock is from the Precambrian metamorphic basement, but on the surface it can be found only in the eastern part of the island where it forms high mountain ranges. The basic rock of Taiwan is Cenozoic geosynclinal sediment. Judging from the character of the stratification and the significant break in sedimentation, during the Eocene and Miocene there were strong orogenic movements and a general uplift began and subsequently continued. The processes of folding involved predominantly the deposits of the central and eastern parts of the island where mountain chains were formed. The western part of the island was uplifted latest, and here there developed littoral depressions which are uplifted areas of the sea bottom.

The uplifting was complicated by the disjunctive dislocations which were marked by particular intensity during the Neogene-Quaternary Age. The faults and fissures which can be observed chiefly along the axis of the island and also show a north-northeast strike broke the mountain chains into individual blocks, and various sections of the island began to experience movements which differed both in direction and amplitude. At the same time, on Taiwan and in the territory of the nearby seas there was particularly intensive volcanic activity, as a consequence of which lava flows poured out on the surface of the island, and in the Taiwan Straits a number of islands arose. These include the Pescadores formed of basalt lava, and other smaller ones.

At the present the tectonic movements in this area undoubtedly are continuing and have a differentiated character. The recent movements in the eastern part of the island have been marked by particular intensity and this can be clearly seen in the relief. Here first of all there are numerous recent faults which have determined the direction of the valleys. Moreover, parallel to the coast there stretches a young anticlinal ridge the rapid development of which can be seen from the antecedent character of the river valleys cutting through it. According to the data of seismologists, on Taiwan and in the neighboring areas of the ocean from 1909 to 1952 there were about 25 earthquakes of force 8-9 and more (G. P. Gorshkov, 1960).

Fluvial erosion and aggradation are important exogenic processes within Taiwan which have played a very great role in the formation of the sculptural relief features. In the alpine areas one can observe traces of glaciation.

In the topography of Taiwan one can establish two basic parts--mountainous and plain. The mountains of Taiwan

occupy virtually two-thirds of the island and consist of four
basic ranges running parallel to one another.   A significant
portion of the Taiwan islands reaches very great altitudes
(22 peaks are higher than 3, 500 meters), and this is not
characteristic for the remaining islands of this area; they
also show sharp alpine landforms with the extensive development of traces of ancient glaciation and a dense deeply incised river network.   The plains of Taiwan are typically flat
depressions; they are composed of alluvial-marine deposits.

CHAPTER **2** THE NATURAL
ZONING OF
CHINA

V. T. Zaychikov
USSR Academy of Sciences
Institute of Geography

With the exceptional extensiveness of the territory of
China and the contrast in its natural conditions, naturally
one might expect great differences in the landscapes of this
nation. In fact, in natural terms, individual portions of
China differ sharply, comprising unique complexes of natural conditions. This circumstance makes it essential in
studying the physical geography of China to view the nature
of this land not only in terms of its basic components, but
also in terms of its individual natural regions.

In the geographical study of China, the regional ap-
proach has long been used. Even in the early geographical
work of the Chinese Yükung which dates, as is supposed, to
the eighth-fifth centuries B.C., a zoning of the nation is
given. In this work all of China which at that time comprised only the eastern portion of the present territory of
the state was divided into nine major regions: Chingchou
comprising the territory of the northern half of the Great
China Plain and the nearby mountainous regions; Yungchou
lying more to the west of the former in the Loess Region;
Yuchou in the basin of the headwaters of the Hwang Ho;
Hsuchou in the basin of the lower reaches of the same river;
Yenchou in the basin of the lower courses of the Chiho;
Ch'inchou occupying the Shantung Peninsula; Lienchou in the
Szechwan Basin; Chingchou in the basin of the middle
reaches the Yangtze and Yangchou covering the entire south-
east from the lower courses of the Yangtze, including Kiangs
and Kwantung.

Characteristically, the regions given in Yükung are
not connected with the existing administrative division of
the nation at that time and basically are major physical-
geographical areas. Within these regions, they give a description of the nature and the economy.

The regional description of Chinese geography is
characteristic also for later geographical works by Chinese. These are particularly detailed in the very old multi-
volume basic work Tifangchi (Descriptions of the Locality).
In the geographical literature on China published in European languages, regional descriptions have also predominated. This literature has made extensive use of the tradi-
tional division of China into the eastern and western halves
with a subsequent subdividing of each of the major portions
into smaller regions. The eastern half of the nation is
usually divided into Manchuria or Northeastern China covering the territory of the northeast of the Great China Plain;
North China; South China separated by the longitudinal
Ch'inling Range; and Southwest China covering the Yunnan
Uplands and Kweichow. Frequently in these works they
give a more detailed dividing, in particular they establish
Central China as a particular region covering basically the
middle and lower courses of the Yangtze. For the western
half of the nation, the most characteristic division is into
the Chinese Gobi, the Tarim Basin, Dzungaria, the Eastern
Tien Shan, the Kunlun and Tibet.

Among the authors of various works on the geography
of China, one can note a basic difference in the setting of the
boundaries for the given regions, as well as in the composition and content. It is rather difficult to evaluate the various systems used for the zoning of China since virtually in
all of these works describing the regions, as a rule, they
have not given explanations as to the principles and methods
of establishing the regions.

Only most recently have the questions of the physical-
geographical zoning of China been worked out in the writings
of geographers in the Chinese People's Republic.

As a result of the research, in 1956, they prepared
and published a preliminary variation for the natural zoning

of China* which was subsequently basically reworked and accepted in final form in 1959.

The zoning worked out by Chinese scientists for the nation consists of a number of systems of special types of zoning (geomorphological, climatic, hydrological, hydro-geological, soil, geobotanical, zoogeographical), as well as systems of integrated natural zoning for the nation. For each of the designated types of zoning, they have compiled maps and extensive texts which explain the principles used for dividing the nation into the various regions and which give detailed descriptions of the established regions.

In zoning the nation, the Chinese scientists have con-sidered the uniqueness of the territory of China, the com-plexity of the structure and the great diversity in its nat-ural conditions which make particular demands in terms of selecting the classifying features. The integrated natural zoning which has been worked out is ultimately based upon the bioclimatic principle which reflects the relationships of the climate with the soil cover, vegetation and animal world, and also with agriculture. This factor has been given preference as the chief one (in any event for the higher stages of zoning) in the aim of more fully reflecting the zonal patterns of nature in the zoning.

The establishing of the regions under this classifica-tion (bioclimatic) has been preceded by a preliminary divid-ing of the entire territory of the nation into basic major por-tions--eastern monsoon, Mongolian-Sinkiang Upland and the Tsinghai-Tibetan Upland (done not by the zonal principle), and also by dividing the territory into thermal belts. The establishing of the latter can be explained by the necessity of previously showing the territorial differences in the dis-tribution of heat.

----

*This work was published in a Russian translation by the Foreign Literature Publishing House in 1957 under the title Fizikogeograficheskoye rayonirovaniye Kitaya (The Physical-Geographical Zoning of China), No. 1, Moscow, Foreign Literature Publishing House, 1957.

In using the differences in the total active temperatures (having in mind the air temperature total during the
days with a mean daily temperature of more than 10°), the
entire territory of China can be divided into six thermal
belts which follow one another from north to south; the cold-
temperate (with a total active temperature less than 1,700°),
temperate (1,700-3,200°), warm-temperate (3,200-4,500°),
subtropical (4,500-8,000°), tropical (8,000-9,000°) and
equatorial (approximately 9,500°).

Each of these thermal belts, in turn, can be divided
into areas which in the described zoning of the Chinese geographers is viewed as the largest region (first degree). As
the basis for establishing the areas they have used the humidity indices (the ratio of possible evaporability to the
amount of precipitation). Most completely these areas are
shown in the temperate and warm-temperate belts (humid,
semihumid, semiarid and arid).

The subsequent and second-in-number taxonomic unit
is the natural zone and subzone. These are established in
the areas in terms of the internal differences in the soil
types and the classes of vegetation formation--for example,
the zone of the forest-steppe and the leached black soils,
the zone of steppes and black soils. Thus, at this level in
the taxonomic ladder, the climatic features which have been
used to establish the thermal belts and the areas are sup-
plemented by the biogeographical.

As a total within China they have established 29 natural zones. The next taxonomic subdivisions in this zoning
are the province, district and region. The provinces are
established according to the intrazonal bioclimatic differences and features of the topography. In turn, they are
broken down into districts depending upon the topography
and lithology, and the districts into regions. It should be
noted that in the zoning done by the Chinese scientists, the
provinces, districts and regions have been reflected chiefly
only in the taxonomic system. In the regional descriptions,
the characteristics of these subdivisions are absent and on
the maps there are no boundaries for the districts and regions. It is supposed that these lowest-rank subdivisions
will be established and mapped later with further detailiza-
tion of the zoning.

Particularly valuable in this work has been the sys-
tematization of the natural landscapes according to the bioclimatic features with the use of quantitative indices (the
total active temperatures, the dryness indices, the runoff
indices, etc.). As a result of the research they have worked
out and depicted on a map the natural system of landscapes
in the nation and, which is equally important, they have
shown the relationships and patterns for the combinations of
the individual landscapes. The situation of the individual
regions is somewhat different in the total system of landscapes for the nation. For example, previously the Liaotung Peninsula was viewed as an organic portion of Northeastern China, but according to the new zoning they have
established a commonness in the natural conditions of this
territory with Northern China (the same balance of heat and
moisture, a commonness in the soil-vegetation cover).

The consistent use of the bioclimatic principle in the
zoning has helped to introduce greater clarity in determining
the boundaries for the individual landscapes, for example,
of Southern China.

In contrast to the former understanding of this region
which covered an extensive territory in the south of the
Yangtze including both the tropical and subtropical areas, in
the new zoning the subtropical territories have been clearly
delimited from the extreme south with its tropical landscapes.

At the same time we should note that in the designated
system of zoning there are certain disputed ideas; for example, the basic taxonomic units are construed chiefly according to the latitudinal-zonal principle without proper con-
sideration to the structure of the surface and certain other
factors. However, in zoning such a complex territory as
China is in terms of its structure, one can scarcely use the
latitudinal-zonal principle as the chief one in working out a
system of regions, even of the highest rank. If the surface
of this land were more homogeneous, and if it were not bordered by the great ocean basin, the latitudinal-zonal factors
undoubtedly would be much more expressed. But China is
predominantly a mountainous land with very high uplands
which create an extremely complex surface with great contrasts in the hypsometric levels, inclines and exposures for

the slopes. On the other hand, in occupying the border position on the continent directly next to the ocean, China has
constantly experienced the consequences of the fight between
continental and oceanic influences. If there were not the
Eastern Asian and Indian monsoons, China which lies basically within the latitudes of the high-pressure subtropical
belt would undoubtedly be a desert. It is because of the monsoons that significant areas of the subtropical territories in
the eastern and southern portions of the republic receive a
great deal of moisture and are marked by the distribution of
forest landscapes.

But the influence of the monsoons, like the mountainousness of the territory of China and in general all of Eastern Asia, has fundamentally changed the type of zonality
which is characteristic for the extensive plains of the northern and western portions of Eurasia; instead of the longitudinal-
horizontal zones which are found in the plains of the Western Siberia and Europe, here the natural zones assume a
strike which is close to meridional. The influence of the
oceanic monsoons and the mountainousness of the territory
have caused a unique and complex zonal structure for nature.
While in the east of China the latitudinal zonality has been
somewhat shifted but is still clearly traceable, in the western alpine portion of the nation we can clearly see the patterns of vertical zonality. Under these conditions, in the
physical-geographical zoning of the nation the orographic
factor, like the particular features in atmospheric circulation, undoubtedly in all stages of the zoning should be given
much more significance than has been done in the designated work.

The designated zoning has been worked out by Chinese
scientists for the purposes of agricultural production, and
due to this it does not as sharply show the bioclimatic as-
pect. However, undoubtedly its major significance is for
the physical-geographical study of China. In preparing this
chapter, the materials of the described zoning have
been widely used in general descriptions of the physical geography of the nation and particularly in the regional portion
of the work. In it they have considered the basic criteria
for dividing China into regions, and these data have been
used in constructing the system of physical-geographic regions in the monograph. The latter undoubtedly differs

from the system of zoning by the Chinese scientists since
the monograph is aimed at a general geographic study of
China for which both the bioclimatic and orotectonic aspects
are important.

The zoning used in the monograph proceeds from the
belonging of the Chinese territory to four natural areas of
Asia--Eastern Asia, Southern Asia, Central Asia and the
Tsinghai-Tibetan Uplands--which differ sharply in terms of
the character of the natural conditions. These major portions of Asia comprising the territory of China can be broken
down into smaller units. Thus, in the eastern portion of the
nation, as the basic regions we have maintained the division
used in geographical literature into the Northeastern, Northern, Southeastern and Southwestern China. However, the
composition of the territory for each of these regions has
been changed considering the data of zoning done by the Chinese scientists: In the northeast of China they have included in the monsoon portion of the land the territories of
the temperate belt. In the north of China there are the territories of a transitional character from temperate to subtropical, and finally, to the southeast and southwest there are
the subtropics. The latter have been divided into the given
two regions in line with the great difference in the structure
of the surface caused by fundamental differences in the character of the subtropical landscapes for these regions.

For the Central Asiatic portion we have also kept the
name "Northwest China" which is used in literature. This
region covers the territory of the steppes and deserts
stretching in a belt from the Khingan to the Pamirs. In
Northwest China we have not included the Tsaidam Depression and the western portion of the Nanshan which have similar bioclimatic conditions for this region but orotectonically
are closely linked with the Tsinghai-Tibetan Uplands. According to this latter feature, the Tsaidam Depression and
the Western Nanshan are viewed as a portion of the Tsinghai-
Tibetan Uplands as natural portions of it.

In describing the listed basic regions of China, in each
of them we have had to individually view also the smaller
natural complexes. They have been established depending
upon the character of the natural conditions of the region,

their internal differences and features, but making sure that the scheme of the regions was not too broken up and that the established parts actually had basic distinguishing features.

CHAPTER **3** NORTHEAST
CHINA

N. M. Kazakova
USSR Academy of Sciences
Institute of Geography

Northeast China is the northernmost region of the
land. It lies on the edge of the continent and thus is under
the intensive influence of both the continental and oceanic
pressures. Various portions of this region have different
temperature conditions, a differing degree of moisture, and
various soil, floristic and faunistic complexes. In essence
this is a transitional region from the sharply continental
Siberia and Central Asia to the humid monsoon maritime region, and therefore its nature is extremely unique and is
marked by great contrasts. The contrasts are further intensified by the character of the topography, where the chief
feature is the alternation between mountains and low plains
extending in a meridional direction. The mountains as a
whole are not very high--as a rule, not more than 1,000-
1,500 meters above sea level, and only individual ranges
and peaks rise up to 2,500-2,700 meters and somewhat
higher.

The climate of Northeast China is marked by a very
cold and little-snow winter which is typical for a larger
portion of the region and a humid summer which is not hot.
Towards the south there is a gradual rise in temperature,
but only in the southernmost portions of the region is the
winter significantly warmer. The thinness of the snow
cover helps in the deep freezing of the soil and this, in
turn, leads to the formation of a seasonal permafrost layer
which covers large areas. The greatest amount of

precipitation, as a rule, falls in July, and the summer
rains frequently have a torrential character. The amount
of precipitation drops basically (if one discards the influence of the topography) from the southeast to the northwest.
In line with the cyclonic disturbances, the amount of precipitation fluctuates sharply over the years.

The river network of Northeast China is rather dense.
The river regime is caused basically by the regime of precipitation which shows an unevenness of runoff which is both
seasonal and over many years. The low water levels here
are in the winter when the amount of precipitation is least
and falls in a solid state. The highest are in the middle
of the summer and this is due to the maximum amount of
precipitation and to the increase in the amount of groundwater due to the thawing of the seasonal permafrost and the
low water permeability of the soil. The diverse topography
of Northeast China with the significant fluctuations in the
relative altitudes and in places rather sharp transitions
from mountains to lowland plains has helped in the acceler-
ated river runoff and overflows in the plains where the
floodwaters ordinarily cover extensive areas.

The existence of a permafrost horizon at a shallow
depth has caused the extensive development of permafrost
processes in the relief formation and in particular the predominance of lateral erosion processes and also the strong
development of swamping processes due to which in the
northern part of the region there has been a very broad development of swamps and swampy areas which have developed in general more or less independently of the landforms
and the elevation. The swamping, in its turn, has caused
the extensive development of meadow and gley soil formation processes and has created favorable conditions for
growing meadow and swamp vegetation.

At the same time the weathering and erosion processes have occurred relatively slowly in the northern part.
The frost weathering processes show the greatest intensity
and these processes are particularly seen on the barren
peaks and slopes of mountains, and as a result of this, rock
streams have formed here which in places cover significant
areas. In line with the very slight weathering processes,
the soil formation processes have occurred slowly. The

soils, with the exception of the valleys and the low portions
of the slopes, are thin (usually 20-50 cm.), poor in nutrients, while the soil temperature due to the closeness of the
frost layer is low, and therefore here only modest plants
will grow.

In the southern and particularly in the eastern portions of the region, where the air temperature is higher,
the amount of precipitation is greater and soil freezing is
absent, and thus the processes of physical weathering and
river erosion begin to take on greater significance, and
here riverbed erosion predominates. The degree of intensity of these processes depends upon a number of factors
including the lithology of the rock, the vegetation cover, etc.
The soil formation processes also occur much more intensively, and therefore the soil is thicker and richer in nutrients, and the vegetation is diverse.

The territory of Northeast China lies within the forest,
forest-steppe and steppe zones. A larger portion of the region lies in the forest and steppe zones. The forest zone includes the northern portion of the Greater Khingan, the Chinese portion of the Lesser Khingan and the Eastern Manchurian Mountains. In the steppe zone are the southern half of
the Greater Khingan and the Northeast Plain. In the forest-
steppe zone are the northern portion of the Northeast Plain,
the northeast portion of the Lesser Khingan, the middle portion of the Greater Khingan, and also the Sankiang and the
Chinese portion of the Khingan Depression.

The latitudinal direction of the geographical zone
within Northeast China has thus been greatly disturbed because of the geographical placement of the
region and the meridional orientation of the orographic
units. Thus, in the western colder and drier portion of the
region far to the south, following the direction of the Greater
Khingan, stretches a tongue of tayga forests reaching approximately up to 47° n. lat. At the same latitudes in the mountains of the warmer and moister eastern portion there have
developed coniferous-broad-leafed forests of the Far Eastern type, and the southern boundary of these forests drops
beyond the limit of the region. On the plain enclosed within
the mountains virtually up to 48° n. lat. there rise steppes
with a transition from the drier southern to the moister

northern varieties; above lies the forest-steppe which reaches into the Zeya-Bureya Depression of the Soviet Union, i.e., to the north of 50° n. lat. At the same time, to the west of the Greater Khingan on the same latitudes one will find dry steppes and typical semideserts.

The geographical zones thus take on a common direction from northwest to southeast and this is caused by the moistening influence of the ocean. The boundaries of the individual landscape zones to a very great degree have been subordinate to the topography and therefore are extremely winding. In truth, at present the natural landscapes here to one degree or another have been changed by the economic activity of man, but nevertheless the basic patterns in the distribution of the landscape zones can be traced rather clearly.

The significant extent of Northeast China from north to south and from west to east and the diverse topography of the region thus lead to the great landscape differences in its individual parts.

The slight glaciation of the mountains in Northeast China here has not had a direct effect upon the formation of the present landscapes. The strong glaciation of the neighboring mountains of Siberia and Mongolia, as was correctly noted by E. M. Murzayev (1955), here can be seen only indirectly, in the general cooling of the climate which, however, has not caused fundamental changes in the organic world since at present the relics of Tertiary and Upper Mesozoic plants and animals are numerous here. A. N. Krishtofovich feels that the modern flora of the Far East is Tertiary temperate flora which has reigned here since the end of the Cretaceous Age (A. N. Krishtofovich, 1936).

The largest physical-geographic units of Northeast China are the Greater Khingan, the Chinese portion of the Lesser Khingan, the Eastern Manchurian Mountains, the Northeast Plain and the Sankiang Depression.

THE GREATER KHINGAN

This is a well-expressed medium-elevation range (with average elevations of 1,200-1,300 meters above sea level, maximum 2,034 meters), oriented generally almost meridionally with a characteristic sharp asymmetry in the western and eastern slopes. The latter has been caused by the presence of a major Mesozoic fault along the eastern slope of the mountains, and also by the subsequent uplifting of their western portion and the subsidence of the Northeast Plain. The mountains are composed predominantly of igneous rock, and in the northern and central portions one will widely find granites and basalts, and in the south liparites and quartz trachytes. The sedimentary rock is encountered only in certain areas and generally does not cover large areas.

In the topography of the Greater Khingan there predominate gentle smooth landforms: mountains with flat peaks and gentle slopes and broad flat-bottomed valleys. The mountains, as a rule, are covered by fragments of bedrock and fine-grained material of the weathering crust. Towards the bottom the slopes level out and change into slightly inclined deluvial trains which border the foothills. The valleys are usually composed of friable deposits, they have well-expressed terraces and in the north are usually swampy. The valley heads are particularly broad and slightly incut. An exception is the eastern steep slope of the Greater Khingan which is broken up by narrow deeply incut river valleys and in general is much better watered which is due to the climatic features in the territory of Northeast China.

Due to the significant extent of the Greater Khingan from north to south (it stretches along the meridian for almost 10°), the character of the climate, soils and vegetation in the northern and southern portions of it differs sharply.

The northern portion of the mountains (approximately to the north of the Khalkhin-Gol and T'aoerh rivers) is the coldest territory not only for Northeast China, but for all of Eastern China in general. The winter here is extremely severe, dry and long, lasting seven months. The mean temperatures are -28°, with maximums dropping down to

-50° C., the amount of winter precipitation is about 200 mm. (maximum 400 mm.) of the 500 mm. annually, the soil is deeply frozen, and permafrost has developed over large areas.

Due to the low air temperatures during the larger portion of the year, to the presence of permafrost and the gentle topography, the moisture in the soil (regardless of the slight amount of atmospheric precipitation) is in general sufficient for the development of forest vegetation, but the specific composition of the forests here is poor. The Daurian larch (Larix Gmelinii, L. dahurica) is most widely found in the mountains of the northern portion of the Greater Khingan; besides it on individual areas there has been rather good development of pine (Pinus sylvestris var. mongolica), Asian white birch (Betual platyphylla) and aspen (Populus tremula), in the south one will frequently encounter the Mongolian oak (Quercus mongolica). In the undergrowth and on the deforested areas one will widely find a shrub grassy vegetation but its specific composition is also monotonous. Of the shrubs one will most frequently encounter rhododendron (Rhododendron mucronulata); in addition, here there grow foxberry (Vaccininium vitis-idaea), wild rosemary (Lednum palustre), and alder (Alnus fruticosa). Of the grasses there is rough blue-joint reedgrass (Calamagrostis langsdorfii), lily of the valley (Convallaria majalis), several species of sedge and moss, chiefly sphagnum.

The vegetation of the northern part of the Greater Khingan is related to the Daurian flora. Here predominate forests and the largest areas are covered by forests consisting of Daurian larch followed by birch, aspen and pine groves and the birch and aspen groves are in essence the secondary forests of the Daurian larch forests. A more limited area is covered by shrub and swamp associations. The former are made up of associations of Pinus pumila, Daurian juniper (Juniperus dahurica) and dwarf arctic birch (Betaul fruticosa); the latter of sedge, sphagnum mosses and reedgrass (Calamagrostis hirsuta).

The light coniferous tayga of Northeast China is, as is known, the southernmost variation of the Eurasian tayga and differs from it in the unique character of the soil formation processes. Thus, while for the tayga of the more northern latitudes there is a characteristic virtually exclusive predominance of podzol formation, for the tayga of Northeast China with the warmer and drier climate, along with the podzol formation predominating here, the appearance of a sod process is also typical. The podzol formation in the majority of instances has been accompanied by a gley process which has encompassed the lower portion of the soil profile which has been due to the frost. In the area where mixed forests have developed, the podzol formation has been combined with brown soil formation and as a result various varieties of brown soils have also been formed. The basic soils in the northern portion of the Greater Khingan are soddy-podzolic, brown-podzolic, gley brown-podzolic, meadow and swamp.

Vertical zonality is generally not very clearly expressed within this portion of the Greater Khingan. Of course, the climate, soil and vegetation change somewhat with altitude, but there are no sharp changes here. If one tries to follow the character of the vegetation in the various altitude belts, then the following emerges. The upper forest boundary here lies at elevations about 1,400 meters above sea level. The upper belt (from 1,200 to 1,400 meters) is made up of a shrub growth of Pinus pumila with sparse short-trunked specimens of larch, lichens and mosses. Below 1,200 meters grows a coniferous forest consisting chiefly of larch, but on the southern-exposure slopes pine groves are common. In the lower portions of the slopes the larch tayga is replaced by the secondary birch-larch and birch-aspen forest. To the south of 52-50° n. lat., the lower portions of the slopes are covered by forest-steppe. Along the river valleys the steppe meadows stretch far to the north. In the forests of the northern portion of the Greater Khingan live marten, the northern deer, elk, the blue hare and other animals typical for the Siberian Tayga with many fur-bearing animals among them.

Most widely found in the northern portion of the Greater Khingan are landscapes of larch-rhododendron forests developed predominantly on the brown podzolic soils. Also widely found are landscapes of a larch-grassy forest on the soddy-podzolic soils usually confined to the lower and gentler slopes. The higher areas and the steep slopes are covered by larch and Pinus pumila. In the forests on the

very rocky slopes where only creeping plants can grow, one
will encounter thickets of Daurian juniper, ferns and lichens.
On the poorly drained areas of terraces and gentle slopes
one will find larch-ledum areas on gley brown-podzolic
soils. Where the drainage is particularly bad, for example,
on areas with permafrost, ledum-sphagnum larch forests
will grow. On relatively dry areas, usually on the steep
southern slopes, pine-rhododendron-foxberry associations
will grow. The leafy forests are represented usually by
grassy and rhododendron birch and aspen forests. Along the
banks of rivers on the low terraces there have developed
meadow and particularly the meadow-swamp landscapes
made up of sedge, sphagnum mosses, swamp rhododendron
and willow. Here on the swampy soils one will frequently
encounter a relatively thick layer of peat.

As one moves to the south, the amount of coniferous
strains gradually drops, and there are more and more mixed
forests which, in turn, are replaced by forest-steppe. In
the southern portion of the Greater Khingan, the forest-
steppe landscapes no longer cover the slopes, but conversely,
the upper portions of the mountains (above 1,500 meters
above sea level). The tree varieties here are more diverse--
Mongolian oak (Quercus mongolica), Mongolian linden (Tilia
mongolica), birch (Betula Ermanii and B. platphylla), willow (Salix viminea), elm (Ulmus propinqua), pine (Pinus
mongolica), cherry (Prunus padus), etc.; of the grasses
steppe associations appear--feather grass (Stipa baicalensis), koeleria (Koeleria gracilis), etc.

In general the climate in the southern portion of the
Greater Khingan is significantly warmer than the north and
is very dry. Mean January temperatures are -14, -16°, the
snow cover is thin and of short duration; the snow lasts all
of one and a half or two months. The annual amount of precipitation drops to 250-300 mm.; summer precipitation falls
basically in the form of lightning storms and this causes intensive erosion and flooding in the piedmont plains. During
the spring the precipitation is slight (less than 15 per cent
of the annual amount), the temperature sharply rises and
there are very strong winds, frequently dry winds.

The vegetation in the southern portion of the Greater
Khingan is basically steppe and is related predominantly to

the Mongolian flora; here there are no forest associations, there are few meadow associations, and shrubs are rarely encountered. The annual amount of precipitation here favors the growth of a tall-grass vegetation. The steppes, as a rule, have a virtually solid grass cover; among the grasses predominate gramen, but one will also encounter legumes and Compositae. The specific composition of the steppes at the various altitudes changes insignificantly in general. The steppes are basically feather grass but one will also encounter Aneurolepidium chinense, bistort (Cleistogenus squarrosa), koeleria (Koeleria gracilis), sage (Artemisia frigida, etc.), Siberian tansy (Tanacetum sibiricum), astragalus (Astragalus adsurgens), caragana (Caragana microphylla), and alfalfa (Medicargo ruthenica). The chief soil formation processes are the sod processes and carbonization, and as a result various varieties of chestnut soils have developed. Among the animals rodents predominate such as hamsters, susliks and zokors.

Thus, the landscapes in the southern portion of the Greater Khingan are significantly more homogeneous than the landscapes in the north. Here predominate landscapes of feather grass steppes on the dark chestnut soils. Only in individual areas of this territory which stand out in terms of the microrelief and lithology does the character of the soils and vegetation change somewhat. For example, in low areas where rainwater accumulates temporarily and the depth of the water table is from 2 to 4 meters, the sod processes become more intense and are accompanied by slight gleization and sometimes salination. As a result meadow dark-chestnut soils are formed on which grow predominantly shiny chiy (Lasiagrostis splendens), vostrets (Aneurolepidium chinense), and sometimes brome (Bromus inecmis), poa (Poa subfatigata); on the heavily swamped areas of the floodplains and low terraces reed grows. In those areas where the groundwater level lies at a depth of 1-2 meters meadow salt swamps are formed and more rarely alkali areas; the salinization is basically sulfate. On the sands primitive chestnut and sandy chestnut soils have developed and on them grow wildrye (Elymus mollis), tickseed (Corispemum thelelegium), caragana (Caragana zahibrucneri) and certain species of shrubs, for example, the Siberian apricot (Prunus sibiricum), hawthorn (Crataegus

pinnatifida), lespedeze (Lespedeza bicolor), etc. On areas
of shifting sands grows Agrophyllum arenarium.

THE CHINESE PORTION OF THE
LESSER KHINGAN

The Chinese portion of the Lesser Khingan--the lowest
mountains in Northeast China--occupies the smallest area of
all of the mountainous systems in the region. This is a typical denudation low-mountain relief where elevations on the
average are 400-600 meters above sea level and only individual sparse peaks somewhat exceed 1,000 meters. In terms
of the general appearance of the topography, the Chinese
portion of the Lesser Khingan is very similar to the northern
portion of the Greater Khingan, regardless of the fact that
the pre-Neogene history in the development of these mountain systems was not the same. While the Greater Khingan
and the southern portion of the Lesser Khingan (to the south
of the line running between the towns of T'eli and Poshan)
composed of crystalline rock began to be formed in the Upper Paleozoic and during the Yenshan Age the mountain
ranges rose here, the northern portion of the Lesser Khingan composed of Mesozoic sandstone and shales and young
basalts up until the Quaternary Age was an intermontane
trough which connected the northeastern and Zeya-Bureya
plains. A general uplift in the Lesser Khingan recently has
disturbed this link and the mountains were formed in their
present state.

This uplift brought about a fundamental change in the
river system of the basin in the present middle portion of the
Amur. Thus, on the basis of our geomorphological observations, it may be supposed that during this time there was
formed that portion in the middle course of the Amur which
lies between the town of Heihe in the north and the Sankiang
Plain in the south. Here where the southern portion of the
Lesser Khingan abuts the Bureya Range where the river
flows along a narrow valley, the river evidently used a fault
with a northwest strike. The Sungari River also made its
way along a fault which passes along the boundary of the Lesser Khingan and the Eastern Manchurian Mountains. At the
same time, there occurred the subsidence of the Sankiang

Basin and this caused the capturing of the river systems of
the Zeya-Bureya and the Northeast Plain by the Amur.

In terms of its natural features, the Chinese portion of
the Lesser Khingan occupies an intermediate position with
the northern portion close to the northern portion of the
Greater Khingan, and the southern to the northern portion of
the Eastern Manchurian Mountains. The winter and summer
temperatures are here somewhat higher than in the Greater
Khingan (mean January temperature is -26°, mean July temperature +22°), and there is more precipitation. As we have
already noted, permafrost develops here.

The weathering processes, particularly in the south,
occur somewhat more intensively and due to this the soils
are thicker and richer in nutrients.

Of the vegetation associations, here predominate forests with a specific composition that is more diverse than in
the Greater Khingan but poorer than in the Eastern Manchurian Mountains. In the northern lower Chinese portion of the
Lesser Khingan one will encounter landscapes of the forest-
steppe which, on the one hand, as we have already noticed,
extend directly into the Zeya-Bureya Depression, and on the
other hand, in the form of a narrow tongue are connected
with the forest steppe of the Northeast Plain.

The soil formation in the designated region has occurred basically according to the type of podzol formation
which is usually accompanied by a gley process and by
brown soil formation; within the Chinese portion of the Lesser Khingan, podzolic and brown forest soils have basically
developed, and in the valleys there are meadow-swamp and
swamp soils.

The basic landscapes in this portion of the Lesser
Khingan are in the north larch-birch forests and forest-
steppe, and in the south coniferous-broad-leafed forests,
while along the river valleys and depressions there are
swampy and wet meadows. The transition of one forest type
into another is gradual. The landscapes of the larch-birch
forests on the slightly podzolic soils with a predominance of
Daurian larch and tayga fauna change directly into the forests of the Greater Khingan and in essence are analogous to

them. The forest-steppe landscape in terms of the specific composition of the vegetation is very close to the forest-steppe of the Zeya-Bureya Plain and territorially only the Amur River separates them. Here the basic vegetation formations are, according to P. D. Yaroshenko (1958), shrub oak groves with a predominance of Mongolian oak (Quercus mongolica) with the absence of Daurian birch (Betula dahurica), lespedeza (Lespedeza bicolor), and certain others which are frequently confined to the slopes of mountains and hills, and steppe meadows with poa (Poa angustifolia), koeleria (Koeleria gracilis), bedstraw (Galium boreale and G. verum), sage (Artemisia selengensis and A. manshurica), clover (Trifolium lupinaster), vetch (Vicia amoena), etc., along the low terraces above the floodplain. Along the river valleys here one will encounter forests of Daurian larch (Larix dahurica), elm (Ulmus propinqua), poplar (Populus suaveolens), maple (Acer ginuala), willow (Salix hsinganica and S. triandra), etc.; on the dunes there are oak-pine forests, along the depressions birch thickets together with wet meadows and swampy thickets. The landscapes of the coniferous-broad-leafed forests on the brown forest soils with a fauna of the mixed forests represent a northern variety of the Eastern Manchurian forests of the Far Eastern type with the vegetation cover related to the Manchurian flora. In the coniferous broad-leafed forests in the Chinese portion of the Lesser Khingan there predominates Korean cedar (Pinus koraiensis), and aside from this there is larch (Larix dahurica), jeddo spruce (Picea jezoensis), yew (Taxus chinensis), birch and elms.

THE EASTERN MANCHURIAN MOUNTAINS

The Eastern Manchurian Mountains, or--as they are called--the Eastern Manchurian mountainous land, occupy a significant area and are very complex in natural terms, and this to a significant degree has been caused by the complexity of the topography in this territory.

The Eastern Manchurian Mountains are the highest mountains in Northeast China. Their elevations on the average are 1,500-1,700 meters above sea level, and individual peaks exceed 2,000-2,500 meters. The central portion of this mountain system is the highest: The ranges of Changkuangts'ailing and Laoyehling, and the Ch'angpaishan Plateau.

Within the latter lies the highest peak, Mount Pait'oushan (Paektusan) which borders North Korea.

A characteristic feature of the Eastern Manchurian Mountains is the alternation of ranges with a northeastern strike and longitudinal intermontane basins which are broadest in the northern portion of the mountains. The ranges are composed predominantly of granites and metamorphic rock and more rarely sedimentary rock; they have, as a rule, rather flat level watershed areas and steep very rugged slopes. The intermontane tectonic depressions have been filled usually with friable Meso-Cenozoic and recent deposits. The presence of these large intermontane troughs to a significant degree has caused the distribution of the hydrographic network and the largest rivers are longitudinal and consecutive. As in the Khingan Mountains, the present rivers in no way correspond to the valley widths. Aside from the longitudinal valleys the mountains are heavily broken up by cross valleys which differ in the alternation of narrow rocky and broad sections. In the eastern portion of the mountains where during the Neogene and Quaternary ages the volcanic eruptions were particularly strong, extensive basalt plateaus have greatly developed along with the cones of extinct volcanos and crater lakes. These heavy lava eruptions which occurred along the lines of the revived Mesozoic faults and covered enormous areas to a significant degree transformed the ancient relief and brought about changes in the direction of the river network. The lavas filled in the valleys, caused changes in the rivers, rejuvenated certain sections of them and developed new lakes (for example, Lake Chinpo), waterfalls (T'ienshuilou) and new channels.

The general picture of the hydrographic network here generally has a radial character. The rivers in the northern and eastern portions of the mountains such as the Sungari, Mutankiang, Mulingho and others are related to the Amur Basin, the rivers in the southwestern portion to the basins of the Liaoho and Yalungkiang, and the rivers in the southeastern portion are in the system of the T'umenkiang River. The rivers cutting through the Eastern Manchurian Mountains, as a rule, carry a great deal of water; there are frequent rapids; they flow rapidly, have a steep drop and have greatly eroded the slopes. In contrast to the Khingan, here the role of river channel erosion is very great.

In climatic terms, the Eastern Manchurian Mountains
are the wettest portion of Northeast China. The amount of
annual precipitation here exceeds 750 mm. and in the southern part reaches (and sometimes even exceeds) 1, 000 mm.;
the maximum amount of precipitation (up to 1, 600 mm.)
will be found on the southeastern slope of the Ch'angpaishan.
The air temperatures, particularly the winter ones, here are
significantly higher than in the Khingan (mean January temperatures fluctuate from -20° in the north up to -10° and
less in the south), although on the high peaks of the Ch'angpaishan snow will be found for more than six months a year.

In comparison with the above described mountains of
the Khingan, the natural conditions of the Eastern Manchurian Mountains are significantly more favorable for the
growing of diverse vegetation. The warm period of the year
is longer here, the summer temperatures are higher, there
is a greater amount of annual precipitation, and soil freezing is virtually absent. The weathering processes occur
here more intensively, and therefore the soil cover is significantly thicker and richer in nutrients.

The vegetation of the Eastern Manchurian Mountains
is related to the Manchurian flora. Here predominate forests with a very diverse specific composition and with many
endemics. The basic soil-forming processes are clay accumulation, sod processes and podzolization. On level
areas, as in the Khingan Mountains, swamping processes
have widely developed, but here they have been caused not
by the presence of a frost horizon but by the poor evaporation.

The animal world is rich and diverse. Here one will
find the lynx, leopard, bear, raccoon dog and many other
species typical for the forests of the Far Eastern type.

The great extent of the Eastern Manchurian Mountains, the sharp fluctuations in elevation and the varying degree of ruggedness lead to fundamental landscape differences for the individual portions of this mountainous territory. First of all here, in contrast to the other mountains
of Northeast China, vertical zonality is very clearly expressed. The Chinese scientists have established in the
Eastern Manchurian Mountains the following vegetation belts

(Chu Tse-fan et al., 1958); 1) secondary mixed leafy forests predominate at elevations from 250 to 500 meters; 2) from 500 to 1,000 meters--coniferous-broad-leafed forests; 3) from 1,000 to 1,800 meters--coniferous forests; 4) from 1,800 to 2,200 meters--alpine leafy forests with an admixture of conifers; 5) above 2,200 meters--alpine meadows and shrubs.

Elevations from 500 to 1,000 meters are the most widely found in the Eastern Manchurian Mountains, and due to this vegetation of precisely this belt predominates and it is represented by mixed coniferous and deciduous leafy forests. The dominant coniferous strains are here the Korean cedar (Pinus koraiensis), the Manchurian fir (Abies holophylla), the Khingan fir (Abies nephrolepis), the jeddo and Siberian spruce (Picea jezoensis and P. obovata); the basic deciduous strains are the Asian white birch, the Daurian and yellow birth (Betula platyphylla, B. dahurica and B. lutea), the Mongolian oak (Quercus mongolica), elm (Ulmus propinqua), the Manchurian walnut (Juglans manshurica), the Amur cork (Phellodendron amurense), the Manchurian and Amur linden (Tilia manshurica and T. amurens), the mono and Manchurian maple (Acer mono and A. manshuricum), Maakia amurensis, the Manchurian ash (Fraxinis manshurica), etc. In the undergrowth there are such shrubs as filbert (Corylus manshurica), barberry (Berberis amurensis), spindle-tree (Evonimus), elder (Sambacus), viburnum (Viburnum), etc., which frequently form impassable thickets. Here there are also numerous lianas such as bower (Actinidia arguta, A. kolomikta), Amur grape (Vitis amurensis), Chinese magnolia vine (Schizandra chinensis), etc. The species of grass vegetation are also very diverse, and of them most frequently one will encounter Gryopteris crassirhizoma, Lepisorus ussuriensis, Rjrrosid petiolosa, cinnamon fern (Osmunaa cinnamomea), horsetail (Equisetum hiemale), lilies (Lilium aistichum) and many others.

Within this altitude belt, the designated forest composition generally changes little. Of course, in individual areas, one will frequently observe various combinations of vegetation species, but this is not due so much to the absolute altitude as to the specifics of the local conditions such as the steepness of the slopes, the character of the drainage, moisture, etc.

The natural conditions of the lower altitude belt (below 500 meters) are generally little different from the conditions described above, and therefore the natural forests on elevations up to 1,000 meters were, of course, rather homogeneous. At present, as a result of the felling, in the lower belt of the mountains the forests will virtually not be found. For the cedar forest the secondary forests are the broad-leafed forests consisting of Mongolian oak, maple, elm, ash and also Asian white birch and aspen. One or another may predominate at present in the given altitude belt.

At elevations up to 1,000 meters there predominate brown forest slightly podzolized soils. They have developed on high terraces, hills and mountain slopes beneath the mixed coniferous-broad-leafed forests where there is good drainage and the mechanical composition of the parent rock is not heavy. On the gentle areas with poor drainage and on the low terraces beneath the meadow and forest vegetation, depending upon the degree of moisture, there will develop meadow brown forest soils, podzolic-gley and swamp soils. The latter frequently contain a thick peat horizon.

In the following altitude belt (1,000-1,800 meters) there predominate coniferous forests the specific composition of which, in contrast to the lower portions of the mountains, as the altitude increases changes rather sharply. Thus, in the lower part of this belt (approximately up to 1,400 meters) there predominates Korean cedar, and along with this one will encounter the broad-leafed varieties of trees, shrubs, and grasses grow poorer, and of the lianas only the magnolia vine is encountered, while in the depressions there are swampy sedge and sphagnum meadows. Above the amount of cedar drops and at the same time there is an increase in the amount of Jeddo spruce, Khingan fir, Korean Daurian larch (Larix olgensis), and one begins to find rock and Manshu white birch (Betula ermanii, B. manshurica). Shrubs and grasses are very poorly developed but there is much moss.

At elevations of 1,800-2,200 meters mixed forests predominate of Korean Daurian larch and rock birch, and the Khingan fir and Jeddo spruce also grow but in a smaller amount. Beneath the forest canopy one will encounter from time to time Pinus pumila. Higher than 1,000 meters

absolute elevation, soddy-podzolic soils predominate beneath the coniferous forests.

In the upper belt (above 2,200 meters) one will find
only low shrubs, grasses, mosses and lichens. Most widely
found here is the wild rosemary, foxberry, blueberry, rhododendron (Rhododendron chrysanthum and R. redowskia-
num), willow (Salix rotundifolia) and juniper (Juniperus communis). The soils are basically alpine meadow.

In economic terms, the mountainous territories of
Northeast China are of great interest. Besides the minerals
which these mountains possess undoubtedly in abundance,
here is concentrated a significant portion of the nation's forest reserves.

The minerals have best of all been surveyed in the
Eastern Manchurian Mountains. The complex developmental
conditions of this territory have caused the formation of all
sorts of mineral sphere. According to the geological data
(A. M. Smirnov, 1954; Sun Shu and Yu. A. Khodak, 1959,
etc.), in the pre-Paleozoic crystalline rock one will find
gold, graphite, magnesite, iron ores, niobite-tantalite and
other rare metals. Certain deposits of these minerals are
very important in economic terms. Thus, for example, the
magnesite deposit at Tashih-ch'iao in the southern portion of
the mountains is one of the richest in the world; besides magnesite it contains also talc deposits. In the Muling Basin, in
the northern portion of the mountains, the largest graphite
deposit in Northeast China is found at Liumao (A. M.
Smirnov, 1954). The Anshan Basin is an important iron ore
basin.

In the Hercynian granitoids one will find a number of
polymetallic deposits, frequently with gold (for example, the
T'ienpaoshan deposit), and also iron (the Hsiaoling deposit)
and graphite (close to Mingcha) deposits. In the Upper Paleozoic sedimentary rock there are hematite beds, bauxite, refractory clays and coals; the latter, however, are marked
by low ash content. The Mesozoic sedimentary suites are
known for their coals--brown semianthracites; these deposits also have oil shales and bectonite clays; a portion of the
chalk conglomerates is gold-bearing. Polymetallic mineralization is found in the Mesozoic granites: copper, lead,

zinc, cadmium, molybdenum, wolfram and fluorite. In the
Cenozoic minerals one will find Paleogene bituminous coals
and oil shales (for example, the Fushun deposit); placer
gold is encountered in the Pliocene gravel beds and in the
Tertiary terrace and riverbed deposits.

The minerals of the Greater Khingan and the Chinese
portion of the Lesser Khingan have been little studied. Work
in recent years on the western slopes in the northern portion
of the Greater Khingan has turned up deposits and manifestations of lead, zinc, molybdenum, wolfram, copper, tin, antimony, iron, gold (in placers), and also brown coal, graphite and fluorite (V. K. Chaykovskiy, 1959). Most widely
found here are minerals of magmatic origin. The geologists have supposed that the mineralization has been due to
the granite intrusions, predominantly of Mesozoic age, and
has been confined to the tectonic faults and fissures
(Nagibina, M. S., 1959; Chaykovskiy, V. K., 1959). In the
mountains of the Chinese portion of the Lesser Khingan, at
present they have discovered deposits of graphite, iron,
gold, nickel, polymetals, copper, rare metals, fluorite, antimony and molybdenum (Wang Shiu-chang et al., 1959; Sun
Shu and Yu. A. Khodak, 1959).

The forests of Northeast China in the past were very
extensive but over the passage of time, particularly during
the Japanese occupation, they have been greatly felled, but
even now at present they cover extensive areas of the Eastern Manchurian Mountains, the Chinese portion of the Lesser Khingan and the northern portion of the Greater Khingan.
Above we have listed the basic tree varieties growing in the
forests of Northeast China. The majority of these trees is
commercial. Thus, for example, the Daurian larch is of
important economic significance, and it serves as an important lumber source for China. As we have already pointed
out, this tree makes few demands upon the natural conditions, it endures the severe winters and late frosts well, and
will easily grow on permafrost soils and on any landforms.
Moreover, the Daurian larch multiplies very rapidly and
this is also a valuable quality of this strain. The Korean
cedar is widely used as construction material and it has
great elasticity. The Jeddo spruce also gives good lumber
and the wood of the yew is also excellent, although this tree
grows very slowly. Along with the utilization in lumber, the

forest areas are also of great water-retention and anti-
erosion significance; the forests of Northeast China are a
valuable resource and are carefully protected; reforesta-
tion work is being carried out. As we have already noted,
the natural conditions in the northern and eastern portions
of the region are completely favorable for raising forest
vegetation and due to this they are very hopeful for the further development of forestry here. Moreover, in the forests many valuable animals can be raised and used for
for hunting.

THE NORTHEAST PLAIN

The Northeast Plain lies in an intermontane trough and
is filled with a thick layer of friable sandy-gravel, clay and
loess-like lacustrine-alluvial deposits, and it has an egress
to the sea.

The steady subsidence of this territory and the formation of the basin began in the Mesozoic. Against a background of general subsidence, individual portions of the plain
have undergone both stronger subsidences and weak uplifts
which can be clearly seen in the contemporary topography.
A characteristic feature of the plain topography is the absence of a general gradual rise in the surface from the sea
into the interior of the region and the presence of the following basic hypsometric levels: lower (0-50 meters) which is
the Liaho Depression lying in the southern maritime and
most intensively subsiding portion of the plain; middle (120-
200 meters) which is the Nenkiang-Sungari Depression lying
in the northern part of the plain in the basins of the Nenkiang and Sungari rivers; and the upper (160-270 meters)
which is the divide of the Sungari and Liaoho rivers lying in
the central part. The uplifting of the latter has intensified
in recent times and has been accompanied by a rejuvenation
of previous faults from which there have been lava eruptions.
A chain of volcanic cones lies along the southern boundary of
the divide, and also along the northern edge of the Northeast
Plain. The uplifting of the designated divide has caused
sharp changes in the direction of the rivers on this plain, and
the picture of the river network assumed an appearance close
to the present one.

The plains of the two lower levels have a flat surface and are heavily swamped, while the plain of the upper level is marked by a hilly relief. The hills are composed of granites covered by Meso-Cenozoic sediments; aeolian forms are also widely found, particularly in the west.

Within the Northeast Plain are found the Sungari, Nenkiang, Liaoho and their tributaries. Various areas of the plain have been unevenly irrigated. The northeastern and northwestern portions of it have had the greatest amount of water and these areas are drained by the rivers of the Sungari Basin, and also the southeastern portion drained by the rivers of the Liaoho Basin. The central portion of the Nenkiang-Sungari Depression and the southwestern portion of the Northeast Plain are virtually devoid of actual currents; for them there are typical small lakelets, frequently bitter-salt, swamps and salt bogs. The current of the rivers is extremely slow due to the insignificant slope of the locale. The river valleys are wide, flat and with a series of aggradation terraces. The rivers during the low period flow in winding channels which are narrow in comparison with the valleys, and there are numerous streams, meanders, low islands and shoals. During the flood period, the rivers, as a rule, overflow their banks, inundating extensive areas.

The border areas of the Northeast Plain lying in the foothills at elevations of 200-300 meters above sea level are composed of proluvial deposits and have a somewhat different character to the surface than the remaining area of the plain. At present erosion processes have predominated here over the aggradation processes, and therefore, although the incline of the surface of these plains is slight (5-10°), their ruggedness is somewhat greater. Characteristic features here are: low monadnocks which are bedrock or erosion; small dish-shaped basins 1-2 meters deep, covering an area of 100-1,000 square meters, with a flat bottom and steep slopes evidently formed as a result of corrosion; and also ravines.

The climate of the Northeast Plain, particularly in terms of the precipitation regime, represents something of a mid-ground between the moist Eastern Manchurian Mountains and the drier Khingan. The annual amount of precipitation in the northwest is 400-500 mm., in the south and

southeast 600-700 mm., with the winter and spring precipitation being insignificant, and therefore, during the spring
when the temperature rises rather rapidly, dry winds frequently develop here. In the northern portion of the plain,
as we have already pointed out, permafrost develops. The
dominant portion of the summer precipitation here with the
conditions of the flat topography, the heavy composition of
the soil and the presence of a frozen horizon remains on the
surface, and this leads to the intensive swamping of the lowest portions of the plain.

The vegetation of the Northeast Plain is chiefly steppe
and meadow-steppe, and in the north and on the foothills a
forest-steppe has developed. The basic soil-forming process
within the plain has been sod processes; moreover, swamping, salination and carbonatization have also played a certain
role here. According to recent data of soil research, in the
northern portion of the plain various sorts of meadow soils
have been formed and are widely found (Sung Ta-ch'uan,
1958; V. A. Kovda, E. E. Bekker et al., 1958). Certain researchers call these soils meadow-black earth (I. P. Gerasimov and Ma Yung-chih, 1958) or degradation black earth and
black earth-like soils of plains (T. P. Gordeyev, 1954). The
meadow soils on various areas of the plain are not the same.
On the more elevated areas including on the river terraces
where the water table is at a depth of about 3 meters, the
meadow dark-colored soils are found. On the low areas
where the groundwater level lies at a depth of about 2 meters
and is supersaturated with rain and floodwaters, for example, in the river floodplains, meadow dark-colored shallow
soils have developed. On the lowest areas where the groundwater lies at depths of from 1 to 1.5 meters, the meadow
process of soil formation has been combined with the swamp
process, and gley-meadow soils have developed. On those
areas where the groundwater level is at a depth of 1 meter,
there has been intensive salting of the soils; the salting is
basically soda and this has been caused by the chemism of
the groundwaters. In the piedmont well-drained areas of the
plain, the leached black earths have developed.

In the southern portion of the Northeast Plain, according to I. P. Gerasimov and Ma Yung-chih (1958), on the
lower portions of the plain, there have developed cinnamonic
and meadow-cinnamonic primitive soils, while on the more

elevated areas and in the foothills there are brown forest
soils. In the western portion of the plain and in a narrow
strip along the eastern and partially the western slope of the
Greater Khingan, where the climate is drier and the carbonization processes are intense, on sandy and sandy loam deposits there has been a development of black earths which
are typical and calcareous. A significant portion of these
soils, like the soils in the southern portion of the plain, is
used in crop raising. The animal world of the plain is represented basically by rodents among which there are many
hamsters, susliks, zokors, i.e., species analogous to
those which inhabit the southern portion of the Greater
Khingan.

The basic landscapes of the Northeast Plain are, thus,
forest-steppe, steppe, meadow-steppe and cultivated. A
forest-steppe covers the northern portion of the Nenkiang-
Sungari Depression and foothills. At present the forest-
steppe to a significant degree has been changed by the economic activity of man. The tree strains have been preserved basically in gorges and in ravines in the form of
small groves and insular forests of leafy and coniferous va-
rities such as the Daurian and Manchurian complexes. In
the forests aspen and elm predominate and one will also find
Mongolian oak, Manchurian linden, Daurian birch, etc. The
dominant vegetation formations here are the steppe meadows
with poa (Poa angustifolia), koeleria (Koeleria gracilis), bedstraw (Galium verum), feather grass (Stipa baicalensis),
stellera (Stellera chamaejasme), vetch (Vicia amoena), etc.,
which usually occupy the terraces above the floodplain, and
meadow-steppes with a dominance of tansy (Tanacetum sibiricum), and also bedstraw, koeleria and others on ridges
(Yaroshenko, 1958). As a whole, the steppe meadows of the
Nenkiang-Sungari Depression are more steppe-like than the
meadows in the south of the Lesser Khingan.

Of the remaining larger portion of the Northeast Plain
there is a predominance of steppe and meadow-steppe landscapes with broad representation of the Daurian, Mongolian
and Northern Chinese species of vegetation. The primary
steppes here also have been greatly destroyed. The remaining virgin plain areas are covered basically by gramen motley grass vegetation with a predominance of feather grass
and Aleurolepidium chinense.

The enormous extent of the plain, the differences in the microrelief, the microclimate and character of the soil cover have caused the diverse specific composition of the steppes and meadows in the Northeast Plain. In those areas bordering on the forest-steppe, feather grass predominates (Stipa baicalensis) as well as bistort (Polygonum divaricatum) and Aleurolepidium chinense, and here also one will encounter tree vegetation, predominantly elm, in the form of small groves and individual trees. In the central and western parts where the climate is drier the main species of grasses are clover (Trifolium sibiricum), arundinella (Arundinella hirta), feather grass (Stipa baicalensis), astragalus (Astragalus melilotoides), and several species of sage (Artemisia capillata, A. japonica, A. sieversiana and A. vulgaris), and in areas there are individual specimens of elm (Ulmus pumila, U. macrocarpa) and Mongolian oak. In the southwestern portion where sandy areas are widely found, there grows sage (Artemisia halodendron), caragana (Caragana rosea), and ephedra (Ephedra distachya). In addition, significant areas of the plain are covered by the vegetation of salt swamps and more rarely black alkali soils with a predominance of astragalus and lespedeza. The salt swamps are most widely found in the lower reaches of the Nenkiang River and on low areas composed of heavy loams and clays, particularly along the shores of the numerous soda lakes. The river floodplains are either covered by meadows or everglades. In the southern portion of the plain cultivated landscapes predominate.

THE SANKIANG AND NORTH HANKAI DEPRESSIONS

The Sankiang and North Hankai depressions are the lowest plains in Northeast China. The Sankiang Plain, or the so-called Three River Area, is connected in the southwest by a narrow strip of the Sungari plains with the Northeast Plain, and in the north extends into the Amur depressions of the Soviet Union. Along the western, northern and eastern borders of this plain flow the Sungari, the Amur and the Ussuri bordering on the USSR. The North Hankai Depression extends directly into the Hankai depressions of the Soviet Union and is watered by the Ussuri River and its tributaries.

As we have already noted, both the Sankiang and the North Hankai aggradation plains lie in the intermontane tectonic troughs and are composed of thick beds of friable sandy-clay deposits of a lacustrine-alluvial origin. There altitudes are not significant, less than 100 meters above sea level, and the surface is flat; the relative elevations of the Sankiang Plain fluctuate within the limits of 50 meters, and the North Hankai from 10 to 20 meters. In places one will encounter individual isolated peaks or groups of peaks up to 500 meters relative elevation which are monadnocks of the indigenous relief. Close to the mountains the surface of the plains becomes somewhat more hilly. Within the plains the rivers flow in broad flat valleys with a series of terraces; the drop of the channel and the current speed are insignificant; for example, the speed of the Sungari is 0.9-1.2 meters per second (Bedarev, 1934).

The climate of the Sankiang and North Hankai intermontane troughs differs somewhat from the climate of the mountains surrounding them. In comparison with the Lesser Khingan it is warmer here, but in comparison with the Eastern Manchurian mountains it is drier. The winter temperatures within the plains are -20°, -22°, summer temperatures +20°, +22°, annual precipitation is 500 mm., in places somewhat more, the snow cover is shallow and the layer of seasonal freezing lies at a relatively shallow depth. The low central areas of the plains have the warmest and wettest climate.

The low flat surfaces of these plains are periodically subjected to heavy inundations. The inundations are particularly strong on the Sankiang Plain where they arise both as a result of flooding on the Sungari and under the influence of overflows from the Amur where the rise in the water level occurs due to flooding from the tributaries in the upper and middle portions of its basin.

The little evaporation, the insignificant drop in the locality, poor drainage and abundant moisture have caused the significant development of swamps and meadows in the plains, and this is a typical feature of the contemporary landscape for these territories. Chinese scientists in using paleogeographic data have assumed that in the past these plains were covered with forests--coniferous, leafy and mixed. The forests alternated with meadows and swamps which covered the lowest areas. As a consequence of the economic activity of man, the forests were cut down and at present they have remained only in the foothills surrounding the plains and in individual areas on the plains.

Within the Sankiang Plain, different varieties of meadow soils have developed as well as the unique "pankiang" soils and the brown forest soils. The meadow dark-colored soils which have formed beneath the meadow vegetation basically occupy the river floodplains. The "pankiang" soils formed on deposits of a heavy mechanical composition beneath the cover of the forest and meadow vegetation have broadly developed on the low terraces, frequently together with the meadow dark-colored soils. The brown forest soils have developed chiefly on the upper terraces which are composed of sandy deposits and on coniform hills beneath the forest vegetation.

The basic present landscapes of the Sankiang and North Hankai plains are meadow and meadow-swamp with areas of forest-steppe. The meadows are chiefly motley grass and on the Sankiang Plain one will frequently encounter meadow-rue, polygonum, sage, reedgrass, etc., and on the North Hankai Plain, according to the data of P. D. Yaroshenko, one will find arundinella (Arundinella anomala). The latter gramen is related to a tropical genus and this has provided the basis for the mentioned author who assumed that the landscapes of the Hankai Depression are close to the landscapes of the subtropical type (P. D. Yaroshenko, 1958). The forest areas in the plains are formed by deciduous broad-leafed varieties such as Mongolian oak, Asian white birch, aspen, etc.

The plains of Northeast China in terms of their natural conditions are very valuable for agriculture. The basic farming areas of the region are located here. This is helped by the warm moist summer and the good soils which in the predominant majority are sandy loam and contain a large amount of organic substances, having a good granular structure and neutral or slightly acidy reaction (Chen Chao-shun, 1953); the level topography facilitates working the fields with agricultural machinery. However, even now in Northeast China there are numerous virgin lands and many of them can be used without preliminary reclamation work or farming measures. These are, for example, significant areas of the Sankiang and North Hankai plains, and also individual areas of the Northeast Plain, particularly the northern part of it.

Moreover, on individual areas of the plains, and also in the southern part of the Greater Khingan, tall-grass vegetation grows excellently. The steppes have, as a rule, virtually a solid grass cover and among the grasses there predominate the gramens and also the Compositae are encountered. They are all fodder plants, and therefore the steppes are excellent natural pastures.

At the same time, agriculture in Northeast China is greatly damaged by natural calamities such as droughts and particularly floodings. The general oversaturating of the soils also does significant damage and is caused by the abundant summer precipitation and by the presence of freezing which is found on the predominant area of the plains. The most radical measure for combatting inundation is regulating the river drainage by building high dams and large reservoirs. This will also facilitate various reclamation projects which will help to control the oversaturating of the soils, the lack of moisture in the soils and also swamping and soil salting.

CHAPTER 4 NORTH CHINA

N. M. Kazakova
USSR Academy of Sciences
Institute of Geography

North China lies within the temperate belt, between
the Yellow Sea and the Central Asiatic deserts. The largest
mountain systems of North China are the Shansi Mountains
extending almost meridionally and the Jehol Uplands which
abut them on the north and basically are directed latitudinally. Along with the Ch'inling Range, also lying within
North China, these mountains virtually form a continuous
chain which stretches in the form of a broken line from the
Liaotung Gulf in the northeast as far as the Nanshan Mountains in the southwest, and plays a very great role in the
formation of the climate and the landscape of the territories
lying to either side of it. These mountains are a natural
barrier which stops a large portion of the precipitation
brought in by the summer monsoons, and because of it the
landscapes in the eastern and western portions of the region
have a completely different appearance. At the same time,
the difference between the north and the south is much less
severe and this is caused chiefly by the absence of ranges
lying longitudinally.

Among the mountainous territories including the
Liaotung and Shantung peninsulas, in North China there is
also the North China low plain occupying an enormous area
in the eastern portion, and the unique territory of loess hills
and plateaus lying in the west.

Over the larger portion of North China, with the exception of the maritime area, the climate is continental. The
amount of atmospheric precipitation fluctuates approximately
from 250 mm. in the northwest to 800 mm. in the maritime

area. The winter is dry and rather cold, with minimum temperatures in the southernmost portions of the region down to -15, -20°, and in the northern areas they reach -30°. Winter precipitation is insignificant and only 2-6 per cent of the total annual amount. At the same time, the northwest winds are extremely strong, and they frequently turn into storms which carry a mass of dust and sand. The summer is hot and wet. The mean July temperatures are distributed rather uniquely. The lowest temperatures (+22°) are observed here in the west and in the north, while the highest (more than +28°) will be found in the Weiho Valley and in the North China Depression; on the remaining territory the temperatures are 24-26°. Maximum temperatures exceed 40°. The amount of summer precipitation is very high and comprises 70-80 per cent of the annual.

In the spring the temperature rises sharply; as in the winter, the winds are very strong, while the amount of precipitation is insignificant, and therefore there are frequent dry winds, dust storms and droughts. As for all regions with a sharply continental climate, for the climate of North China there are typical great amplitudes in the annual and daily temperatures. The annual amplitudes are also great in Northeast China and in Inner Mongolia and comprise on the average about 30°, and in some years reach up to 55-70° Daily amplitudes here are less than in Mongolia, Sinkiang and Tibet, but are greater than in other regions of China. The highest daily amplitudes are in the spring and autumn, on the order of 10-15°.

The basic rivers of North China are the Hwang Ho, the Huaiho, the Haiho and their tributaries. Like the rivers of Northeast China, they are fed by snow and rain, but the amount of snow water in the water balance of the rivers is even less here. In the North China Depression and in the foothills groundwaters play a rather large role in feeding the rivers, but on the remaining territory of the region they lie too deeply (in places below 30 meters and more), and therefore their role in feeding the rivers is insignificant. The discharges of the rivers in North China, due to the small amount of atmospheric precipitation, are low, particularly in the lower reaches; during individual years certain rivers dry up. The rise and fall of the waters depend basically upon the amount of atmospheric precipitation and only the spring

flooding, known under the name of "peach blossom flooding,"
may be caused by the thawing of snow in the mountains. The
greatest fall of the waters is observed in the winter during
the period of stable ice on open water, and this is explained
by the brief flood period and the lack of groundwater. The
highest water levels are found in the period of summer rains.
The latter usually cause sharp flooding which within the
North China Depression frequently assume the character of
inundations. A distinguishing feature of the river regime in
North China is the great amount of load for which the rivers
in this region hold first place in the nation. The load is particularly great in those rivers which flow through the locality composed of loess deposits.

In general in North China the loess deposits are very
widely found. The thickness of them is particularly great in
the west where in certain areas it exceeds 100 meters. On
the highest ranges and peaks in the western portion of the region, the Shansi Mountains and the Jehol Uplands, the loess
cover is absent. On the North China Depression over-
deposited loess has developed, while on the Shantung and
Liaotung peninsulas the loess deposits will be found only in
certain areas, chiefly along the valleys. The presence of
loess deposits is reflected not only on the character of the
drainage but in general has a very important and in certain
areas decisive influence upon the course of the present physical
geographic processes. Thus, for example, in the west,
within the Loess Province the erosion processes are extremely intensive, particularly river channel, and due to
this, as we have already noted, the surface here is strongly
and deeply cut up by valleys and ravines. In being a very
friable rock, the loess is easily washed away, and the rivers
carry in their waters a mass of suspended material which is
deposited in the North China Depression. Due to this there
has been a continuous silting of the channels, runoff is difficult, and the rivers have long flowed above the surrounding
locality, kept in by man-made embankments. In particularly
rainy years, the banks may break and enormous areas will
be inundated, and the channels will stray, and the traces of
this are numerous within the depression. In the mountains
where the loess cover is absent, weathering processes predominate, and in the west--in the Shansi Mountains and in
the Jehol Uplands--physical weathering processes predominate, and in the east--in the Shantung and Liaotung Mountains

where the period with relatively high temperatures and humidity is rather protracted--in the summer both physical and chemical weathering are intense.

The loess deposits which cover, thus, a large portion of the surface of North China, also influence the features of the soil cover. The soils which are a result of the transformation of primary and redeposited loess which has a friable structure, a weak base reaction and is rich in calcium, have analogous properties. These soils are very fertile and have long been used for farming, and due to this to a significant degree they have lost their natural properties and cannot be classified in any genetic type with sufficient precision. Chinese soil scientists usually call such heavily altered soils by the local name--"hei-lu-t'u."

The territory of North China lies in the forest, forest-steppe and steppe zones. The forest zone includes the extreme eastern portion of the region, the Liaotung and Shantung peninsulas, and also the Shansi Mountains and the Jehol Uplands. In the forest-steppe zone lie the southern part of the loess hill region, the slopes of the Shansi Mountains and the North China Depression; the steppe zone includes the western part of the region. The geographic zonality on the territory of North China, thus, is complex. Over the predominant portion of it, the geographic zones are extended in a meridional direction and this is explained by the influence of the ocean; in the extreme western, more precisely in the southwestern part, there is basically a latitudinal direction which is characteristic for the interior parts of Asia. A very important type of natural vegetation in the forest zone is the deciduous forests of the temperate belt with a predominance of oak. The maritime climate of the peninsular portion of the region is particularly favorable for the growth of forests as this is characterized by relatively slight seasonal fluctuations in temperature and a very significant relative humidity. The vegetation here is diverse and a large portion of the trees and shrubs, particularly in Shantung, belongs to the southern species of the Japanese and Korean type. The climatic conditions of the Shansi Mountains and the Jehol Uplands lying on the same latitudes as the Shantung and Liaotung peninsulas are less favorable for forests. Regardless of the generally rather large amount of atmospheric precipitation which the southern and eastern slopes receive, the cold and dry winter limits the growth of

trees, and the specific composition of the forests here is
not so rich as in the maritime area; here northern species
are frequent. In the northwestern parts of these mountains
where the amount of precipitation drops sharply, phytocen-
oses of a transitional character will be found more and
more frequently, in the form of xerophyte forests and forest-
steppes. In the western part of the region during the year only
a small amount of precipitation falls and in combination with
the dry cold winter and windy dry spring frequented by
sandstorms, this does not favor the development of forests.
The natural vegetation here is forest-steppe and steppe, and
the transition from one landscape type to another occurs in
a strict sequence--from the Ch'inling forests in the south,
through the forest-steppe to the dry steppes and semideserts
of the north limited by the Ordos.

At present as a consequence of the centuries-old plowing and the intensive erosion caused by it, the primary vegetation cover of North China has been almost completely
destroyed. The natural vegetation has been preserved only
in the northwest and in small areas in the mountains. A significant area in the region is cultivated and is represented
by cultivated landscapes. With the passage of time the animal world of North China has also greatly changed. The destruction of the forests has greatly reduced the amount of
forest animals here, and at present, steppe rodents predominate on a larger portion of the region: hamsters, voles,
zokors, etc.

The basic physical-geographic units of North China are:
the Liaotung and Shantung Mountains, the North China Depression, the Jehol Uplands and the Shansi Mountains, the
loess hills and plateaus.

THE LIAOTUNG AND SHANTUNG MOUNTAINS

The Liaotung and Shantung peninsulas are parts of a
single whole, and their history shows that before the recent
subsidence of the bottom of the Pohai Gulf they had a great
deal in common.

The mountains of the Liaotung Peninsula at present are
a southern extension of the Eastern Manchurian Mountains

and have an analogous northeast strike, but are lower. They
bear the common name of Liaotunshanti or the Fenshuiling
and consist of a series of more or less parallel mountain
ranges composed of ancient crystalline rock. The main
range comprising the skeleton of the peninsula is the Ch'en-
shan Range, and individual peaks somewhat exceed 1,000
meters. Here lies the highest peak of the peninsula, Mount
Puyungshan, with an altitude of 1,132 meters. The remaining mountains are significantly lower and rarely exceed
1,000 meters, on the average they reach 300-500 meters
above sea level and are thus a typical low-mountain relief.
The mountains in places have sharp peaks and pointed ridges
which have developed in the relief under the influence of
weathering and erosion processes and have been greatly cut
by the river valleys.

The basic rivers of the peninsula are the Huankiang
and Yunweiho (tributaries of the Yalu River), and also the
Tayangho, Yingnaho, Hunho and T'aitseho. The river valleys are narrow without large alluvial plains.

The Shantung Mountains are a particular mountain
mass in the relief separating the Chiaolai Plain into two un-
equal parts, and this plain crosses the peninsula in meridional direction. Like the Liaotung Mountains, they are basically composed of archaic crystalline shales and granites,
and also of Lower Paleozoic sedimentary rock, and are
basically a low-mountain area and hilly mountain area, but
certain peaks are somewhat higher with the tallest mountain,
T'aishan, reaching 1,545 meters above sea level. Faults,
as we have noted, have played a major role in creating the
present relief of the Shantung Mountains, and as a result of
this many mountains are horsts, while the valleys occupy
the grabens. In the relief of Shantung one can clearly establish the highest mountains in the southwestern part, the
low-mountain and hill mountain area of the northeast, the
central plain and the piedmont areas.

The mountains lying in the southwest consist of a series
of faulted ranges formed along faults of a northeast and northwest strike and due to this they have a reticular structure.
The largest ranges are the Hsingshan, Lushan and T'aishan
stretching in a northeast direction parallel to one another.
The elevations of these mountains on the average are not less

than 1,000 meters above sea level, but the relative elevations are very high, on the order of 650-800 meters. The general pattern of the river network here has a radial character, and the direction of many rivers is subordinate to the structures, and as a consequence of this certain rivers such as the Hsingt'ai, Moning and others flow into the grabens while others such as the Tawengho and Ssushui flow into the syncline basins.

The mountains lying in the northeast have very low elevations, on the average less than 500 meters above sea level, and among them only certain peaks and ridges rise up to 500 and, more rarely, 1,000 meters, and only one mountain, Loashan, reaches an elevation of 1,132 meters. Certain mountains are composed of granites and have a rounded configuration, many have been separated as a result of erosion, and have been heavily incut by deep valleys and are marked by their sharp landforms.

The Shantung plains which lie in the central and piedmont portions of it are denudation and are usually covered by a very thin mantle of alluvial and proluvial deposits. The Chiaolai Plain occupies the largest area, it has an elevation of less than 50 meters and a relatively homogeneous flat or inundating surface, on which individual low monadnocks develop which are composed of bedrock. The chief river of the plain is Chiaolai.

The climate of the Liaotung and particularly the Shantung peninsulas is warmer and drier than the climate of the Eastern Manchurian Mountains. The annual mean amount of precipitation is 600-800 mm., and the variability in the amount of precipitation over the seasons of the year is greater than in Northeast China, however, on the predominant portion of the territory, droughts, particularly in the spring, are a rare phenomenon, since the relative humidity is comparatively high. An exception is the southwest portion of the Shantung where due to the greater distance from the sea there is less precipitation than along the coast, with the soils being poor in moisture during the spring; the temperature rises rapidly and this brings about rather frequent spring droughts.

In line with the particular features of the climatic regime, and in particular due to the relatively extended period with relatively high temperatures and humidity, weathering processes here occur rather intensively, and for a larger portion of the territory, as we have noted, both the processes of physical and in the summer chemical weathering are intensive. In the western portion of Shantung, where the amount of precipitation is less and the amplitude in the fluctuations of daily temperatures is greater, physical weathering predominates over chemical. The timing of atmospheric precipitation to the summer period causes a rapid rise and fall in the erosion processes, which are particularly intensive on the steep slopes in the upper portions of the mountains. During heavy rains mud slides frequently develop here which greatly destroy the slopes.

The vegetation cover of the Liaotung and Shantung Mountains is very unique. On the Liaotung Peninsula there are numerous representatives of Manchurian flora, for example, the alder (Alnus japonica), the yellow birch (Betula costata), the Amur barberry (Berberis amurensis), and cherry (Prunus padus). On the Shantung Peninsula, along with the northern species of plants, a whole series of southern species appears, for example, styrax (Styrax obassia), Lindera obtusiloba, which is a representative of the laurel family with falling leaves, wingnut (Pretocarya stenoptere), magnolia (Magnolia parviflora), and others. Moreover, here one will encounter individual species of North China flora.

At present, however, the natural vegetation has been greatly destroyed and the forests have remained only in individual areas, chiefly on the upper parts of mountains. The basic tree strains of the remaining forests are various species of oak such as the daimyo (Quercus dentata), the oriental oak (Q. variabilis), the liaotung (Q. liaotungensis), the sawtooth oak (Q. acutissima), the Mongolian oak (Q. mongolica), and pines among which the Japanese red pine (Pinus densiflora) predominates; on the Liaotung Peninsula one will encounter a variety of Chinese pine (Pinus tabulaeformis var. mutadensis), and on the Shantung Peninsula the Masson pine (P. massoniana).

The basic soil-forming processes in the Liaotung and Shantung Mountains are clay accumulation and sod processes,

and as a result various varieties of brown forest and cinnamonic soils have formed. The latter are developed particularly in Shantung (I. P. Gerasimov, Ma Yung-chih, 1958).
However, over a significant area of the mountains, the soil
cover is very thin, since the destruction of the tree vegetation has led to an intensification in the erosion processes,
and thus to a washing-out and redepositing of the friable material. In this regard here, particularly on the steeper
slopes, the skeleton soils of the brown forest type and rocky
earths are widely found. In the lower parts of the slopes and
in the foothills, on the detritus fans and terraces, the soils
are thicker and have a much better developed profile. In the
river valleys with a stratification depth below 2 meters one
will find meadow and brown forest soils.

At present in the Liaotung and Shantung Mountains
there are cultivated landscapes predominating; there are
also many rocky expanses. The forest landscapes have been
best preserved on the Liaotung Peninsula, chiefly in the
Ch'engshan Mountains, where in the upper parts grow forests of a variety of Chinese pine, and in the Lower parts,
forests with a predominance of the liaotung oak and Manchurian linden. Beyond these mountains one will encounter only
low man-made forests of oak, linden, aspen, Persian walnut,
etc.

Only 2.3 per cent of the Shantung Mountains are covered by forests, i.e., they are virtually completely deforested (Kao Fan, 1952). Forests are encountered only in the
form of small residual areas scattered on the slopes of
mountains and in the foothills as well as in the form of
groves along the river valleys. One can observe a certain
pattern in the distribution of the tree strains. Thus, in the
upper belt of mountains on the shallow and rocky soils one
will find the pine and on the peaks there are alpine meadows
of Sarcanthus scolopendriifolins, Habenaria eincarifolia,
etc. In the lower belt of the mountains and on the detritus
fans where the soil cover is thicker, there are mixed forests of oak, elm, ash, linden and other broad-leafed trees;
in the undergrowth there is the tall ailanthus, lespedeza,
fruit trees in combination with a grassy vegetation. In the
foothills and valleys, aside from the listed varieties there
is also the Chinese scholar's tree (Sophora japonica), the
white mulberry (Morus alba), the Persian walnut (Juglans

regia), the silk tree (Koelreuteria panuculata), acacia (Albizzia julibsissin, A. Kalcore) and certain others.

Judging from the character of the soils, it may be assumed that in the past the Liaotung and Shantung Mountains were covered by forests while on the piedmont plains there was evidently a vegetation of the savanna type, i.e., there predominated a grassy vegetation among which were scattered individual shrubs and trees.

THE NORTH CHINA DEPRESSION

The North China lowland plain is one of the largest plains in China (its area equals 300,000 sq. km.) and it lies, as we have already noted, in a broad submontane depression which has been filled with a thick layer of Meso-Cenozoic deposits. According to the data from drilling and geophysical research, the thickness of the Quaternary deposits alone here reaches 800-1,000 meters (V. G. Lebedev, 1959b). Among the latter alluvial deposits predominate. The surface of the North China Plain is flat and slightly inclined towards the Yellow Sea, and the absolute elevation of the larger portion of it does not exceed 50 meters, increasing only to the west as one approaches the mountains, although even here the elevation reaches not more than 75-100 meters above sea level. Among this enormous flat lowland plain there is only one area lying along the southern border of the Shantung Mountains where there is a relief of outlier ridges and hills (up to 400 meters above sea level) composed of bedrock and overcovered by Quaternary sands and redeposited loesses.

The numerous rivers which flow over the plain are basically related to the river basins of the Haiho, the Hwang Ho and the Huaiho, and there are particularly many tributaries of the Huaiho River, and due to this the southern portion of the North China Plain is broken up much more heavily than the northern. In line with the intensive accumulation of friable deposits which, as has been noted, occurs within the plain, its microrelief has an unusual character. The river channels lying higher than the surrounding locality are local watersheds and the areas between the channels are depressions with lakes and swamps. Here the location of either is very unstable since, with particularly heavy

rises in the river waters, they overflow their banks and
change the direction of the current, and thus naturally the
relief is also changed.

On individual portions of the North China Plain which
are little reinforced by vegetation, the aeolian processes
achieve rather significant development. This has been aided
by the small amount of precipitation and the extremely
strong winds in the winter and spring months, and this leads
to the formation of aeolian and frequently shifting landforms
on the surface of the plain which is composed of friable deposits.

The complex microrelief and the poor drainage due
to the fact that the runoff occurs chiefly in elevated channels
and in the depressions between them water accumulates and
surplus moistening develops cause the unique hydrological
conditions on this territory. Of great significance, as has
been noted, are the underground waters with the stratification depth and the mineralization playing an important role
in the formation and development of the landscapes.

The vegetation of the North China Plain is basically
related to the North China flora and among it one will encounter elements of the Manchurian and Mongolian floras.
Regardless of the rather southerly position of the plain, the
winter is still relatively cold (in the north the mean January
temperatures are -6°), and therefore subtropical plants are
encountered here in a significantly smaller amount. At
present a larger area of the North China Plain is cultivated
and planted with crops. The natural vegetation is found in
the river floodplains and in the depressions of the relief
where there are thickets of reed, grassy vegetation represented predominantly by legumes and the crowfoot family,
and also various shrubs with the tamarisk predominating.
On the dunes one will find Agriophyllum arenarium, Caris-
permum puberulum and Trilulus terrestis, etc. The vegetation cover of the salined soils which have developed particularly along the seacoast is represented chiefly by such
plants from the goosefoot, gramen and Compositae families
and various species of Suaeda (Suaeda ussuriensis, S. glauca,
etc.) and Russian thistle, glasswort (Salicornia herbacea),
Aeluropus litoralis, Crypsis aculeata, Scozzonera mongolica and Artemisia anethifolia (Ch'ien Ch'ung-shu et al.,

1957). The designated authors write that depending upon the
character of the tide or upon a change in the groundwater
level, these plants lie either in the form of a broad strip or
in individual groups. Among the grassy vegetation one will
also encounter certain halophyte shrubs such as various
species of tamarisk and nitraria (Nitraria Schoberi, etc.).
Around population points, along roads and near hills there
are artificial plantings of trees consisting of arbor vitae,
pine and poplar.

According to the data of I. P. Gerasimov and Ma
Yung-chih (1958), cinnamonic soils are the zonal soils
within the North China Plain. Aside from them a significant
area is covered by the intrazonal soils; meadow, gley, salined and numerous varieties of them. The protracted farming has had a great influence upon the soil formation as the
soils to a greater or lesser degree have lost their natural
features. The cinnamonic soils have developed on the most
elevated areas of the plain, on the terraces and detritus
fans where the drainage is good and the depth of the groundwater stratification is more than 4 meters. Depending upon
the degree of moisture here either cinnamonic calcareous
soils have formed or calcareous leached (non-calcareous).
The former are found chiefly on the northern drier portion
of the plain, and the second in the southern. In the lower
parts of the plain where the drainage is poor and the groundwater level lies at a depth of 1.5-2.5 meters, chiefly meadow
soils have formed. On the particularly low and flat areas
with a heavy mechanical composition to the earth, the stratification depth of the groundwaters fluctuates from 1.5 to 2
meters and sometimes less than 1.5 meters, with the formation of meadow-swamp and in certain places salined soils.
On the maritime sections of the plain which have been subjected to the tides, the groundwater level is at a depth less
than 1.5 meters, and the soils are heavily salined. Like-
wise the soils are salined which make up a larger portion of
the salt swamps.

THE JEHOL UPLANDS AND THE
SHANSI MOUNTAINS

The topography of this region is extremely complex
and diverse. The Jehol Uplands which have an average elevation of about 1,500 meters are characterized by a steppe-
like drop in the surface from the northwest to the southeast
and this has been caused by the general slope of the structures and the major faults with a northeast strike, and also
by the presence of a number of small ranges with different
orientation which is related to the large number of inter-
crossing faults. In accordance with the basic fault lines
here one can establish three chief structural-orographic
stages: the upper with elevations of 1,800-2,000 meters
which includes the divide range and plateau of Weich'ang; the
middle with an elevation of approximately 1,100 meters with
the Chienshengling Range, and the lower of 300-400 meters
absolute elevation with the Sunglingshan Range (Chou T'ing-
ju, Liu P'ei-T'ung, 1956). The ranges are composed of
Precambrian crystalline shales, gneisses and granites, and
also Mesozoic sedimentary and effusive rock, and the plateaus are made up of young basalts.

A characteristic feature of the topography in the Jehol
Uplands is the extreme ruggedness, and the lower mountains in the southeastern part are particularly rugged which
is due to the tectonic and climatic features of this territory.

The rivers of the Jehol Uplands are related either to
the basin of the Liaoho River or drain into the sea. In places
they flow over the intermontane depressions in broad valleys,
but in other places they sometimes cut through the ranges
forming deep gorges. Typical for the given territory is the
fact that certain rivers, for example, the Luanho, have cut
through all the ranges of the uplands, even the watershed
range, and have reached the border of the Mongolian plains.
A large portion of the young lava Weich'ang Plateau is already so cut up that it has the appearance of table mountains;
here there are frequent stream capturings and rejuvenation
phenomena. Aside from the Luanho, the Laohaho and Ta-
lingho are also major rivers of the uplands.

The Shansi Mountains are a complex system of medium elevation ranges and intermontane depressions oriented from the northeast to the southwest, and also plateau areas lying between them. The complex topography reflects the complicated tectonic conditions of this territory; the ranges have, as a rule, an anticline structure inherited as far back as the Mesozoic, while the plateaus are synclinal, and the intermontane basins are fault troughs. The absolute elevations for the ranges of the Shansi Mountains are on the average 2,000-3,000 meters, and the maximum--Mount Peishan-- is 3,204 meters, while the elevation of the interior plateau is 500-1,000 meters, and the intermontane depressions lie at varying altitudes, approximately from 400 to almost 1,500 meters. The mountains are composed of ancient crystalline rock which is exposed in the axial parts of the highest ranges and by sedimentary rock from the Paleozoic. Typical for the ranges of the Shansi Mountains is a sharply expressed asymmetry caused by the disjunctive tectonics. The external mountain slopes facing the North China Plain are steep and cliff-like; the interior ones facing the central plateau are gentle. The slopes of the ranges and the plateau have been heavily broken up by narrow river valleys and ravines, and the rivers frequently utilize the tectonic fissures. At the same time the upper portions of the mountains have a rather level surface. Within the plateau there are also numerous small depressions which have been filled with loess deposits and have a hilly relief. The steepest intermontane depression, or more accurately a strip of depressions, is the graben-depressions lying in the middle portion of the Shansi Mountains--the Tait'ung in the north and the Fenho in the south--and a series of intermediate ones in which the river channel has made its way. The depressions are filled with lacustrine, lacustrine-alluvial and loess deposits and are aggradation terraced plains connected by narrow sections of valleys from the rivers flowing through them. The border areas of the plains are composed of deposits from the detritus fans and are somewhat more broken up.

The climate of the Shansi Mountains and the Jehol Uplands is significantly drier than in the eastern portion of the region. The annual amount of precipitation is all of 300-500 mm., dropping as one moves to the northwest. A characteristic climatic feature of the given territory is the significant

fluctuations in the microclimatic conditions for the individual parts and this is due to the great complexity of the
topography.

Of the present physical-geographic processes within
the Jehol Uplands and the Shansi Mountains, the processes
of weathering and erosion are particularly strong, and the
intensity of the latter is strengthened even further due to the
presence of the loess deposits. In contrast to the eastern
portion of the region, and in particular the Shantung Mountains, where the temperature and moisture are lower, the
processes of physical weathering clearly predominate over
the processes of chemical weathering.

The vegetation cover of the Jehol Uplands and the
Shansi Mountains, along with the complex relief conditions
and the microclimate itself, is rather diverse. The amount
of atmospheric precipitation falling here is favorable to the
development of tree vegetation, but the cold and dry winter
still limits the growth of the plants; the specific composition of the vegetation is here not as rich as in the east of the
region. Of great significance in the distribution of the vegetation associations is the orientation of the slopes. As
Chinese researchers write, on the southern slopes where
there is intensive evaporation, the soils are dry and the air
humidity is rather low, and a xerophyte type of vegetation
predominates; on the northern slopes where there is relatively little sunlight and evaporation is low and the air and
soil humidity is significant, mesophytes predominate.
These two types of vegetation make up an amazing contrast
(Ch'ien Ch'ung-shu et al., 1957).

The basic soil-forming processes are podzolic and
soddy and as the forests are felled the latter begins to acquire greater and greater significance. As a result the
basic soils in the Jehol Uplands and the Shansi Mountains
are varying varieties of brown forest and cinnamonic soils.
In the upper belt of the mountains the mountain meadow-
steppe soils have developed; in the intermontane plains there
are alluvial soils. At present due to the fact that the primary vegetation has been virtually completely destroyed,
the soils also have greatly changed.

The basic landscapes of the described mountains, aside
from the cultivated ones, are at present shrub and grass.
The forests, predominantly secondary, have been preserved
only on individual areas of the northern mountain slopes. In
the distribution of the landscape types, aside from the exposure, the elevation above sea level is also of important significance. According to the data of the designated authors,
on the northern mountain slopes at an elevation of less than
1, 600 meters one will encounter leafy forests with a predominance of alien oak (Quercus aliena) and Mongolian (Q. mongolica), in the lower portions of the slopes the liaotung oak
(Q. liaotungensis), in the upper ones accompanied by the
Mongolian linden (Tilia mongolica) and the Manchurian linden (T. manshurica), the mono maple (Acer mono) and the
truncated maple (A. trunealum), the Chinese ash (Fraxinus
chinensis), Turchaninov hornbeam (Carpinus turczaninowii),
and on the grassy slopes there predominate various species
of sage and feather grass. At an elevation from 1, 600 to
2, 500 meters where the climate is colder and the soils are
shallower, one will encounter subalpine coniferous forests
represented by spruce (Picea asperata, P. neoveitchii), an
insignificant amount of Asian white fir (Abies nephrolepis)
and the Himalayan larch (Larix Gmelini var. Principic-
Rupprechtii), but most frequently on these sites secondary birch and aspen forests will be growing. There are few
other tree strains and the chief ones are hazel, mountain
ash, willow, honeysuckle, lilac, spiraea and cotoneaster;
there are also plants with climbing stems such as the shin-
leaf, majanthemum, lily of the valley, etc. At elevations
above 2, 500 meters there are alpine meadows composed of
a large number of plants belonging to the type of plants in the
Chinese portion of the Himalayas, for example, several species of saussurea and buzul'nik and also plants of the sub-
artic type such as Papaver medicanle and Polygonum vivi-
parum.

On the southern slopes at an elevation up to 1, 000 meters one will encounter sparse forests of oak or pine but
spiny shrubs predominate such as the buckthorn, honeylocust
(Gleditschia heterophylla), etc.; on the slopes covered by
wild grasses the leading place is held by the themeda (Themeda triaudre), and also grassy plants are common from
the families of Gramineae, Compositae, Leguminosae and
Ranunculaceae as well as various species of sage and feather

grass. At an elevation from 1, 000 to 2, 000 meters there
are shrub species dominant such as Siberian filbert and the
David ostriosis; above 2, 000 meters there is an abundance
of various species of subalpine meadow plants among which
one can sometimes encounter individual specimens of dragon
spruce (Ch'ien Ch'ungshu et al., 1957).

THE LOESS HILLS AND PLATEAUS

This territory is a structured trough built with a thick
layer of continental sediments covered by loess. The average elevation of the surface is 1, 200-1, 500 meters, and individual ranges composed of bedrock are higher and in the
Liup'anshan reach 2, 936 meters absolute elevation. The
thickness of the loess beds is not as great as was previously
supposed, but it frequently reaches and in places exceeds
100 meters. The exceptional development of the loess deposits and thus the unique loess topography distinguish this
territory from the other basins of China and to a significant
degree have caused the specific natural features. Under the
influence of the heavy summer downpours, the friable loess
deposits are broken up by rills and ravines, and due to this
the territory has long since lost its plateau-like character
and is a combination of loess hills, ravines and ridges of
differing shape and profile and sections of rugged loess plateaus. The relative elevations of the hills by and large are
100-150 meters, and rarely more. Among them two types
are most widely found, the extended spurs ("liang") which
make up the interfluve of the ravines and hills with a rounded
shape ("mao") which are scattered individually. The best
preserved plateau areas are the Chinchih Plateau lying in the
middle course of the Ch'ingho and the Loch'uan Plateau in the
middle course of the Loho.

The rivers of the given territory are related to the
Hwang Ho Basin which borders it on the northwest and east,
and to the basin of the major Hwang Ho tributary, the Weiho
River, flowing along the southern border. The river network here is not thick, but the ravines reach colossal dimen
sions in covering enormous areas. It has been computed
that the ravines cover approximately one-half of the entire
territory, and the depth of the erosion incutting is 100-150
meters, and sometimes more than 200 meters.

The climate of the given territory is distinct from the climate of the above-described mountains chiefly in the greater aridness which is particularly strong in its northern part, with the annual amount of precipitation fluctuating within the limits of from 250 mm. in the northwest up to 500 mm. in the south. The temperature conditions are approximately the same, with the exception of sharper fluctuations in the annual and daily temperatures. Very typical are droughts which occur here not only in the spring months, but also during the summer.

The given territory is a transition from forest-steppe and the remains of this can be traced in the southeast portion, to a dry steppe which is widely developed in the northwest. As a consequence of the tilling over the millenium, the primary vegetation cover has been almost completely reduced and the secondary as a result of tilling has been heavily destroyed, and therefore the natural flora can be recreated only from a small amount of plants growing in a suppressed condition. The remains of the secondary forests can be encountered only in the mountain ranges such as the Liup'anshan and others, and along the river valleys. The soil cover in a natural state was evidently made up by different varieties of cinnamonic soils which in moving northwest and with the increase in dryness were replaced by gray-cinnamonic soils. At present the soils, like the vegetation, have already been significantly changed. Under the influence of years of plowing, a large portion of the given territory, as we have pointed out, has lost its natural properties and cannot be related to any of the listed soil types; usually they are called "hei-lu-t'u" (black soils). The cinnamonic and mountain meadow-steppe forests have been preserved only on the ranges; along the river valleys and ravines there have developed meadow, salined and in places swampy soils.

The dominant landscapes of the given territory are thus cultivated. Only in individual areas unsuitable for agricultural working such as on the steep slopes and the hills and along the ravines will one encounter small areas of dry steppe and forest-steppe.

As was stated by M. P. Petrov who worked in the loess region of China, according to the computations of

Chinese botanists, the natural vegetation here covers not
more than 2-3 per cent.

The microrelief has a significant influence upon the
distribution of this residual vegetation. Thus, according to
the data of M. P. Petrov, on the placor areas where the
steppe vegetation has been preserved only in small spots
will one encounter feather grass (Stipa bungeana, S. gran-
dis), Aneurolepidium dasystachus, and several species of
sage (Artemisia giraldi, A. sacrorum, A. capillaris, etc.),
and certain other plants. On the slopes of the ravines, sup-
plementing the designated species, one will encounter several species of shrubs as well as spiraea, lespedeza, ephedra, etc. The shrubs are encountered in the form of solitary or very suppressed specimens, and on the southern
slopes of the ravines they are particularly rare and xeromorphic species predominate among them. Along the bottoms of the ravines where the moisture conditions are more
favorable and sometimes even abundant, the vegetation has a
more mesophilic and sometimes hygrophilic character (M. P.
Petrov, 1959a).

On the sections bordering the Ordos where there are
shifting sands, i. e., in the semidesert zone, several species of sage (Artemisia salsoides, A. ordosica, A. sphae-
rocephalla) grow very sparsely as well as Agriophyllum
arenarium), juniper (Juniperus chinensis), caragana (Caragana korshinskii), willow (Salix mongolica, S. Cheilophylla)
and certain other plants.

On the salined soils which are rather common in the
described territory there will be predominantly Russian
thistle (Salsola collina), suaeda (Suaeda ussuriensis, S.
glauca), winterfat (Eurotia cerotoides), tamarisk (Tamarix chinensis), etc.

On the mountain ranges with an elevation up to 2,000
meters above sea level there are secondary forests with a
dominance of liaotung oak, Asian white birch, poplar, and
one will frequently encounter eastern biota; of the shrubs
there is the ostriopsis; of the grasses sage. At elevations
from 2,000 to 3,000 meters (for example, in the Liup'anshan Mountains) areas of relic forests have remained where
the chief strains are pine (Chinese and Armand), the eastern

biota and the liaotung oak.

As follows from what has been given above, the natural conditions of a significant portion of North China are rather favorable for raising many agricultural crops, and due to this it is one of the most important farming regions of the nation. The basic agricultural lands lie within the North China Depression and in the southern portion of the Loess Province, and besides these all of the areas in the mountains and river valleys suitable for farming are also plowed. Very little virgin land remains here which could be used for planting; chiefly these lands are concentrated along the shores of the Pohai Gulf. Here the lands, as we have noted, are salty, and therefore the utilization of them requires certain meliorative work. Work on meliorating these territories is being done on a rather broad scale, and the termination of it is a task of the immediate future.

For further increasing the agriculture of North China it is very important to control the inundation and droughts. In truth, in recent years as work has developed on regulating the river regime of this territory, the danger of natural calamities has been significantly reduced, but it is impossible to consider them finally eliminated. Here the danger of flooding within the North China plains is increased in comparison, for example, with Northeast China due to the great amount of suspended material which the rivers of the region carry.

In the western portion of the region, particularly within the Loess Province, the plague of agriculture is washout and soil erosion. The development of these processes, aside from the properties of the loess itself, has been further exacerbated by incorrect farming and above all by the intensive destruction of the vegetation cover. Over time these processes have assumed a threatening character. Therefore an immediate task of the future is to recreate the vegetation by forestation, grass planting, etc. Certain measures are already being undertaken.

North China is not only a major farming region but it is also rich in minerals. Of the greatest economic significance here is the hard coal, and North China is first in the nation in the holding of hard coal and iron ore reserves.

The larger portion of the coals is found in the sandstones
and sandstone shales of the Permean and Carboniferous ages and the thickness of the whole seams is significant
and in places exceeds 5 meters. In North China there predominate bituminous coals, and there is significantly less
anthracite. The largest coal basins lie in the west of the
region, in the Shensi-Shansi Basin (the Tat'ung deposit and
a number of others) and in the foothills along the borders of
the North China Plain. The largest iron ore deposits are
the Lungyang and Ishui.

Aside from coal and iron ore North China also has oil
deposits. They are concentrated chiefly in the western portion of the region where they are confined to the monocline
and anticline structures. The largest oil deposit is the
Tench'ang. Chinese geologists assume that the oil-bearing
zone may occupy a significant area here, but this territory
has not yet been sufficiently studied (Chang Keng et al.,
1958).

Of the other minerals in North China there are deposits of copper, manganese, wolfram, lead, zinc and certain
other nonferrous metals concentrated chiefly in the Jehol
Uplands and in the northern part of the Shansi Mountains, as
well as deposits of all sorts of nonmetallic minerals
(Severnyy Kitay, [North China], 1958). Thus, in the T'aihangshan Mountains and Jehol there are deposits of asbestos,
graphite and mica; in the Shansi Mountains there is sulfur-
ous pyrite and gypsum; in Shantung there are bauxites and
in the western portion of the region and along the seacoast
there are rich deposits of salt and soda. Of the nonmetallic minerals in the region one will widely find limestone and refractory clays and the deposits are located close
to the hard coal and iron ore basins.

CHAPTER **5** SOUTHEASTERN CHINA:
THE MONSOON
SUBTROPICS

V. T. Zaychikov
USSR Academy of Sciences
Institute of Geography

The territory of China lying to the south of the
Ch'inling-Huaiyenshan Mountains, in literature, has been
called Central China. This term, however, has not always
had the same meaning. In economical-geographical zoning,
Central China includes the territory of the middle courses
of the Yangtze with three administrative provinces--Hunan,
Hupei and Kiangsi. In the physical-geographic zoning Central China means a more extensive territory including, besides the middle reaches of the Yangtze, also its lower
courses and the Szechwan Basin. Sometimes Central China
is understood as a more extensive natural region also including the basin of the South Chinese river, the Sikiang.

One may also frequently encounter such names as
Central-South China which includes the territory of China
from the Hwang Ho River in the north to the South China Sea
in the south, and South China (which in some instances is
treated as the region covering the coastal strip of Fukien,
Chekiang and the Island of Taiwan, and in other instances
has the territory of Fukien and Chekiang provinces, and finally, even more broadly, including Fukien, Kwangtung,
Kwangsi and Taiwan).

This division which has a certain historical sense and
a bearing to the past dividing of China into China itself and
the western territories inhabited by non-Chinese nationali-
ties does not reflect the actual geographical position of the
region in the land. From this viewpoint, the term of
"Southeast Asia" is more precise. In this work the

area of Southeastern China includes the zone of humid subtropics which is characterized by specific features of natural conditions which sharply delimit this region from the
area of North China which neighbors it.

This distinction can be observed in the entire appearance of nature. In contrast to the predominantly level North
China, the subtropical region is characterized by a very
rugged relief bringing together high mountains, low-mountain
areas broken up by river valleys, hills and belts of alluvial
plains stretching along the river channels. The distinc-
tions from North China are just as fundamental in the climate as well.

Southeast China lies predominantly in the zone of the
subtropical belt. Only the extreme northern and southern
portions of it show a transitional character in nature bringing it close in the south to the landscapes of the tropics and
in the north to the temperate belts.

However, the subtropical climate of Southeast China
has its own particular features which distinguish the Chinese
humid subtropics from the subtropics in the other regions of
Eurasia. The basic feature of it is due to the cooling effect
of the winter monsoon when masses of cold continental air
reach into the low latitudes, making the climate of Southeast China variable and cooler than on the respective latitudes in the west of the continent.

While in Europe and Transcaucasia the subtropic
boundary runs approximately between 30 and 43°, in certain areas moving to the north or south depending upon prox-
imity to the sea or the amount of protection by mountains
against north winds, in the east of the Asian continent, the
subtropic zone lies significantly farther south, on a latitude
of approximately 22-31°. In the east of China, characteristic indications of subtropism may be observed in essence
only on the latitude of the middle and lower reaches of the
Yangtze River. In the town of Wuhan which lies on the bank
of this river, the mean annual air temperature is 16.9°.
The warm period, with mean monthly temperatures above
15° (only at such temperatures will there be the vegetation
of the subtropical plants which require the most warmth)
lasts seven months, from April through October inclusively;

in March and November, the mean monthly temperatures
fluctuate from 10 to 13°, corresponding to the minimum heat
conditions of marked vegetation for the majority of cultivated plants in the temperate and subtropical zones. The
remaining three months of the year show mean monthly temperatures below 10°; in December 6.5°, in January 3.9° and
in February 5.4°. During all of the winter months there are
frosts which at times are rather severe with absolute minimums down to -18°. During the winter there are frequent
instances where the bodies of water and soils will freeze.
During the cold 1955 winter, in Wuhan the soil froze down to
11 cm. in depth.

The cold winters frequently disturb the subtropical conditions of this region. The vegetation period lasts not more
than 270 days a year and the periodic heavy frosts have a
lethal effect upon the wintering of the perennial subtropical
plants.

The character of the vegetation in the Middle Yangtze
corresponds to these climatic conditions. The forests show
a dominance of broad-leafed deciduous trees, chiefly oak
(Quercus dentata, Q. liaotungensis), which are also found
in North China. In contrast to North China, here, as a rule,
one will also encounter evergreen leafy varieties but the
proportional amount of them is not great, not more than 10
per cent, and these varieties are shown chiefly in the lower
story and underbrush.

Under the protection of the higher trees one will find
the evergreen oak (Q. glauca), the rhododendron (Rhododendron ovatum), holly (Ilex cornuta) and tea (Thea cuspidata).

Of the cultivated evergreens the following are characteristic: camellia and the tea bush. More thermophilic
trees such as the citrus will grow in Wuhan, although they
will not bear fruit.

Thus, in terms of the agroclimatic and general landscape features, the valley of the Middle and Lower Yangtze
can very conditionally be related to the subtropics proper,
although the valley lies in lower latitudes. This territory
may rightly be viewed as the northern boundary for the Chinese subtropics.

The territory lying to the north of it, approximately
up to the Huaiho River, shows a transitional landscape character, generally maintaining the features of nature in North
China, but with a few subtropical elements, in particular,
with the distribution of individual subtropical plants which
are more resistant to cold.

In truth, to the west of Wuhan where the Ch'inling
Range has created a shelter against the incursions of the
northern cold winds, the subtropical boundary shifts somewhat to the north. In the west of Hupei Province and Szechwan Province, the subtropical forests extend significantly
farther north of the Yangtze Valley.

The relatively cold winter is also characteristic for
the more southern subtropical territories of China. In
Ch'angsha which lies more than 250 km. to the south of
Wuhan, the average mean temperatures for several years
running have been 4.4° in January, 6.2° in February, and
7.2° in December, and only in Wuchow lying on the latitude
of the Tropic of Cancer do the monthly mean temperatures
remain above 10° all year long. Particularly indicative are
the extreme temperatures which in the variable atmosphere
of the Southern Asiatic subtropics reach great contrasts.
The means of the absolute minimums for January are -5°
in Wuhan, -4° in Ch'angsha and -3° in Wuchow; the mean of
the absolute minimums of July in the corresponding points
are: 38, 38 and 35°.

The Chinese subtropics differ from the subtropics in
the western portions of the continent not only in terms of the
conditions of the thermal regime such as being colder in the
winter period, but also in terms of the moisture conditions.
In terms of the amount of annual precipitation, the Chinese
subtropics stand closer to the moist subtropics of our Western Transcaucasia. During the year in various portions of
Southeast China there falls from 1,100 up to 2,000 mm. of
precipitation; on the Black Sea Coast in the region of the
Kolkhid Depression there are 1,500-1,700 mm. However,
the annual distribution and the regime of the precipitation
are markedly different for the monsoon subtropics of China.
In contrast to Western Transcaucasia where precipitation
falls rather evenly all year round and particularly significant amounts fall in the autumn, in the monsoon subtropics,

with the exception of certain localities, the basic mass of
precipitation falls in the summer period with a relatively dry
spring, autumn and winter. During the summer here there
is a surplus moisture, while in the remaining part of the
year there is a lack of moisture which tells particularly upon
the growth and development of vegetation.

Under the conditions of the variable climate and chiefly
the cold dry winters, vegetation in the Chinese subtropics
does not develop year-round. While green tones are characteristic for the winter landscapes on a large portion of these
subtropics, particularly in the southern and western regions,
in terms of brightness and lushness of the green colors these
regions are far inferior to the humid subtropics of Western
Transcaucasia. Areas of evergreen subtropical forests and
luxuriant fields green during the winter alternate with the
brown tones of the dry grasses on the slopes of the hills and
the barren groves of deciduous trees.

In the evergreen forests proper of the Chinese subtropics there is a rather significant admixture of subtropical
deciduous varieties such as Rhus suicedanea, Albiggia kal-
kovix, Clerodendron inandarinarum, Cornus controversa.
Many of the evergreens in these forests are related to varieties resistant to a lack of moisture. The edificators of
the Chinese subtropical evergreen forests are certain forms
of castanopsis such as C. cyrei, C. carlesii, C. cuspidata,
C. armata and C. concinna, and many species from the
laurel family--Lindera glauca, the camphor tree (Cinnamomum camphora, etc.) and Cryptocarya. We should note
the distribution of vegetation favoring dry areas, particularly the laurels, in the subtropical forests of Southeast
China which is marked by an abundance of precipitation and
air humidity. This can be explained by the fact that a thin
soil layer is closely underlaid by waterproof rock and the
rainwaters are little retained on the steep slopes and rapidly
run off over the surface. Thus, the actual soil properties
here are more important than the climatic factor, a circumstance which V. L. Komarov noted during his travels in
Eastern Asia.

Very frequently in Southeast China one will find groves
of Masson pine (Pinus massioniana) which usually occupy the
territories of felled evergreen forests, cypress, Japanese

cryptomeria (Cryptomeria japonica) and Chinese yew
(Taxus chinensis). Of the moisture-loving conifers there is
China fir (Cunninghamia sinensis) which is found along the
banks of rivers and the shady slopes of mountains, forming
in such areas large forests.

The particular features of nature in the Chinese subtropics are also felt on the composition and farming methods
for the subtropical crops. Among the field crops rice is
most widely grown, and for raising it they have had to extensively use artificial irrigation and built irrigation devices.
Individual regions of the Chinese subtropics in terms of the
thermal conditions make it possible to raise two crops of
rice a year on one field, however, this cannot be done everywhere, only in the southern limits of this zone where the
vegetation period with mean monthly temperatures above
15-17° lasts not less than 250 days and also under the conditions of using the corresponding farming systems. They
also use methods of interrow rice planting with strains that
differ in terms of the growth time or second cropping; the
northern boundary for the two-harvest rice system with interrow planting reaches 30°, while the second method of
second cropping requires a longer warm period and will be
found significantly farther south, approximately 25o
n. lat.

While the monsoon character of the natural conditions
in the Chinese subtropics as a whole is favorable to the
spread of rice growing, the raising of cotton, and particularly the fine-staple varieties, is difficult due to the abundance of precipitation during the flowering period of this
plant. More favorable are conditions for another fiber crop,
China grass, which has the same requirements for heat and
moisture.

Also characteristic is the composition of the tree industrial and fruit crops which are successfully raised in the
monsoon subtropics. These include the tung tree, the tallow
tree, the lacquer tree, the sasanqua camellia, the tea tree,
citrus, the Japanese medlar, the lichee, dragon's eye, and
banana. Many of these plants are endemic for China. They
are very sensitive to cold, particularly when young, and the
spread of them into the various parts of Southeast China
greatly depends upon the regional conditions of the individual

regions, particularly their protection against the northern winds.

In such an extensive area as subtropical China, the regional differences naturally are great. They stand out most clearly in comparing the mountainous and plain regions, but there are just as important contrasts between the eastern and western areas and between the northern and southern parts. If we take into account only the most basic regional features, on the designated region we can establish its basic subdivisions: the Yangtze Plain, the Szechwan Basin, the southeastern subtropics, the Kweichow Plateau and the Island of Taiwan.

THE YANGTZE PLAIN

The Yangtze Plain covers the extensive valley of the great Chinese river in its middle and lower courses--from the town of Ich'ang to the mouth. It is particularly wide in the delta area and in the places where the Yangtze receives its major tributaries, including large areas of lowlands along the lower reaches of these rivers and also the lowlands around the largest lakes in China--Tungt'ing, P'oyang and T'ai--which are hydrologically linked with the Yangtze.

After the North China Plain, the Yangtze Plain which is genetically closely linked to it is the largest in the east of the Chinese People's Republic. It is the most populated and the most developed part of all Middle China. Here, in the Yangtze Valley and the neighboring plains of lakes Tungt'ing, P'oyang, the lower reaches of the Hanshui and the Yangtze Delta with a total area of approximately 180,000 sq. km. is concentrated significantly more than 100,000 inhabitants [sic]; this gives an average population density of 500 persons per 1 sq. km. Therefore one is not surprised by the profound transformation in this portion of the land which has been carried out as a result of the centuries-long effect of intensive farming on it. The artifically levelled surface is the most important characteristic feature in all the physical geography of the Yangtze Plain.

Virtually the entire territory of the plain is under intensive crop raising. Its surface has been converted into a system of flat terraces descending in steps along the

slopes of the valleys. Retained by low earth embankments
designed for holding back the water on the surface of the
rice paddies, these terraces form a unique type of terrace
relief which contrasts to the background of the forested
slopes of elevations surrounding the plain.

The plain territory and particularly the portion near
the mouth of the river is covered by a network of artificial
channels which have been created gradually for draining the
low areas subjected to inundation as well as for irrigating
the fields and navigation. The smaller drainage ditches
and channels which lead off of these main lines in all directions here have formed an unusually developed and dense
network of artificial waterways equipped with locks and
other devices which make it possible to control the runoff
of ground--and irrigation waters. But the lowlands have
not been sufficiently protected against incursion of floodwater, and controlling flooding remains one of the chief problems in the transformation of this territory.

This problem is particularly pressing for the plains
in the middle reaches of the Yangtze which have been repeatedly subjected to disastrous flooding. In August 1931,
heavy flooding caused by an abundance of cyclonic depressions flooded virtually all of the plain, having caused great
destruction. The town of Hankow for four months was covered with a layer of water 5-7 meters deep. The 1954 flood
was even larger. During this year in the region of Hankow
during the six summer months there was more than 184 cm.
of precipitation and this was 55 cm. above the index
for the 1931 summer precipitation. However, the amount
of river overflow and the scale of destruction done were incomparably less due chiefly to the hydrotechnical installations which had been put into operation during the years
of communist power, in particular the Chinchiang water control system. The majority of the newly built and repaired
dams withstood the pressure of the floodwater, protecting
large areas with dense population against inundation.

But the existing protective installations do not
prevent the danger of overflowing by the Yangtze with very
high floods. This danger can be fully eliminated only by fundamentally changing the river and controlling its runoff.

The Yangtze Plain in China is called the land of rivers and canals. In fact it is difficult to find another such territory which could be compared with it in terms of the extent of natural and artificial waterways. However, for this plain there are characteristic not only exceptionally high density in the river network but also a great uniqueness of these water installations and their close interlinking. The core of this integrated water system is the Yangtze River. By using the regulating and other installations of this system depending upon the degree of moisture in the season, the water is put on the fields (or surpluses drained off) as it is needed for flooding the rice paddies, for periodically irrigating other crops and for maintaining the groundwater level. This entire network is intensively used by water transport which is the main means of communication in Southeast China.

For the Yangtze Plain there is characteristic a profound change in the components of living nature--the soils, vegetation cover and animal world. Not less than two-thirds of the plain area is under rice soils which are one of the unique types of cultivated soils. They have been formed over a long period under the specific conditions of rice growing. In arranging the area for rice fields, man has completely transformed the primary soil horizons having artificially replaced them with new soils of earth and other material constantly brought in. The protracted inundation and anaerobiosis have given the soils of the rice paddies sharply expressed features of gleyness bringing them close to swamp soils, as a unique cultivated variation of the latter.

The zonal soil types (yellow-cinnamonic soils, yellow-brown soils) which are used for grain crops are also greatly changed on the plain. They also have undergone a long path of agricultural development and have greatly altered the initial structure and composition.

The Yangtze Plain is characterized by intensive farming, with each piece being considered and utilized in crop raising, truck farming or orchard raising; in the summer rice prevails on the fields occupying all of the land suitable for raising this crop, totalling up to 70-80 per cent of the summer planting; during the winter and spring the fields are under wheat, barley, vegetable crops, and clover which provides good green fertilizer. Everywhere one will see small groves of oak, Simon poplar (Populus simonii), silk tree (Albizzia Julibrissin) and mulberry scattered around the edges of villages and along the banks of canals and lakes. These plantings comprise the basic element in the cultivated landscape of the plain.

THE SZECHWAN BASIN

When one travels up the river from Ich'ang lying at the western edge of the Yangtze Plain, one is struck by the sharp changes in the landscape. The valley becomes very narrow and the mountains come right up to the river, raising steep cliffs over the rapid current. For more than 200 km. the powerful river travels in the deep Wushan narrows which the river cut in the Paleozoic limestones of the border range on its way to the plain expanses of the maritime area.

Above the Wushan cut in the upper reaches of the Yangtze lies the Szechwan Basin which is one of the richest regions of the nation in terms of natural resources and a major granary. It is a typical intermontane basin, very large in size, covering not less than one half the basin in the upper course of the great Chinese river with its major tributaries, the Chilingkiang, Minkiang and Ch'ienkiang.

The mountains surrounding the basin on all sides are higher in the west and north and this tells upon the geography of this entire region. Protected against the penetration of cold northern winds, this area is much warmer in the winter than the plains of Southeast China lying more to the south.

The mean minimal January temperature in Chungking is 5.6°, and in Hukow lying further east in the valley of the Middle Yangtze on almost the same latitude it is all of 0.4°. The period of possible frosts in Szechwan is a little more than two months and the frosts which occur here are slight, with temperatures not below -2°, while in the valley of the Middle and Lower Yangtze which during the winter is under the influence of the Siberian anticyclone, this period lasts up to 3-4 months with frosts reaching 10° and below. Naturally the vegetation period in Szechwan is significantly

longer; in fact, it lasts almost year-round while in the east
of Southeast China it begins with the beginning of March and
terminates at the end of November, lasting only about nine
months. Szechwan is distinct for its high humidity since the
western and northern mountain framework of the basin, like
a giant screen, retains the moisture of the maritime monsoons penetrating along the Yangtze Valley. The annual
amount of precipitation is more than 1, 000 mm.; in the distribution of precipitation over the territory one can observe
a relatively small amount of precipitation in the interior low
portion of the basin (800-1, 200 mm.) and an increase in the
peripheral mountain slopes, particularly in the west of
Szechwan where the annual amounts reach 1, 250-1, 750 mm.
In being marked by smaller winter precipitation in comparison with the other parts of Southeast China, Szechwan is
richer in spring and particularly autumn rains, although the
spring droughts are still a rather frequent phonomenon, and
this is due to the high temperatures and great evaporability.

The high evaporation and temperature indices, with
the virtually complete absence of wind, have caused the
great cloudiness and heavy fogs which are one of the characteristic features of the basin. In Chungking there are not
more than 30 clear days during the year. The annual number of clear days in Ch'engtu is even less, only 25. It is
overcast all the remaining time, although in a very unique
manner: the characteristic luminescence of the mists covering the basin in a film illuminates the surrounding locality,
framing the contours of objects with pale crowns.

The abundance of surface runoff formed on the mountains surrounding the basin provides a good deal of water
for the hydrographic network of Szechwan which abounds in
rivers. They are all marked by a significant fall in the
channels, by an abundance of rapids and cascades and are
therefore difficult for navigation. These rivers are rich in
hydropower; in terms of the reserves of power resources,
Szechwan holds one of the leading places in China.

In contrast to the river network in the valley of the
Middle and Lower Yangtze, the Szechwan rivers which are
marked by a great channel incutting and a rapid current can
handle the highest flooding relatively easily. Therefore,
with the exception of the Ch'engtu Plain the territory of the

basin is virtually free of flooding. On the Ch'engtu Plain, when the Minkiang River carries enormous amounts of detritus, overflows can be prevented by using the Tukiang hydroengineering installations.

On the other hand, the great amount of surface runoff in the mountain locality in Szechwan has caused an intense erosion process. The activity of running water has altered the onetime flat surface of the lake bottom of the basin, having turned it into a locality that is greatly broken up with chaotic hills. In the north where the topography is more rugged, the relative elevation of the erosion hills reaches 100 meters, and in the south of the basin the hills do not exceed 50 meters and have a softer rounded surface. Between the hills in one place or another along the river channels there are areas of alluvial plains which are completely planted with rice. Of them, the largest--the Ch'engtu Plain-- through the centuries-long labor of the farmers has been turned into one of the richest farming areas of the land with a magnificent system of artificial irrigation and drainage.

The lack of arable land on the plains has forced the population to cultivate the slopes of the hills, building terraces on them which frequently cover the slopes from top to bottom. The terracing has slowed down the erosion and has made it possible to cultivate additional areas by using the steeper slopes with grades up to 45° and more. In extending farther, terracing in Szechwan has covered extensive hill areas, having turned them into a classical province of terraced farming. The uniqueness of the Szechwan landscapes is further emphasized by the characteristic color of the "purple soils" found here which have developed on the calcareous purple shales of Cretaceous Age.

The mild warm climate and the developed irrigation system have helped to make the Szechwan Basin a major center of subtropical agriculture which is specialized in raising rice, oil crops and citrus. Virtually all of the irrigated lands are planted in rice during the summer; after the summer harvest a large portion of these lands is planted in wheat and bean crops which mature in the winter. On the unirrigated lands, chiefly on the slopes of the hills or the brows of the fields, they raise corn, kaoliang and soy. Industrial crops are rather significant in the summer plantings, particularly sugar cane and tobacco, and after the harvesting of these crops the fields are planted with winter rape. At the foot of the hills and on the low portions of the slopes with purple soils having a neutral reaction, fruit raising is very important, particularly citrus, while the higher belt with acid yellow soils developed on Jurassic sandstones is planted with tea represented here in its shrub and tree forms. The plantings of the tea tree which produce the coarser varieties of Szechwan tea make up extensive groves. Everywhere along the groves and near villages one will see tree plantings among which Ficus lacor is common which is the most frequently found tree in Szechwan.

Wild vegetation in the Szechwan Basin has been preserved on the mountain slopes surrounding the basin where the influence of man has been relatively weak. In the lower strip along the river valleys it is represented by subtropical forests of evergreen oak, castanopsis, Schima and long-stemmed beech. In these forests there are significant plantings of tung and other valuable trees. After the felling of these forests they were replaced by forests of Masson pines with rhododendrons. At elevations above 2,200 meters the forests assume a mixed character of evergreen, leafy, deciduous and coniferous. Above 2,600 meters there are pure fir forests.

The Szechwan Basin and the mountains surrounding it are rich in minerals. In the center of the basin are concentrated the reserves of oil and natural gas. Along the edge of the basin are located extensive coal fields which are particularly large in the region of the folded anticlines of Eastern Szechwan. The border regions of the basin and the Szechwan Mountains are rich in iron, copper, gold, nickel, antimony, lead, zinc and silver. Salt deposits are found everywhere.

THE SOUTHEASTERN SUBTROPICS

The southeastern subtropics cover a small area of Southeast China--the area of the South China Mountains, the lake basins of Tungt'ing and P'oyang and the basin of the Chukiang River. In this region are located totally or by and large six major South China provinces: Chekiang, Fukien,

Kiangsi, Hunan, Kwangtung and the Kwangsi-Chuang Autonomous Region with a total area of more than 900, 000 sq.
km. and a population of up to 130 million persons.

In the physical-geographic sense this region is complex. The relief is made up of a chaotic accumulation of
low mountains and hills which are extremely diverse in
terms of geomorphology. In the larger ranges there is a
dominant direction from northeast to southwest corresponding to the strike of the Sinian system. However, the numerous spurs of the longitudinal ranges, the transverse chains
and the individual mountains and hills separated by deep and
sometimes rather narrow valleys have created a confused
labyrinth of elevations which sometimes has a characteristic pattern like a grid. The mountains of the southeast
coast stretching in a belt along the South China Sea show
such a character of reticular structure.

The mountains differ greatly in terms of the rock comprising them, and among the rock a leading place is held by
metamorphic rock, limestones, red sandstones, shales,
clays and granites, and therefore the weathering and denudation which are particularly intensive here due to the heavy
downpours and sharp temperature fluctuations have created
an improbable diversity in the landforms. Smooth dome-
shaped surfaces which are characteristic for the higher hills
composed of granites rise over cuestas of red sandstone with
picturesque tower-like shapes. Limestone outcroppings
carved out by karst stand in contrast to the soft outlines of
the clay slopes.

In Southeast China there is little plain territory. Individual areas of lowlands stretch in narrow strips along the
lower reaches of rivers and the seashore. The area of
them is small and all in all does not exceed one-fifth of the
territory in the region. Here particularly there is a lack of
arable land, and it is almost completely concentrated deep
in the valleys and on the seacoast, and these areas have been
turned into solid strips of irrigated rice paddies. However,
in contrast to Szechwan or the Loess Region which have a
high level of terrace forming, in the southeastern subtropics
of China one is struck by the contrast between the plains
where they have utilized each centimeter of land, and the
slopes of the elevations which are little used in farming.

Here one will very infrequently encounter mountain terraces
and only on slopes not steeper than 20-25°. Usually even
relatively gentle slopes which lie near cultivated lowlands
with a dense agricultural population are covered with tall
grass and are not used even for pasturing livestock kept in
barns. These lands could be extensively used for planting
industrial and fruit areas which would increase the fund of
agricultural land. Characteristically, in the Eastern
Szechwan Mountains the tung plantings run up the slopes of
the mountains to the very peaks, and they are planted on
rocky soils which are completely unsuitable for field crops.

For developing agriculture in the southeastern subtropics, soil melioration is of great importance. The zonal
soil types here are yellow earths and red earths which have
developed on the ancient allite weathering crust. Particularly characteristic are the red earths which are widely
found in hilly localities up to an altitude of 1,000 meters.
Depending upon the character of the parent rock, these soils
will differ sharply. The thickest red earths are formed on
sandstones and clays; they are marked by a slightly acid
reaction. On limestones the red weathering products are
shallow. The bright-red tint and elevated acidity of the red
earths will be found in outcroppings of flinty shales. In being found in a rugged locality with intensive precipitation,
these soils have been heavily eroded, washed out and are
poor in organic substances and not fertile. A significant
portion of them is left fallow. Therefore the question of improving the red soils and using them in farming is being
given great attention in China as one of the basic problems
in developing subtropical agriculture.

For a large territory in the southeastern subtropics
with such a diverse structure in the surface naturally there
will be differences in the climatic conditions and a difference
in the duration of the vegetation period.

As a whole the southeastern subtropics are warmer
than the Yangtze Plain, but in the northern half due to the
fall of hoarfrost, the vegetation period is limited approximately to 9-10 months; only in the southern half of the subtropics where hoarfrosts are virtually absent do plants veg-
etate year-round.

Everywhere the dry period is significantly shorter and not as sharply expressed as in the more northern regions of China. The warm climate and the abundance of moisture have helped in the development of a lush subtropical vegetation.

In the valleys and on the plains cultivated vegetation predominates, and along with the subtropical and tropical field and orchard crops, one will find many plantings of citrus, Japanese medlar, lichee, dragon's eye (Euphoria longana, Lam.), and banana.

On the mountain slopes up to 1,000-1,100 meters, there are evergreen leafy forests which are the most typical for the natural vegetation cover of the southeastern subtropics. These forests are represented by many associations, chiefly by species of castanopsis (Castanopsis tibetana, C. caspidata, C. eyrei, C. fissa, C. fordii, etc.), Elacocarpus sylvestris, Schima (Schima confertiflora) and ficus (Ficus wightiana).

But usually these forests have been heavily felled and are preserved only in the inaccessible mountainous regions with a sparse population. In the felling areas, the evergreen leafy forests have been replaced by tall-grass meadows or planted coniferous forests where one will most frequently find the Masson pine, Chinese fir, Japanese cryptomeria and cypress. These rapidly growing varieties are raised by the population due to the demands for construction materials.

Everywhere in the southeastern subtropics, particularly close to the rural settlements, one will encounter bamboo groves which sometimes occupy large areas of the mountain slopes rising up to an elevation of about 1,500 meters. These groves are also predominantly planted; due to rapid multiplication which in the bamboo occurs by the development of underground runners, the bamboo plants grow rapidly and are easily replaced after felling. Frequently the bamboos grow in mixed forests with the Masson pine and the Chinese fir.

In the mountains composed of limestones, as in the higher stage of the mountains, the evergreen leafy forests

are replaced by mixed forests comprised of a predominance
of deciduous varieties. In the more elevated portions of the
mountains, above 1,500 meters, one will find a low forest
composed of many rhododendrons and also coniferous forests, shrubs and mountain-top meadows.

To the west of the described region of the southeastern
subtropics lie the Kweichow Uplands occupying the territory
of Kweichou Province, the south of Szechwan and the north
of the Kwangsi-Chuang Autonomous Region. This ancient
platform area by the Yenshan mountain-forming movements
was contorted into folds and broken up by faults which can
be seen particularly along the edges of the uplands which by
and large are a rugged mountainous locale with steep inaccessible ranges. The uplands have a mean elevation of about
1,000 meters, being a step between the westerly more elevated Yunnan Uplands and the low-mountain, hilly Southeast
China bordering the Kweichow Uplands on the east. The uplands drop towards the northeast and southeast having caused
the basic directions in the river drainage in the northern
part into the Yangtze and in the south into the Sikiang; the
middle portion of the uplands forms the divide between these
two major Chinese rivers. The relief of the Kweichow Uplands is given its characteristic features by the distribution
of karst phenomena which have developed on limestones
which have been put down over many geological periods from
the Cambrian to the Triassic and in certain areas reach exceptionally great thickness.

The limestone landforms are represented here in their
most characteristic features providing the fullest collection
of surface and underground karst formations, beginning with
the dry plateaus and basins in the Permean limestones in the
middle portion of Kweichow and the classical "stone forests"
in the basin of the Nanp'ankiang River up to the smallest
landforms such as corries, pits, wells and caves. Many
streams and even rivers begin in the underground cavities
or, in flowing over the surface, fall into sinkholes which are
particularly numerous on steep slopes and along the borders
of the uplands; travelling a certain portion of the way in
underground beds, the rivers once again appear on the surface.

The ruggedness of the relief and the distribution of karst have made an impression upon the economic development of the area. On the territory of the Kweichow Plateau relatively little of the land is plowed and very little of the land is under irrigated rice paddies as it is difficult to make them due to the permeability of the rock. The very high filtration of irrigation water is characteristic both for the irrigated fields themselves and for the irrigation network and reservoirs.

The farming areas are concentrated in the valleys and in the intermontane basins where the gentle relief and the thick detritus deposits have made it possible to develop magnificent lands, sometimes with artificial irrigation, producing stable harvests of rice, corn and sweet potatoes. But in the basins formed by limestone corrosion and having a shallow soil cover, droughts do significant damage to the plantings.

River overflows also do serious harm, and these are particularly frequent in the area where sinkholes are found. During flooding the sinkholes cannot handle the great discharges and the river water, in flowing out on the surface, forms temporary lakes sometimes up to 20-30 meters deep.

The particular features of the orography of the Kweichow Uplands have also told on their climate which is characterized by a warmer winter than in the east, by a relatively cool summer and rather frequent overcast weather. The microclimatic differences are particularly significant here and are due to the altitude zonality and the exposure of the slopes.

The more elevated west of the uplands having an average elevation of more than 1,500 meters has the shortest vegetation period in Southeast China, all of 160 days, although the minimum temperatures do not have such sharp drops as can be observed in the southeastern subtropics. The minimum temperatures in T'ungtse over a protracted period have shown -5° while in Ch'angsha lying more to the east but on the same latitude the temperatures are -7.8°.

In the east of the Kweichow Plateau, it is warmer and the vegetation period lasts one month longer than in the west. Here in the sheltered valleys one will predominantly find subtropical crops with a predominance of tea, Asiatic tree cotton, the lacquer tree, the tung tree, sumac, citrus, persimmon and khiva (?).

On the territory of the Kweichow Uplands, significant areas of natural forests have been preserved. Most frequently one will find stands of Masson pine and China fir which are encountered everywhere and form the basic areas of forests. In the mountain valleys, particularly in the upper reaches of the main river of the uplands, the Wukiang, evergreen leafy forests are common and these are encountered on the yellow-earth soils at an elevation of approximately 1,000-1,200 meters. In these forests predominate species of castanopsis and Cyclobalanopsis; in the lower portions there are trees from the laurel family as well as camellia, magnolia, eucomia, and Chinese pistache, the products of which are widely used in pharmacology. The wettest portions of the valleys are covered by bamboo thickets while on the dry slopes cypress groves are dominant.

The mountain belt above 1,200 meters is made up of beech forests in which one may encounter many valuable hardwoods such as Schima, naked panasia and indigofera which are widely used in construction. Although in Kweichow the natural forests have been better preserved than in the east, here also fellings are rather frequent, particularly close to the roads and logging rivers, and these have been covered by overgrowths of oak and shrub meadows.

ISLAND OF TAIWAN

The mountainous Island of Taiwan is separated from continental China by a wide strait with a number of small islands and it has a number of characteristic natural features. In terms of the geological structure which is a typical anticlinorium projecting above the surface of the seawater, Taiwan strikes one in the magnificence and ruggedness of the mountains which occupy a large portion of its surface. The system of tall mountain ranges stretching from the north to the south along the axial line of the island has created a barrier which is difficult to cross up to 3,950 meters high which isolates the eastern coast of the island from the west.

In the east, in coming almost to the sea itself, the mountains drop off in steep slopes, leaving only a narrow strip for the coastal lowland. In the west the area of the maritime plain is significantly larger. The plains of Taiwan composed of river debris are completely worked and heavily populated, forming a sharp contrast to the mountainous territories which are covered by natural forests and almost uninhabited.

A characteristic feature of Taiwan is the volcanism and seismicity of its individual areas which shows that the island belongs to the zone of active tectonic structures. In this century the island has been struck by destructive earthquakes on the average of once a year; earthquakes are most frequent in the east and north of the island. In the north of Taiwan lies the most famous group of volcanos, the Tait'üngshan. Along the fault lines in the Yushan and Ts'ukaoshan Mountains are concentrated more than 100 thermal springs which are very popular due to their therapeutic properties.

The shore line of Taiwan is clearly outlined but not very incut. The shore is poor in harbors and in places there are coral reefs which make navigation difficult. On the west of the island navigation is difficult due to the shallowness of the sea and the number of sandy shoals and spits. The eastern shore line of the fault type has steep walls and to a great degree has been subjected to the sea tides and also is not suitable for navigation. The best harbors are found in the north of the island which is marked by a relatively greater incutting of the shore.

The climate on Taiwan is the warmest and, more important, the most even in China. Here there are no sharp temperature fluctuations which can be observed in the continental portion of the land even along the coast of the subtropical and tropical zones. In T'aipei, the mean temperatures in January and February are above 14-15°, and in July the temperature does not exceed 28°. The temperatures are evener in T'aitung which lies on the east coast where the mean temperatures in January-February do not drop below 18°, and in July do not rise above 28°. On the island, aside from its mountain areas, there are no frosts and the absolute minimums do not drop below 6°.

The island is rich in precipitation and in the distribution of it one can observe a much greater seasonal evenness in comparison with the continental areas of China. The abundant summer precipitation due to the southwest monsoons and typhoons in the winter is replaced by the significant precipitation caused by the northeast monsoon. The dry air of this continental monsoon in passing over the surface of the sea, is saturated with moisture and, in reaching Taiwan, causes the winter precipitation in the west of the island. As a result, the island receives an enormous amount of precipitation, and the annual total in the mountain territories exceeds 2,500 mm., while on the plains it fluctuates between 1,500 and 2,500 mm. Only in the strip of piedmont terraces does the amount of precipitation fall below these indices.

The high indices for sunlight, heat and moisture set Taiwan apart in the subtropical zone of China as a region of humid subtropics with a year-round vegetation period and the most favorable conditions for the wintering of thermophilic plants. The western plain occupying the alluvial lowlands along the western coast of Taiwan is an area of exceptionally intensive rice growing with two harvests a year. The rice planted in January and February matures by June and July, and after working the field is once again planted in rice which is ready in October-November. Sugar cane is also an important crop on the island and plantations of it occupy extensive areas of the western plain between T'aichung and Kaoshiung.

The mountain slopes facing the plain are solidly planted with the tea bush which produces a great amount of tea and which, like sugar, is a major export crop of Taiwan. A description of the agricultural landscapes on Taiwan would be incomplete if we did not mention the rich banana plantations which completely surround many of the Taiwan settlements, in particular in the region of T'aichung and Kaoshiung. The banana plantations alternate with pineapple plantations which are planted particularly on the piedmont plains. Everywhere there are plantings of mandarin oranges and oranges, and in the southerly parts of the island which have tropical climatic features there are such tropical fruit trees as mangos with large orange-colored fruits which

have a sweet taste and aroma, yangt'ao, the tree pineapple
and the coconut palm.

The mountains of Taiwan are rich in natural forests
and the good state of preservation has helped in their unusually rapid recreation. The subtropical forests which lie
in the lower stage with a marked predominance of trees
from the laurel and tea families, in particular the camphor
tree and Schima, above 1,500 meters are replaced by the
stage of deciduous broad-leafed forests and coniferous forests of Taiwan pine, China fir and above this there is a belt
of tall-trunked cypress forests; finally, at about 3,500 meters there are spruce-fir forests with a predominance of
Abies kawakami which in the upper stage of the forests is
replaced by rhododendron shrubs and alpine meadows.

CHAPTER

6

SOUTH CHINA: THE
TROPICAL REGION

V. T. Zaychikov and D. V. Panfilov
USSR Academy of Sciences
Institute of Geography

The features of tropical nature are endemic only to a
very small portion of the territory of China, including the
south of Yunnan, the southern coast, the Island of Hainan
and the southern extremity of Taiwan. In terms of area
(somewhat more than 40,000 sq. km.) this region does not
exceed one per cent of the total territory of China, but it
plays a major role in the national economy as a deliverer
of rubber, coffee, black pepper and many other types of
tropical products.

The most basic feature of the natural conditions in
this region distinguishing it from the other neighboring subtropics is the more even temperature regime and the much
smaller amount of winter minimums which do not disturb
the vegetation of the thermophilic plants. The mean monthly
temperatures in no month of the year drop below 13°, and
absolute minimums usually have a positive value. In comparison with the other regions, the daily temperature
changes are also insignificant.

This territory is the wettest in China with an annual amou
of precipitation up to 2,500 mm., although one will observe
just as sharp a contrast in the regime and distribution of the
precipitation as in the monsoon subtropics. Individual territories of the tropics have relatively less moisture and with
the high evaporation level endemic to the tropics will be dry.

Particularly characteristic are the biogeographical
features of the tropical region. The humid tropical forests

which are endemic to it differ sharply from the subtropical
and particularly from the forests of the temperate latitudes.
They are set apart by the greater diversity of the flora and
most importantly by the absence of homogeneous forest
stands consisting of one or several tree varieties. On the
other hand, the extreme diversity in the specific composition
is combined here with an unusually rapid development of the
plant organisms and the extremely intensive and complete
utilization of space by them. With enough moisture the tropical forest grows heavily, its cover becomes completely
solid and the trees reach an enormous height.

The average height of the tropical forests in China is
40-50 meters which is approximately double the average
height of the forests in the temperate belt. Individual trees
reach 60 meters in height.

Under the tall canopy grow lower trees. Thus, in the
forest there are at least three or four stories. The humid
tropical forest is also marked by the developed root system
which projects above the surface of the ground sometimes
rising up to 2 meters and providing an additional support for
the trees against falling. The adventitious roots which extend from the trunk give the tropical forest a particular
coloring. Finally, for the tropical forest there is also a
characteristic unusual abundance of lianas and epiphytes.
The tree trunks are usually thickly covered by lianas and
the number of species may be many score. In climbing up
the trunks, the lianas in the tropical Chinese forest reach
colossal dimensions--up to 50-70 meters long and 10-25 cm.
in diameter.

Of the epiphytes most widely found are orchids and
ferns which cover the trunks and branches of the trees. They
appear in the forks of branches and on any protuberance or
crack in the bark of the trunk, forming "baskets" with its
own soil formed from the dying vegetation, the addition of
mineral particles by termites and various invertebrates
which have died beneath the epiphytes.

In the tropical forests with the solid canopy constant
semidarkness prevails which has forced the plants to climb
upwards or adapt to the conditions of darkness. At the same
time, the cover of the tropical forest helps maintain constant

temperatures and humidity beneath the canopy. Therefore, in these forests the plants can easily endure the dry season of the year remaining green with the preserved soil and ground moisture and partially atmospheric moisture received by the leaves and air roots. After the felling or destruction of the tropical forest it naturally loses this quality and thus the ability to recreate itself. Usually a felled humid tropical forest is replaced by a secondary forest of strains which shed their leaves in the dry season of the year or savannas.

In the tropical region of China, as throughout all of Southern Asia, the savannas are widely found and have generally appeared as a result of cutting the forests. The thick grass cover of them is usually poor in terms of the specific composition, and hard pointed-leafed gramen predominate up to 2 meters high. For the coasts of the tropical region groves of coconut palms are typical which adapt well to the conditions of the poor sandy soils and the strong winds which predominate on the coasts. With the great height which is endemic to these palms, they have exceptional flexibility and can resist the strong winds.

On the territories inundated by seawater there are mangrove forests which in the Chinese tropics are represented by several tree varieties. In places the mangrove forests form rather thick dense thickets rising several meters above the water.

The regional differences in the tropical region of China can be seen most clearly between the above listed basic subdivisions: Southern Yunnan, the coastal strip of the southern maritime area, the Island of Hainan and the southern extremity of Taiwan.

SOUTHERN YUNNAN

Southern Yunnan is the warmest part in the continental territory of the Chinese tropics. This is both due to the position of the uplands which protect the tropical localities against the northern winds and to the mountain-valley relief which is favorable for the penetration of oceanic air masses.

Southern Yunnan is basically a low-mountain territory
But individual peaks, particularly in the west, reach 2,500
meters and above. The valleys of the large river crossing
this territory almost meridionally lie not higher than 300-
500 meters; the height of the valley of the Middle Hwang Ho
is all of 150-200 meters.

The mountain ranges which are a southern continuation of the Sino-Tibetan Mountains in the west have an almost meridional strike and in the east are extended from
the northwest to the southeast. The highest divides lie in
the west neighboring the Shansi Uplands, and in the east in
the uplifted southwest and the southern edge of the Yunnan
Uplands. In the middle lower portion of Southern Yunnan
flowing to the south and southeast are the large rivers Lukiang, Lants'angkiang and Hungho. Their valleys are separated by parallel ridges of low but very rugged mountains.

The rivers of Southern Yunnan carry a great deal of
water particularly in the period of summer rains. During
this time they bear the greatest amount of suspended material which turns the water of the Lants'angkiang a chocolate
color and the water of the Hungho an orange-red. In the
river basins erosion and flood denudation phenomena have
strongly developed and these are particularly bad on the deforested slopes.

The features of the tropical climate in Southern Yunnan are most strongly expressed in the valleys of the major
rivers and in the low-mountain areas not higher than 900-
1,000 meters. Here the mean annual air temperature is
about 23-25°. During the coolest time of the year (from
December through February) the mean monthly temperature
is around 18°.

During the year from 1,300 to 1,900 mm. of precipitation fall. Three seasons are clearly expressed: the dry
cool (from November through February), the dry hot
(March, April) and the humid hot (from May through Octo-.
ber). During the winter although cold spells are possible
the absolute minimums do not drop below 2-4°. In March
during the continuous little-cloudy weather the air temperature rises significantly, particularly during the day. At
the end of March and in the beginning of April at midday

temperatures around 30° and higher are common. During
this time of the year at midday the relative air humidity
drops significantly (down to 40-50 per cent), particularly on
deforested territories. During the night in the springtime
heavy fogs and abundant dew are common.

Rains begin in the first ten-day period of December.
In the west of Southern Yunnan the moisture is brought in
chiefly by the monsoon from the Indian Ocean, and in the
east from the South China Sea. With the beginning of the
rains, the air humidity during the daytime increases up to
90-95 per cent, and during the night comes close to 100
per cent. After the sunset fog is common. During the summer, sunny weather predominates during the day, cloudiness is relatively slight, but on certain days at midday
there will be heavy short downpours. During the day the air
temperature rises to 34-36°, sometimes even higher, and
with the very high humidity and lack of wind which is common here, this is difficult weather for man to endure. The
basic amount of precipitation falls during the nighttime
downpours which are accompanied by heavy thunder. During the night the air temperature remains around 26-32°.

At altitudes around 1,200 meters, the climate of
Southern Yunnan is different. Temperatures are significantly lower and in the winter months at night frequently
drop down to 5-8°. During this season fogs are particularly frequent and the air humidity is high. During the summer at these altitudes there are no hot spells and the temperature fluctuations over the day are insignificant; during
the day the ordinary air temperature is 20-24° and at night
19-21°. During the summer there is a great deal of cloudiness, there are constant drizzles and fogs are frequent.

Above 1,900-2,000 meters, at the tops of the mountains the climate is severe and cool. During the winter at
night there are sometimes frosts, hoarfrosts and glazes.
During the summer the mountain peaks, as a rule, are
shrouded in clouds, the air temperature during the day and
at night is about 16-19°, and only on the rare sunny days is
a little above 20°.

The climate in the south of Yunnan is favorable for growing the rich and diverse forest vegetation characteristic for the tropics of Southern Asia.

In the valleys of the major rivers and their tributaries and also on the hills nearby at elevations not above 600 meters one will find mesophillic and humid tropical forests. Trees of these forests reach 45-50 meters in height, and their crowns are arranged in several stories. The forests are evergreen and only in the upper story will one encounter certain deciduous strains. The specific composition of the arboreal vegetation is exceptionally diverse. Here there are common species of Knema, Canarium, Jaruga, Sterculia, Eriolaena, species of Pterospermum, Dalbergia, Pterocarpus, upas-tree (Anthiaris), Artocarpus, Ficus, Xanthoxylon, Chukrasia, Aglaia, Toona, species of Dysoxylum, Nephelium, Arytera, Spondias, Schefflera and other tree varieties. Here the trees form plantings which are amazing in their diversity. In these forests over an area of one hectare there will usually be from 30 to 60 species of trees. Here are common the low Pandanus and palms both the tall up to 10-15 meters and above (Arenga, Caryota) and the lower growing (Pinanga, Livistona, Didymosperma, Calamus). In places, particularly along the edges of forests, tall bamboos form thick groves.

In the forests there are all sorts of lianas, particularly the arboreal ones which are up to 10-20 cm. and more thick. The lianas drop from the crowns of the trees, they hang from one tree trunk to another, they are intertwined or will lie in gigantic loops on the soil surface. Grassy lianas are abundant along the forest edges and on the sunny openings within the forests. Here the grassy and delicate arboreal lianas form a solid canopy descending from the crowns of the trees or thickly clothing the lower portions of the tall tree trunks.

There are few shrubs and grasses in these forests and they are frequently virtually absent. At the same time, there are very many small trees which have just come up from the soil with large leaves and which basically comprise the lowest story of the tropical forest. In opposition to the slight development of grasses on the soil, the epiphytes, many of which are represented by grassy forms, are very

abundant on the bark of the trees and lianas. Epiphytes are
particularly abundant in the moister forests in gorges.
Here one will find Epipremnum, Pothos and Raphidophora,
orchids and also the epiphyte ferns Asplenium nidus and
Drynaria coronans which look like enormous baskets
attached to the bark of the trunks, in the forks of the
branches and on the thick lianas. In the wettest forests
along the bottom of gorges one will find thick groves of various types of large ground grasses such as the wild banana
(Musa), Alocasia, Phrynium and various gingers. Here
also there are Begonia and the large ferns Angiopteris.

At altitudes of 600-1,200 meters, the driest portions
of the slopes of the hills, particularly where the forests
have been destroyed, one will find thick bamboo groves
(Bambusa spinosa) or the tall grassy gramen such as Imperata cylindrica, Themeda, Thysanolaena and Miscanthus.
Among them will be individual surviving trees of the tropical forests as well as trees and shrubs characteristic for
the Southern Chinese savannas: bombax (Gossampinus
malabarica), Albizzia mollis, Erythrina indica, Ficus geocarpa and Phyllanthus emblica.

At elevations from 1,200-1,300 meters up to 1,700-
1,900 meters, the mountain slopes are covered by thick
mountain tropical forests. In them there are particularly
many lianas and epiphytes, in particular orchids. Shrubs
are very abundant as well as the tall large-leafed grasses,
small bamboos, and in places one will encounter the enormous tree ferns Cyathea. On certain areas the soil surface
in the mountain tropical forests is covered by a solid cover
of Selaginella. One should note the abundance and diversity
of mosses which cover the lower portion of the tree trunks
and also rock outcroppings. Among the mosses on the bark
of the trees one will find very commonly the very small
epiphyte ferns of Hymenophillacea.

The mountain peaks (above 1,700-1,900 meters) are
covered by the "moss" subtropical forests consisting of
more homogeneous trees with the tree rhododendron being
common. Here there are many arboreal lianas. In these
forests under the conditions of constant mists, mosses are
particularly abundant and they cover the trunks and branches
of trees, the lianas and soil in a thick layer and will even

grow on the surface of certain tree leaves and shrubs. In
the "moss" forests there are many ground cap mushrooms,
and on the soil one will frequently encounter begonias with
pink flowers. The very peaks of the mountains are overgrown with shrubrhododendron, alder and club-moss. On
the bark of the trees and shrubs and also on the stones one
will find numerous lichens.

Under the conditions of the tropical climate in Southern Yunnan, particularly at elevations up to 900-1,000 meters, the soils are red and yellow earths, sometimes partially lateritized. In the lowland tropical forests the soils
are little developed and not fertile and this has been caused
by the activity of the very abundant termites which carry a
large portion of the dying plant parts down to a depth of 2-4
meters below the surface. As a result the forest floor and
the grass cover in these forests are almost completely absent, while the soil surface is heavily compacted. On the
side of a felled forest in the valleys there are usually cultivated soils, and of them the rice soils are widely found.

In the mountain tropical and subtropical forests where
the activity of termites is impeded by the low temperatures,
the surface horizons of the red and yellow earths are significantly richer in humus, and beneath the "moss" forests
the mountain soils, moreover, are somewhat podzolized.

The animal world in the south of Yunnan is very rich
and represented predominantly by tropical species. Of the
mammals here one will find the fruit-eating bats, pangolins,
loris, several species of monkey including the anthropoid
ape, the gibbon, civet cats, tigers, leopards, bamboo rats,
the muntjac, and in the Mekong Basin, elephants. Of the
birds one will find such tropical dwellers as the peacock,
Indian cock, fruit-eating doves, the large hornbill (Bucerotes), tits, drongo, bulbuls, weaverbirds and Nectariniidae.
Examples of the tropical reptiles would be the crocodile (in
the Mekong River), the python, the dragon lizard and the
water monitor. Of the amphibians there is an abundance of
web-footed frogs. The rich insect fauna in the south of Yunnan is almost exclusively represented by species and genera
of the Indo-Malayan tropical fauna. The same is true for the
fauna of myriopods and arachnids.

Particularly rich and diverse is the animal world in
the lowland tropical forests--on the river terraces and low-
lying hills, and also in the low-lying gorges. There is less
diversity of animals in the mountainous tropical forests,
and here one encounters representatives of certain Holarctic groups. The fauna of the "moss" forests on the mountain tops is even poorer; it is basically of the Holarctic type.

The change in the landscapes in the south of Yunnan is
due basically to the difference in altitude and to the degree
of moistness in the individual regions of the territory. Tropical landscapes comprise the largest area. The lowland
tropical forests and the tropical savannas are found, as a
rule, only up to 1, 200 meters. Higher, basically up to
1, 700-1, 900 meters, the well-moistened slopes are covered
by mountain tropical forests while in localities with insufficient precipitation, particularly in the Hungho Basin, at
these elevations there predominate relatively lesser moisture-
requiring subtropical landscapes with abundant grassy gramen,
fern and semixerophilic shrubs and trees. Some of them are
endemic to the tropical savanna and others to the subtropics
of the Yunnan Uplands lying to the north. Above 1, 900 meters
one will find the humid subtropical "moss forests" with a
poor composition.

In Southern Yunnan the subtropical landscales along the
watersheds descend rather low, while the tropical landscapes
rise high up the wet gorges and in individual areas of mountain
humid tropical forests will be found in gorges at elevations
around 2, 000-2, 300 meters. As a result in the mountains
there are frequent amazing combinations of areas of tropical
and subtropical vegetation which are next to one another at the
same elevations. Here the wetter shady slopes are covered by
the tropical complexes while the slopes facing south are drier wit
subtropical ones. This is explained by the fact that the tropical plants and many animals are basically more moisture-
loving than the subtropical. For the tropical organisms particularly bad is the lack of moisture in the dry period of the
year with the somewhat reduced winter temperatures in the
mountains of Southern Yunnan, i. e. , conditions to which the
subtropical plants and animals are rather adapted. It is this
boundary in the relationship of the tropical and subtropical
organisms to the climate under the situation of the rugged
relief of Southern Yunnan which determines both the basic
boundary between the tropical and subtropical landscapes and

the pattern of a mosaic distribution for the various variations of tropical and subtropical landscapes.

LEICHOW PENINSULA AND
ISLAND OF HAINAN

The strip of the southern coast with the Leichow Peninsula and also a significant portion of the Island of Hainan
is the most variable in terms of temperature conditions in
the tropical region. The Nanling Mountain Chain lying to the
north is low and cannot fully neutralize the cooling effect of
the Siberian anticyclone. The Leichow Peninsula and Hainan
during the winter are usually at the end or in the interior of
the anticyclone ridge, and over their territories strong
northern and northeastern winds develop which assume particular force with a shift of the polar front to the southeastern edge of the continent. At the same time, the air temperatures drop sharply.

In Ch'iungshan which lies on the northern coast of
Hainan, the absolute January minimum over the period from
1924 to 1935 was 6°, and at the point of Nata lying in the interior of the island at the northern edge of the mountains, it
was lower (4.8°). But these are not the lowest indices. In
the particularly cold winter of 1955, over the entire territory of Leichow and the northern half of Hainan there were
negative temperatures with absolute minimums of -2°.

The incursions of cold air masses and the cold spells
caused by them are most noticeable in the periods from
February to March and from November to December. However, these cold spells are brief in the form of three or
four periodic waves and kill off only the tropical plants which
are most sensitive to colds, in particular the Para rubber
tree which is cultivated therefore only in the south of Hainan
which is protected by mountains against the northern winds.

The course and distribution of precipitation on Hainan
Island are more complex. The mean annual precipitation
totals for various portions of its territory fluctuate in great
limits. The maximum amount of precipitation falls in the
southeast where the annual totals reach 2,000-2,800 mm.,
in the northeast of the island the annual amount is 1,500-

1, 800 mm., and in the southwest it drops down to 1, 300-
1, 500 mm., and in the western portion of the island protected by the mountains against the humid air currents of
the tropical cyclines it is the least amount--all of 800-900
mm., and the distance between the points with the maximum
and minimum amounts of precipitation on the island is a
little more than 100 km. On Leichow Peninsula, the eastern
portion is significantly wetter than the western. A great unevenness can also be observed in the seasonal distribution
of precipitation. The wet period of the year (May-October)
is clearly replaced by a dry period (November-April), and
the transition from one period to the next is accompanied by
sharper changes in the intensity of precipitation fall than in
the changes of air temperature.

The economic activity of man has had a great influence upon the appearance of the contemporary landscapes of
Hainan and Leichow. The tropical forest which at one time
covered their territories with the system of slash-and-burn
farming which predominated here for a protracted period
has been virtually completely destroyed. There are virtually no forests on Leichow. On Hainan Island they have
been preserved only in the interior mountainous territory
and partially in the southeastern and southwestern coasts
which have more favorable conditions for the restoration of
the tropical forest vegetation. However, the total area under
forests on the island is insignificant, and does not exceed
15 per cent.

Characteristically, in the regions where the forest
vegetation has been maintained there are secondary forests
which differ in terms of tree composition from the primary
forests. All the remaining area is under agricultural fields,
savannas, and in places covered by impassable thickets of
shrubs and lianas or is barren waste. With these common
features in the nature of Leichow and Hainan, the local landscape differences are characteristic.

The Leichow Peninsula is not complex in terms of the
surface structure, being basically an undulating platform
with soft outlines and steps dropping to the sea. The mean
altitude of them is 10-50 meters. The platforms are composed chiefly of basalts and sedimentary formations of
Quaternary times. Over the surface of the platforms rise

characteristic volcanic cones 100-250 meters tall which are
particularly numerous in the north and south of the peninsula.

With such a character in the relief, it would be difficult to expect great landscape differences over a territory
that is 7,500 sq. km. But nevertheless there are certain
differences, particularly between the western and eastern
parts of the peninsula.

The eastern half of Leichow is wetter with 1,000-
1,500 mm. of annual precipitation, while in the west the
amount does not exceed 1,000 mm. Such a difference in the
degree of moisture to a significant degree is due to the sub-
jection of the eastern coast to the effect of the typhoons
which are accompanied by intensive rains.

The soil cover of the peninsula is rather mottled and
this is due above all to the different features of underlying
rock.

The extreme north of the peninsula in landscape terms
has common features with the north of Kwangtung, that is, a
hilly locality with broad valleys covered by rice paddies.
The hills which stand out with the bright-red color of the
sands and sandy loams are covered with a gramen motley
grass with solitary specimens of Masson pine. In places the
pines form stands.

Virtually the entire remainder of Leichow, with the
exception of the southeast, is deforested. In the northern
part there predominates the dry low-grass steppe with
sparse trees which differs from the Southern Asiatic savannas in terms of grass composition with the most characteristic being Eragrostis amabilis, Eremochloa ciliaris,
Eriachne pallescens. The southern half of Leichow has the
appearance of a typical savanna with a predominance of
Phoenix hanceana, Heteropogon contortus, Aristida chinensis, and on the more elevated areas Pennisetum alopecu-
roides and Eragrostis chariis. At the foot of the slopes and
in the valleys the number of shrubs gradually increases, in
places forming dense impassable thickets.

The steppes of Leichow to a significant degree have a drought character. With the stopping of the rains in the autumn and winter they dry up and yellow. But even in the rainy period with the little water permeability of the clay soils and the high temperatures, a drought situation is frequently created for the steppe vegetation. Steppe fires here are a frequent phenomenon.

For the entire steppe territory there is a characteristic intensive plane and gulley erosion. The soil layer is usually very thin and in places has been completely washed away. There are numerous ravines and rills which regardless of the fact that they rapidly are overgrown continue to increase with each downpour. The steppes are used for pasturing livestock and this also at times does damage due to the excessive destruction of the vegetation cover.

Against the general background of the savanna landscape Southeast Leichow stands out with the humid tropical forests. This region is somewhat more elevated and here begin all of the significant rivers in the south of the peninsula. Thick red earths have been formed on the weathering products of the basalts, and the forest vegetation has a favorable effect upon improving the structure. This portion of Leichow is one of the wettest and this, of course, helps in the relatively better redevelopment of the forests.

Where the forests have remained, they are marked by great lushness and a rich specific composition. They are usually dense with numerous stories and preserve a bright green year-round. The abundance of lianas makes these forests difficult to get through. In them there are numerous ungulates. In the forest thickets there will still be found tigers.

On Hainan Island in terms of the character of the landscapes, the interior mountain area sharply stands out from the maritime lowlands which surround it on all sides.

The mountain area of Hainan which covers approximately one-quarter of the island's territory consists of several mountain chains running southwest and divided by broad valleys. The highest of these chains is the Wuchihshan Mountains (highest point 1, 879 meters) which occupy the

extreme southeast. Somewhat to the west of these mountains and parallel to them stretches the Yingkeling Chain
and finally, further west, the Yachiataling Mountains. All
of the mountains to a great degree have been worn down and
are relatively low elevations, on the average from 500 to
1,000 meters high, and only individual peaks rise more than
1,000 meters.

The Hainan Mountains which were formed in the course
of the Yenshan mountain-forming movements accompanied
by the introduction of major granite intrusions are characterized by the presence of significant resources of minerals both of hydrothermal origin and those formed as a result of contact metamorphism. The most famous is the iron
ore deposit at Shihlushan with magnetite ore reserves of several hundred million tons, the tin deposits in the region of
Nata and others confined to the contact zones of limestones
and granites, copper deposits, lead, manganese, wolfram
and gold.

The mountainous area of Hainan is characterized by
the greatest wetness. However, the degree of moisture for
the individual areas of the region is not the same. The maximum amount of atmospheric precipitation (up to 3,000 mm.
per year) is received on the windward southeastern slopes,
and on the northeastern slopes the amount of precipitation
drops to 1,500-1,800 mm., with still smaller amounts falling in the southwest and the smallest amount falling in the
western parts of the mountains.

As a whole the entire mountainous area of Hainan is
characterized by great surface runoff. The runoff module
for the Hainan mountain rivers is more than two times
above the runoff module for the subtropical regions of continental China, reaching in the rivers of the west 61.2 cu.
m. per sq. km. It is less for the rivers in the northern and
eastern slopes of Hainan, but here is more than 40 cu. m.
per sq. km. significantly above the corresponding index for
the Sikiang Basin.

In the mountain area three of the largest rivers of
Hainan arise and flow through their upper courses; these are
the Nantukiang, the Wanch'uankiang and the Wenhuakiang.
All of them are marked by a great amount of water. The
largest, the Nantukiang, is only 311 km. long, but has an

annual runoff of 7.5 million cu. m. The annual runoff of the
Wanch'uankiang is 6.2 million cu. m., and of the Wenhuakiang 3.3 million cu. m.

The mountain rivers are rich in power resources and
are important as irrigation sources, although the effective-
ness of utilizing them is made difficult by the extreme ir-
regularity of river runoff. For virtually all of the Hainan
rivers the maximum discharges are hundreds of times above
the minimum, and for the Wenhuakiang River which irri-
gates the western slopes, the difference in the extreme
amounts of the discharges is even greater (maximum--
11,680 cu. m. per second, minimum--4 cu. m. per second). The more intense character of precipitation fall and
the high concentration of surface runoff have caused heavier
erosion on the western mountain slopes, particularly in the
areas of lumbering.

The eastern and western halves of the mountain area,
as for all of the Island of Hainan, basically differ also in
terms of the character of the soil-vegetation cover.

The primary vegetation in the eastern windward portion of the Hainan mountain area was tropical rain forests.
At present they have been greatly destroyed. These forests
occupy the piedmont plains, the valleys and mountain slopes
usually below 800 meters and, as an exception, will rise in
the mountains up to 1,000 meters. They are characterized
by an abundance and diversity in vegetation forms and species, with an exceptional role played by the lianas, epiphytes
and parasitic plants. Many features of these forests, for
example, the presence of air roots, the development of
flowers on the tree trunks and large branches make the rain
forests of Hainan similar to analogous forests in the equatorial belt of Asia, in particular the Malayan Archipelago
and Yunnan. In the higher belt in the east of the mountain
area, at an elevation of 800-1,600 meters, these forests
are replaced by forests of another type, with a predominance of laurels, tea and myrtle.

For the west of the mountainous area of the island
which is poorer in precipitation and characterized by a
clearly expressed dry season, another type of vegetation is
found, the tropical monsoon-rain forest. The lower story

of this forest consists of evergreen species such as lichee, olive, Euphoria longana, mango, ficus, etc. In the upper story there are deciduous trees dominant such as Albizzia chinensis, Gossampinus malabarica, etc. In the monsoon-rain forests, the trees are lower than in the tropical rain forests (usually not more than 15-20 meters) and are marked by a broad branchy crown and twisting trunks. The forests have a sparser stand and there are fewer lianas and epiphytes in them.

On the areas where the primary vegetation has been destroyed in the monsoon-rain forests there will be second-ary forests with a much larger proportional amount of de-ciduous varieties, and in the mountains with an admixture of conifers.

The maritime plain which surrounds the mountain area of Hainan in a ring, in terms of its individual parts, is also not homogeneous in landscape terms. The chief distinction here is due to the relatively greater wetness of the eastern coast, although the picture of landscape differentiation is even more complex than in the interior mountainous area of Hainan.

One should first of all note the platform areas and the coastal lowland in the north of the island with sandy soils covered by steppe and partially thickets of spiny shrubs. This portion of the island is most subject to incursions of cold air waves with absolute minimums below 0°. To the south along the eastern coast the wetness of the territory increases. The southeastern maritime portion of Hainan is a region with the lushest, predominantly forest, vegetation. This region is most protected against the incursions of cold air masses and is the center for growing perennial tropical crops.

The western coast of Hainan sharply contrasts to this region with the dry climate and the predominance of savan-nas and deserty steppes which occupy particularly extensive expanses in the southeastern coast of the island.

CHAPTER 7 SOUTHWEST CHINA: THE YUNNAN REGION

D. V. Panfilov
USSR Academy of Sciences
Institute of Geography

The Yunnan region lies in the subtropical belt in the southwest of China, approximately between 23 and 27° n. lat. and 98 and 105° e. long. This is a mountainous region representing in terms of elevation an intermediate step from the grandiose elevations in the area of Tibet to the low-mountain and lowland areas in the east and south of China. The region is effected by the monsoons which bring moisture from the Indian Ocean and from the South China Sea. However, the mountainousness of the territory and its significant uplifting above sea level (on the average about 2,000 meters) limits the air influx of moisture since the wettest and warmest flows of monsoons move at elevations below 1,000-1,200 meters. In rising in the mountains they are cooled and drop the basic amount of moisture along the periphery of the zone being described here--in the meridional ranges of Burma, along the southern edge of the Yunnan Uplands and in the mountains of North Vietnam.

Thus the medium-mountain relief of the region has a basic influence upon reducing the amount of moisture in the climate and on the temperature drops. Here the climate is much more favorable for human life than in the southernmost part of Yunnan Province or in the east of subtropical China. Nature in the Yunnan region, in possessing significant uniqueness, at the same time shows certain features of a transitional nature from the severe situation in Tibet and the Sino-Tibetan Mountains with their cold and temperate climate and the meager vegetation cover and animal world to the warm and humid climate and rich moisture-loving complex of organisms in the subtropics and tropics of Southern China.

The basis of the orography of the region is generally as follows: in the west there run meridional ranges of which the Kaolingkungshan Range is the most significant. Somewhat further east from the northwest to the southeast stretches the Aylaoshan Range. Even farther east are the Yunnan Uplands occupying the larger portion of the region's territory. The orography of Southwest China is heterogeneous. The meridional ranges of the west are younger. They were formed during the Himalayan phase of alpine orogenesis, skirting the Chinese Platform on the southwest along the ranges of Laos and North Vietnam. The orography of the Yunnan Uplands was formed somewhat earlier during the Yenshan movements of the earth's crust which rejuvenated the peneplainized Mesozoic relief of the ancient Chinese Platform. The highest elevations lie in the west of the region where Mount Wuliangshan rises to 3,505 meters. The majority of the mountains, however, does not rise above 2,500 meters. In the valleys of the major rivers the elevations drop down to 400-500 meters. A particularly sharp difference in elevations and the greatest ruggedness of the relief is in the western portion of the region where in the gorges of the large rivers the steep slopes drop from the divides to a depth of 2,000-2,500 meters. The marginal areas are greatly broken up by small rivers which take their source on the Yunnan Uplands. Being rather calm in the upper reaches, they become rapid around the borders of the region where the elevations fall sharply. The interior portions of the region are a locality with rather soft mountain contours. These mountains rise slightly above the levels of the intermontane valleys. Individual valleys are rather enclosed and will have lakes. The largest of them are Erhhai, Tiench'ih and Fuhsienhu.

The climate of the Yunnan region in the majority of areas is cold with slight amplitudes in temperature changes over the year. Ordinary January temperatures are about 4-5°, and in places significantly higher, up to 14-15°. July temperatures are 16-24°. The winters are mild, and occasionally in some areas in December and January temperatures at night will drop down to -3, -5°. During the day during this season temperatures frequently are up to 12-18°, and in lower lying areas even higher. Snow falls rarely and soon runs off. In March the temperatures rise rapidly, during the day up to 25°. However, the nights

during the spring are cool (from 2-3° up to 8-10°). Fog is
common at night. In May the rains begin and the daily temperature amplitudes drop (during the middle of the day the
temperatures are about 26-30°, at night around 22-25°).
The relative air humidity from May through October keeps
at a level of about 80-90 per cent. The greatest amount of
precipitation (1,300-1,500 mm.) falls in the mountains
along the edges of the region, and in the center of the territory the amount of precipitation drops down to 800-900 mm.,
and in the headwaters of the Hungho (Red River) down to
600 mm.; this is the driest spot of the region. The least
amount of moisture brought in by the monsoons is reached
here.

The largest rivers which flow through the territory of
the region--the Lukiang (Salween) and Lants'angkiang
(Mekong)--flow from the mountains of Tibet and the Sino-
Tibetan Mountains and are basically fed by glaciers. Their
tributaries which begin on the territory of the Yunnan region
are relatively short, with steep drops and with rapids. The
smaller rivers and their tributaries which begin on the territory of the region have a significantly calmer current.
These are the rivers in the basins of the Hungho, Sikiang
and the right tributaries of the Yangtze. They are fed exclusively by rainwater and groundwaters. The latter is
caused by the great development of the karst formations in
the Yunnan Uplands. The greatest rise in the water in all
bodies of water (in the large and small rivers and in the
lakes) will be observed during the summer months, particularly in June-August, and this is due to the monsoon rains.
On the large rivers, the water rise occurs also due to the
intensification of glacier and ice thawing in the mountains of
Tibet. The surplus water during the summer is partially
used for economic purposes, chiefly for irrigating rice paddies which occupy the intermontane valleys and nearby mountain slopes.

In line with the particular features of the relief, hydrography and seasonal distribution of precipitation, the
greatest erosion occurs during the summer months in the
basins of the large rivers, particularly on the slopes which
descend directly to their channels, and also along the edges
of the region where the elevations drop sharply. In the interior portions of the region, erosion is weaker. However,

a certain scarcity of moisture during the dry season leads
to little retention of the soil where the forests have been cut.
Therefore during the rainy period erosion on the deforested
areas is very significant, converting the territory into an
economically unusable area. At present erosion is being
controlled by planting artificial forests.

Characteristically, karst processes have developed
very strongly in the Yunnan region. Over enormous areas
limestones and in places sandstones emerge on the surface,
and with the abundance of precipitation this has led to karst
formation. The absorption of water by the karst sinkholes
plays a definite role in intensifying the lack of moisture during the dry season of the year in those areas where there is
the greatest amount of karst topography. Here there are
numerous caves and unusual shapes of limestones caused by
water erosion, in particular the "stone forests" which are
complex cave labyrinths which in the course of erosion
have been deprived of a ceiling consisting of friable rock.
The "stone forests" are found in the central portion of the
Yunnan Uplands and on the neighboring Kweichow Plateau.

Chemical and biological processes have played a
large role in the rock weathering. Of particular great significance have been the organic acids and the carbon dioxide
dissolved in water which have been formed in the soil with
the year-round disintegration of remains of forest vegetation and which have helped in breaking down the calcareous
rock. The mechanical destruction of the rock and the trans-
fer of the products of its destruction have been achieved
predominantly by the rains and surface runoff which has a
particularly strong effect on the clay rock.

The soils are basically clay formed on the decomposition products of friable clay shales and on weathering
crusts of more solid bedrocks; the acids are acidy or calcareous. In places, particularly on the ridges of elevations
and on the steep slopes, where the solid limestones emerge
on the surface, the soil cover is missing or is shallow. In
the river valleys, soils have formed on sandstone alluvial
detritus and they frequently include gravel and pebbles. In
certain lake basins the soils are gley. The amount of humus
in the soil is relatively low, and podzolization in many instances is rather significant, chiefly in the mountain soils

under the conditions of abundant precipitation and the cool
climate. The lateritization processes are little found.

The vegetation of Southwest China is represented by a
very diverse complex of subtropical species. A significant
portion of the territory in the region is covered by forests
consisting of several species of pine and other conifers, as
well as leafy forests of very many species of deciduous and
evergreen trees and shrubs. In the leafy and coniferous-
leafy forests one will widely find oaks. The predominance
of pine forests on the territory and particularly the Yunnan
pine (Pinus yunnanensis) and also oaks and oak-pine forests
is a phenomenon which to a significant degree is secondary.
These forests have replaced the moisture-loving tree-shrub
natural vegetation which was richer in composition and
which for a significant time had been subjected to felling and
burning. The latter led to the drying of the soil and made it
possible for only more arid-resistant varieties of tree to
grow back, predominantly pines and oaks. Large areas are
covered by dry-valley meadows on the slopes of elevations
with a diverse semi-sor (salina) grassy vegetation and
shrubs. This vegetation is also basically secondary, developing on the site of former forests. The valleys are almost completely plowed and planted with rice and cereals
such as wheat and barley and to a lesser degree other cultivated plants. There are numerous rocky wastes with
sparse grassy and shrub vegetation used for pasturing. Individual mountain peaks are covered with dense liana-
entwined "moss" forests consisting of evergreen leafy trees.
The highest peaks are covered by subalpine grasses and
shrub rhododendron.

The richness of the flora in the region which is due to
the favorable conditions of the subtropical climate and the
diversity of the topography have led over a protracted history to the formation of a number of unique landscapes.
These landscapes over scores of millions of years have existed under a situation with the absence of any significant
climatic changes. Even in the Quaternary Age, when the
entire northern half of Eurasia experienced great changes
in the organic world and relief under the effect of the glacier phenomena, in the designated region the landscape situation of the Tertiary Age was maintained. Only landscapes
which are characteristic at present for the upper parts of

the mountains descended, evidently, lower down on the slopes, occupying a greater territory and without the insular distribution as at present. This can be seen from the very great similarity in the specific composition of the plants and animals inhabiting the individual mountain areas of Yunnan alone and being more than 200-300 km. apart. For example, one should note the similarity in the specific composition of organisms on the mountain slopes of the Wuliangshan in the center of Yunnan and the organisms on the top of Mount Taweishan which rises in the southeast of Yunnan along the left bank of the Hungho. The protracted peaceful existence of the organic world in Southwest China can also be seen from the large number of primitive and partially relic plants and animals which have little evolved due to the absence of significant changes in the geographic situation. For example, these are the numerous mammals such as the primitive shrews, moles, spineless hedgehogs, primitive squirrels and Carnivora which are basically endemic for Southwest China. There are also many plants, in particular ferns, relic conifers, Cycas and the primitive angiosperms, the magnolias.

Regardless of the long effect of man upon nature in the Yunnan region, here large areas of ancient landscapes have remained which make it possible to note the basic types of natural historically-formed landscapes in this territory. Here we should point out that each of these landscape types is due not so much to the entire territory but is mosaically scattered with the other types and found only in definite elevations and landforms and with the corresponding climatic conditions.

The basic landscape types of the designated region are the following:

1) The subalpine landscape on the peaks of the highest mountains;
2) the landscape of the "moss" forests at the top of individual high mountain ranges;
3) the landscape of coniferous forests on dry elevations and on the steep slopes of medium-elevation mountains;
4) a landscape of coniferous-leafy and partially ever-green forests with a complex floristic composition on territories with sufficient moisture;
5) the landscape of karst forms where there are significant outcroppings of limestone with sparse tree-shrub and

grassy vegetation;

    6) the landscape of savannas on slopes descending to the valleys of the major rivers;

    7) the landscape of gallery tropical forests of poor compo sition in the low-lying valleys and gorges.

    Aside from these landscapes during prehistoric times there undoubtedly was a unique landscape of the large inter-montane valleys which at present has completely disappeared due to the effect of man. Here evidently there were large swampy expanses around lakes which at present are basically under rice paddies.

    The Yunnan region can be divided into two major phys-ical-geographic sections: Western Yunnan and the Yunnan Uplands. They are characterized by different combinations of landscapes and this is caused by the particular features of the relief and climate on each of the designated territories.

WESTERN YUNNAN

    Western Yunnan is a typical medium-mountain terri-tory with a very rugged relief. The mean elevations above sea level are around 2,000 meters. However, certain peaks rise up to 2,500-3,000 meters, and the highest peak--Mount Wuliangshan--has an elevation of 3,505 meters. The moun-tain ranges are basically parallel to one another. The west-ern ranges are meridional, while the eastern deviate from the meridional direction and are extended from northwest to southeast. In the west of the designated territory one will find the southern part of the Kaolingkungshan Range on the right bank of the Lukiang River. Farther east, between the Lukiang and Lants'angkiang rivers, lie the southern spurs of the Nushan Range. Farther east, on the left bank of the Langts'angkiang, are located the Lunfangshan Range and its continuation towards the southeast, the Wuliangshan Range. In the easternmost portion of the territory among a series of parallel low ranges is the large Aylaoshan Range running along the right bank of the Hungho River.

    This entire system of ranges is a relatively low southern extension of the meridional Sino-Tibetan Mountains

and is related to the southeastern portion of the Himalayan
mountain belt.

The mountains were formed in the era of the Himalayan phase of alpine orogenesis. They show characteristically sharp-pointed peaks and very steep slopes. Between
the parallel ranges run deep gorges with rivers flowing
through them. Here the altitude differences reach 2,000-
2,500 meters.

The rivers to the west of the Kaolingkungshan Range
belong to the Irawadi Basin, and they flow southwest. These
are the small rivers of the Taping, Nanwanho, Lukuangkiang
and their tributaries. They all take their sources in the
mountains on the territory of Western Yunnan.

Flowing from north to south through the central portion of Western Yunnan in deep gorges are the Lukiang and
Lants'angkiang rivers with abundant water. They begin
more than 1,000 km. to the north in the glaciers of Tibet.
In Western Yunnan these rivers receive only short small
tributaries which basically do not increase the mass of water. The east of the territory is covered by rivers related
to the Hungho Basin. On this territory begins the Hungho itself as well as its major tributary, the Amokiang (Black
River), flowing southeast. In contrast to the short tributaries
of the Lukiang and Lants'angkiang in the Yunnan, for the
Hungho on the given territory the tributaries are much
longer flowing between the low parallel ranges and receiving
the water of numerous small tributaries from the side
gorges. The water level in the rivers of Western Yunnan
changes significantly over the year. In the Lukiang and
Lants'angkiang during the middle of the summer (when the
glaciers thaw in Eastern Tibet), the water level rises by 10-
15 meters and remains at this level until autumn.

In the Hungho Basin a heavy water rise occurs in May-
June, at the beginning of the summer rains. However, over
the year the water level in the Hungho and its tributaries
fluctuates constantly reacting to the uneven influx of summer
precipitation. On the Hungho the brief fluctuations in the water level reach several meters. All of the rivers in Western
Yunnan during the summer carry out a large amount of suspended material. During the summer the water in the Hungho

becomes orange-red from the red earth that is washed out.
Lakes are not characteristic for the given region, but in the
extreme north there is the large Erthai Lake which is located
in a narrow intermontane depression, and through this lake
flows the tributary of the Lants'angkiang, the Yangp'ing-
kiang River.

The climate of Western Yunnan is not the same in the
various parts of the territory, and it will change depending
upon the elevations above sea level. In the west (before the
watershed of the Lukiang and the Lants'angkiang), the summer monsoon from the Indian Ocean brings in abundant precipitation. The humid air currents penetrate from north to
south along the meridional ranges. Here about 1,500 mm.
of precipitation fall each year. To the east of the designated divide the climate is somewhat drier, and the moisture comes in basically from the South China Sea, with
about 1,000 mm. of precipitation falling. The smallest
amount of precipitation is found in the headwaters of the
Hungho which is protected against the humid southwest
winds by the Aylaoshan Range, and against the southeast
winds by the Yunnan Uplands. Here about 600 mm. of precipitation fall. In the Western Yunnan the dry and wet periods of the year are clearly expressed. The winter and
spring are clear, with frequent winds. During this season
fog is common, particularly at night. The basic amount of
precipitation (75-80 per cent) falls from May through October. The annual air humidity is rather high--about 70 per
cent. The mean monthly temperatures over the entire year
are positive. The coolest month, January, has a temperature of somewhat above 5°. The summer is not hot with
mean monthly summer temperatures not above 22°, and in
the majority of places the July temperature is about 20°.
In the narrow intermontane valleys and in the gorges of the
major rivers the winter and summer temperatures are
much higher and come close to tropical temperatures, for
example, along the Lukiang and Hungho rivers. In the
mountains above 1,900-2,500 meters the climate is wet.
During the summer at these elevations the slopes of the
mountains are usually shrouded in clouds and drizzles are
frequent. During the winter fog is almost continuous; at
times the temperature drops below 0°, ground frosts occur
and momentary snows may fall.

The natural vegetation cover in Western Yunnan in
many areas has been well preserved due to the sparseness
of the population and the inaccessible topography. On the
dry mountain slopes there predominate forests of Yunnan
pine (Pinus yunnanensis), and in the higher parts of the
mountains (above 2, 000 meters) in significant numbers grow
the Armand pine (Pinus armandii). Many shrub species are
found in the undergrowth. In sufficiently wet mountain regions, of the conifers one will find Keteleeria Evelyniana
and cypress (Cypressus Duclouxiana), and of the leafy trees,
evergreen and deciduous oak (Quercus) and the evergreen
Yunnan machilus (Machilus yunnanensis) which is related to
the laurel family. In the undergrowth one will commonly
find Michelia yunnanensis of the magnolia family with large
fragrant flowers. Further below on the mountain slopes
there are some tropical laurel forests with diverse predominantly evergreen trees such as Castanopsis, Pasania,
Machilus, evergreen oak, Lithocarpus, Lindera, Symplocos,
Celtis, maple (Acer), Photinia, etc. Among the leafy trees
there are several thermophilic conifers, in particular Libo-
cedrus formosana and yew (Cephalotaxus Mannii). In these
forests there are numerous lianas, in the majority from the
same species as in the tropical forests in the south of China:
Schizandra sphaenanthera, Millettia pulchra, Smilax glabra,
S. discotis, and Hedera nepalensis. The undergrowth consists of all sorts of shrubs such as Machilus yunnanensis,
Evonimus, Berchemia yunnanensis, buckthorn (Rhamnus
virgata), Pittosporum, hawthorn (Crataegus scabrifolia),
Eurya nitida, Elaeagnus, pear (Pirus pashia), Picrosma,
Gudrania, honeysuckle (Lonicera), viburnum (Viburnum),
raspberry (Rubus) and Akebia. There are many species of
fern, moss and lichen. Both in these forests and in the
higher mountainous forests epiphyte orchids are common
which grow not only on trunks and on the thick branches of
trees, but also on rock. Close to the tops of the mountains
at elevations of around 2, 200 meters there are areas of forests consisting of alder (Alnus) and even higher are found
the dark-coniferous forests consisting of fir (Abies Delavayi).
In the undergrowth of the fir forests there are numerous arboreal and shrub rhododendron. There are about three
score known species which are remarkably beautiful with
their white, yellow, pink, red and purple flowers. Rhododendrons are also diverse above the boundary of the forests,
in the subalpine belt. Between the rhododendron clumps in

the subalps grow various types of grasses, many of them
with brightly colored flowers, in particular the various primula (Primula calliantha, P. yunnanensis, P. denticulata,
P. sonchifolia, P. serratifolia).

The wettest mountain regions of Western Yunnan at
elevations around 2, 000-2, 500 meters are covered by evergreen "moss" forests which year-round are enclosed in fog
or clouds. These forests are composed, besides various
oaks and large bright-colored spring-flowering tree rhododendrons, of many other tree species such as castanopsis,
pasania, Manglietia, holly (Ilex), photinia, sweetleaf, and
the camphor tree (Cinnamomum). In the "moss" forests
masses of thick lianas hang from the trees. On everything
there is a solid cover of moss--on the trunks and branches
of the trees, lianas and on the individual leaves of trees
and shrubs. On certain areas of the forest a thick moss
layer has completely covered the soil. In these forests one
will encounter various types of shrubs such as Merilliopanax
membranifolius, Evonimus, Eurya, Gaulteria dumicola,
Daphne, jasmine (Jasminum), willow (Salix longiflora),
raspberry and viburnum. There are numerous epiphyte orchids. In the grass story begonias (Begonia) are common
as well as elatostema (Elatostema surculosum and E. platy-
phyllum), Peracarpa carnosa, Geranium nepalense, Aspar-
agus filicinus, Polygonatum, Zingiber, Selaginella and
Lycopodium. The grasses are moisture-loving and many of
them have large leaves and frequently form dense, tall thickets. Close to the southern boundary of the region, particularly in the Lants'angkiang Basin at elevations from 800 to
1, 600 meters, instead of Yunnan pine forests there are forests consisting of the tall and straight thermophilic pine,
Pinus insularis. Along with the pines grow certain subtropical trees such as Schima, castanopsis, pasania, oak
and sweetleaf. In the grass cover there are many brake
ferns (Pteridium aquilinum), and the soil is covered by Hyp-
num mosses. With these pine forests are found thickets of
tropical vegetation along the gorges, and here with the pines
one will see the large leaves of wild bananas. In the pine
forests themselves of this type one will commonly find the
very interesting relic gymnospermous plants, the Cycas,
which grow several meters tall.

In the driest and warmest areas of Southern Yunnan, particularly along the slopes near the Hungho River and its tributaries, at elevations below 1,200 meters, the savanna is found. Gramen predominate in the savanna, chiefly tall ones such as Imperata cylindrica, Themeda, Thysanolaena, Miscanthus, Andropogon, Heteropogon, etc. Of the arboreal vegetation the following are common: Gossampinus malabarica, Albizzia mollis, Dalbergia obtusifolia, Eriolaena malvacea, Colona floribunda, Engelhardtia Colebrookiana, Erythrina indica, Bauhinia, Mallotus, Cassia, Ficus geocarpa, etc. Also characteristic are tree spurge (Euphorbia Royleana) up to 5-6 meters tall and cactus (Opuntia monacantha). Of the shrubs and low trees there are numerous acacia (Acacia Farnesiana), Ziziphus montana, small oaks, nightshade (Solanum), St. John'swort (Hypericum), Ricinus communis, Pistacia Weinmanniifolia, Phylanthus emblica, Sophora vicifolia and Melastoma.

In the grass cover in places the brake fern is common. The savanna has significantly enlarged the territory occupied by it at the expense of the forests destroyed by man. In the very south of Western Yunnan along the banks of the rivers there are areas of gallery tropical forests with a multi-story tree canopy of a very diverse taxonomic composition, with abundant lianas, all sorts of bamboo and large moisture- and heat-requiring grasses.

In accordance with the subtropical climate and vegetation, the soil formation processes on a larger portion of the Western Yunnan territory can be reduced to the formation of soils characteristic for the subtropics of China. Most widely found are the red earths which in the mountain forests are somewhat podzolized. The breakdown of organic substances in the red earths occurs very quickly and there is a lack of phosphorus. In line with this the red earths are marked by low fertility. Due to the great difference in altitudes on the territory of Western Yunnan, there is a well-expressed vertical zonality in the distribution of the soils, similar to the one which occurs in terms of the climate and vegetation.

The river terraces and gentle slopes of the low mountains below 2,000 meters are covered by ordinary red earths which in places show traces of lateritization. From 2,000

to 2,500 meters beneath the pine and evergreen leafy forests
are found mountain podzolized red earths which at elevations
around 2,600-2,700 meters, in places where the pine forests are found, are replaced by the brown forest soils.
Close to the highest peaks beneath the fir forests at elevations above 3,000 meters the mountain sod-podzolic soils
have developed. The peaks themselves, where the subalpine
meadows are found, are covered by mountain-meadow soils.
In Western Yunnan, the vertical change in the soil cover is
expressed much more sharply than in the other territories
of the Yunnan region. Aside from the designated soil types,
along the banks of the large rivers one will widely find alluvial soils, and in areas where rice is grown, the rice soils.

Like the vegetation cover, the animal world in Western Yunnan has been well preserved and is marked by richness. Of the mammals there are many shrews and several
species of moles, including the very primitive ones. One
will frequently encounter the spineless hedgehogs and tupa-
jida. The bat fauna is also diverse. In the south the Ma-
caca monkeys are common. Pangolins dwell close to the
areas of tropical forest and in the savanna. There are numerous small Carnivora of the marten family. The lesser
panda is common. The large Carnivora are numerous, in
particular the tiger and cloudy leopard. Rodents are rather
diverse, particularly the squirrels and flying squirrels as
well as mice and voles. Of the ungulates one most frequently will encounter wild boar and deer. The birds are
very diverse. Pheasants are characteristic for the mountain subtropical landscapes. At elevations below 1,500 meters one will find peacocks and even lower, in the tropical
forests, there are wild chickens. In the forests various
species of doves and cuckoos are abundant. In the south of
Western Yunnan the large rhinoceros bird (Bucerotes) is
common. Over the entire territory there are many woodpeckers and in the area of tropical forests in gorges there
are tits. Of the Passeres, the drongo is numerous. Particularly diverse are the small Passeres. These include the
Nectariniidae which pollinate the large flowers of certain
trees and shrubs. Of the reptiles there are many geckos,
and in the forests the tree agamas are common. There are
rather numerous snakes, particularly racers and grass
snakes. Of them a number of species basically leads an arboreal way of life. There are several species of venomous

snakes and of them the more common are cobras, Bungarus
and Ancistrodon halys. The amphibians are diverse, and tree
frogs are particularly abundant in the wet forests. The insect
fauna is represented by many thousands of species. Very common
are the large and small cockroaches found under the bark of
rotting trees and on the leaves of shrubs, as well as various
species of earwigs. In the coniferous and leafy forests below
2,000 meters and in the savannas termites are common. Song
cicadas are common which fill the forests with their voices.
One will also encounter the large mottled fireflies. There are
many large plant-eating bugs. Of the beetles particularly
numerous are the darkling beetles which live beneath the bark
of rotting trees, leaf beetles and long-horned beetles. In the
hollows of trees and in rock cracks live wild honeybees. Various
species of bumblebees are also common. There are many ants.
One should also note the large beautiful butterflies, particularly
the swallowtails and Danaidae.

The landscapes of Western Yunnan are marked by a
great diversity and a variegated distribution. The most essential feature is clearly manifested in the distribution of
the landscapes--the relation of them to the topography. On
the ranges and small divide elevations there predominate
subtropical landscapes with elements of landscapes from the
temperate belt. Conversely, in the river valleys and gorges
one will find subtropical landscapes with an abundance of
tropical elements. The latter are encountered in gorges
even at rather high elevations, around 2,000-2,500 meters.
In the lowest localities the landscapes assume a completely
tropical character which, however, is not so clearly expressed as in the more southern locales of Yunnan beyond
the Yunnan region.

THE YUNNAN UPLANDS

The Yunnan Uplands are an elevated territory lying on
the average 2,000 meters above sea level. The elevation
differences are relatively small. Only individual mountains
reach 3,000 meters. The majority of the intermontane valleys is at elevations exceeding 1,500 meters. The uplands
drop somewhat from the northwest to the southeast. The
poorly expressed mountain ranges which rise slightly above
the basic level of the uplands are extended from the

southwest to the northeast. The formation of this mountainous region was due to the Yenshan movements when the peneplainized territory was broken up into individual clumps and
uplifted. There are characteristic rounded forms to the
mountain tops. On the uplands one will widely find karst
erosion of the solid Paleozoic limestones, particularly on
the sloping mountain sites where the limestones emerge on
the surface.

Caves are encountered in many localities. The karst
topography has been most developed in the central part of the
territory to the southeast and east of the K'unming. Here
there are large areas of "stone forests." The intermontane
valleys are broad and frequently have the character of semi-
enclosed basins. In them lie the large lakes of Tiench'ih and
Fuhsienhu, and also a number of smaller lakes. The water
of several lakes such as Lake Yangts'unghai to the southeast
of the K'unming has filled the narrow tectonic troughs. The
depth of such lakes is rather significant, many score meters.
The topography of the Yunnan Uplands has been greatly broken up by numerous small rivers which at the edges of the
uplands have cut deep and narrow gorges.

The rivers in the northern half of the Yunnan Uplands
belong to the Yangtze Basin and they flow to the north and
east. These are the P'utuho, Hsiaokiang, Niulankiang and
Yach'iho. The rivers of the southern half of the uplands belong to the Sikiang Basin and basically flow to the east.
Among them is the largest river of the uplands, the Nanp'-
ankiang, and also the Peip'ankiang River. During the dry
period of the year, the amount of water in the rivers drops
sharply, and many of the small rivers turn into streams
flowing among piles of boulders and gravel detritus. By
spring the lake level has dropped by several meters and the
shoals and flat bottoms along the shore have been exposed.
During the summer rains the rivers have rather a large
amount of water. Near the edges of the uplands where the
fall of the rivers is steep they become rapid mountain
streams greatly destroying the hard rock underlying the
channels.

The climate of the Yunnan Uplands is marked by significant mildness. This is one of the most agreeable climates

in China for man. The winter is warm and the summer is
not hot. The annual temperature is about 16-18°, and only
in the south does it rise up to 22°. The year is clearly divided into a dry period and a rainy period. Over the year
in the center of the uplands some 1,000-1,250 mm. of precipitation fall and in other localities of the uplands somewhat less. During the winter months the weather is usually
clear. The nights are cool but the temperature rarely drops
below 0°. The absolute minimum is -5°. During the winter
in sunny weather the temperature by the second half of the
day rises to 12-18°. The mean January temperature is 4°.
Snow falls rarely and rapidly thaws. In December-February
at night there are frequent fogs and during cold nights hoarfrosts. During the dry period of the year, the air humidity
reaches 60 per cent and more and this is of important significance for the life of the evergreen subtropical plants
since this impedes a strong loss of moisture through the
large evaporating surface of the leaves. In the middle of
February in the K'unming there are common nighttime temperatures of 5-10°. During the winter and spring rather
strong winds may develop, particularly in the middle of the
day. The rainy season begins in May. The moisture is
brought in chiefly by the southeast winds while the southwest
winds which pass over the uplands at a high elevation bring
in, as a rule, only transparent clouds. The July temperature depending upon the elevation of the locality fluctuates
between 16 and 24°. In the summer the ordinary air humidity is about 80-90 per cent. The rainy season ends in October.

The natural vegetation cover on the Yunnan Uplands
has not been as well preserved as in Western Yunnan. Forests cover predominantly the hills while the valleys and hilly
localities are under agricultural land--fields and partially
pastures. Sections of the territory where friable clay rock
lies on the surface have been subjected in certain areas to
heavy erosion and are virtually devoid of vegetation. On the
uplands most widely found are forests of Yunnan pine (Pinus
yunnanensis) and rather numerous leafy forests consisting
of evergreen and deciduous species of oak (Quercus). The
pine and oak forests to a significant degree are secondary
occupying, as a subsequence of a certain xerophilic nature
of the trees comprising them, the place of the forests destroyed by man containing more moisture-loving deciduous

and coniferous varieties which were also more diverse in
terms of composition. The Yunnan pine and the oaks frequently form mixed plantings. Along with them grow evergreens such as Castanopsis, Machilus, Cyclobalanopsis,
Schima, Gordonia, and of the conifers Keteleeria Evelyana
and the cypress (Cypressus Duclouxiana) are particularly
common. The undergrowth consists of very diverse species
of shrubs and in them one can encounter Michelia yunnanensis. Small bamboos grow in areas in the forest. On the
high areas of the locality, usually above 2,000 meters, the
Armand pine (Pinus Armandii) appears in large numbers.
In certain areas of the uplands there are coniferous forests
of Keteleeria Evelyana with abundant lichens on the soil, and
forests have been preserved with a predominance of cypress
(Cypressus Duclouxiana). In the southeast of the uplands
there are forests of all sorts of coniferous and evergreen
leafy trees. Here one will commonly find the thermophilic
pine, Pinus insularis, and on the limestones there are three
species of Keteleeria and the wang pine (Pinus Wangii), and
there is a number of other conifers. Of the leafy varieties
there are common Cyclobalanopsis, Castanopsis, Pasania,
Schima, Altingia, Bucklandia, the camphor tree (Cinnamomum), Machilus, Phoebe, species of maple (Acer) with
whollyedged leaves and many others. In these forests shrubs
are diverse and there are numerous lianas and epiphytes,
bamboos are encountered and the ferns are very well represented.

The most widely found soils in the Yunnan Uplands are
red earths. In the mountains and on the hills mountainous
somewhat podzolized red earths predominate, and in the valleys rice soils on red earths are dominant. The red earths
in the majority have an acid reaction and low fertility. In
certain areas of the uplands one will encounter yellow earths
and the mountainous podzolized yellow earths. On the highest mountains beneath the forests are found forest soils. In
the central portion of the uplands on the red parent rock have
been formed the so-called purple soils which have an acid
reaction or are calcareous. On limestones humus carbona-
tic soils have developed which have a base reaction. On the
banks of rivers are alluvial soils. The processes of laterite formation in the soils of the Yunnan Uplands are insignificant. On the Yunnan Uplands vertical zonality in the distribution of the soil cover is not as sharply expressed as in

Western Yunnan. This is explained by the homogeneity in
the altitudes of the territory, by the relatively small differences in the climate for the individual parts and by the predominance of similar types of coniferous and coniferous-
leafy subtropical forests.

   The animal world of the Yunnan Uplands is rather rich
and diverse. The territory inhabited by large mammals has
been greatly reduced as a result of settlement by man.
These mammals to a significant degree dwell only in the
denser mountain forests. Man has had a much smaller effect upon the life of other animals. Of the mammals there
are many shrews and moles. In the central portion of the
uplands one will encounter the tupajita. Bats are abundant
and diverse. In the southeast of the territory in the forests
along the Nanp'ankiang River live the anthropoid gibbons.
Of the carnivorous mammals one will encounter civets,
tigers, leopards, etc. Of the rodents various types of
squirrels and flying squirrels are common. There are numerous small terrestrial rodents such as voles and mice. Of the
ungulates wild boar and deer are encountered. There is a
rich fauna of birds. Characteristic are kites, pheasants,
several species of dove, cuckoos, woodpeckers and Tima-
liidae. In the valleys the drongo, hoopoe and myna are common. The specific composition of the small Passeres is diverse. In the region of the K'unming the Nectariniidae are
common. Of the reptiles the geckos are abundant, and one
will encounter racers and grass snakes including arboreal
ones. Of the amphibia the toads are common. Insects are
diverse, particularly the dragonflies, cockroaches, locusts,
plant-eating bugs, beetles, diptera and lepidopters. In the
forests there are numerous large song cicadas. There are
also very many scale insects which suck the juice of plants.
Ants are diverse, and on flowering plants there are abundant
flower-bud maggots as well as solitary bees, particularly
the halictidae and andrenas. There are many species of
large and brightly colored bees, the carpenter bees. Bumblebees are also abundant and diverse. There are wild
honeybees. Of the tropical insect groups in the center of
the Yunnan Uplands in the coniferous forests termites are
common and in the valleys one will encounter several species of large butterflies from the Papilionidae.

For the Yunnan Uplands a wide distribution of mesophyte subtropical landscapes is characteristic. Here predominate coniferous and evergreen laurel forests in which a
major role is played by the deciduous trees which lose their
leaves in the dry season of the year. Such a composition of
the vegetation has been caused by the dry season which lasts
almost half the year with low air temperatures and soil temperatures during the winter months. Under these conditions
the moisture evaporated by the plants cannot easily be replaced by them due to the retardation of the physiological
processes, in particular the uptake of moisture by the plant
roots and the carrying of it into the organs above the ground.
Measurements of the soil temperature near K'unming in the
second half of February have shown only 7° at a depth of
about 20 cm. in a coniferous-leafy forest with an undergrowth of bamboo. In the southeastern portion of the uplands lying somewhat below the basic territory, the climate
is warmer and moister. Here the landscapes are marked by
a great diversity in the vegetation and fauna, and in the subtropical organisms there are many species of plants and animals which are characteristic for the tropical regions of
South China.

CHAPTER **8** NORTHWEST CHINA: THE MONGOLIAN-SINKIANG REGION

N. M. Kazakova
USSR Academy of Sciences
Institute of Geography

Northwest China covers an enormous area and the predominant portion of it is part of Central Asia. The natural boundaries of the given physical-geographic region are expressed very clearly and fully coincide with the boundaries of the geomorphological area.

The relief features have an enormous influence upon all the remaining natural components in Northwest China. In the chapter devoted to the topography, it was pointed out that the entire interior portion of the region has to a significant degree a levelled surface. Here plains predominate which lie at a high hypsometric level. They are bordered by a ring of high mountain structures including the already mentioned Kunlun, the Nanshan, the mountains of the Greater Khingan and Jehol and also the Eastern or Chinese Tien Shan and the mountains of Border Dzungaria lying in the west. The listed mountain structures are the border mountains of the region and therefore face it in only one of their slopes or only a portion of the slope as the majority of ranges in Border Dzungaria; only the Eastern Tien Shan extend rather deeply into the region separating the Tarim and Dzungarian plains by a high wall.

A characteristic feature of the nature in Northwest China is the extreme aridness which has been caused by the entire course of the Meso-Cenozoic development of this territory.

According to the geological data, this is a very ancient section of dry land where a continental regime has predominated beginning with the Paleozoic and being established once and for all in the Mesozoic Age, and in certain areas even at the end of the Permean Age. In the Upper Jurassic, the climate in the central parts of Northwest China, or more precisely within the Kashun Gobi, the Peishan and the nearby parts of the Tarim, Dzungarian and Alashan plains, began to acquire features of aridness. During the Cretaceous and Tertiary ages, the dryness constantly intensified and spread to neighboring territories. This can be seen from the change in the composition of deposits and particularly from the appearance of red deposits with salts and gypsums instead of coals, bauxites and iron-manganese ores which predominated in the Jurassic Age as well as by the fossil flora and fauna (V. M. Sinitsyn, 1959). In the Neogene-Quaternary Age there was a general elevation of the region and along its edges rose high mountain ranges.

The climate of Northwest China is marked by the extreme continental features which intensify from east to west. The continental features of the climate were caused by the geographic position of the region within the continent and chiefly by the orientation of the mountain systems surrounding it in terms of the prevailing winds. For example, the northern boundary of the region is more or less exposed and due to this the dry cool air masses related to the Mongolian-Siberian anticyclone are free to penetrate into the region. As a result the winter for the given latitudes is very severe (even in the south, in the Tarim plains, there are frosts down to 20°) with strong winds and virtually no snow as the snow falls rarely, and when it does there is little of it and it rapidly disappears.

At the same time, the southern, western and eastern boundaries of the region are closed off by the high mountain structures lying perpendicular to the prevailing winds. Therefore the warm humid air masses formed during the summer above the surface of the oceans penetrate Northwest China with difficulty and are almost completely held back by the orographic barriers. As a result during the warm season of the year over the surface of Northwest China continental air also prevails and there is dry hot weather. It rarely rains and the larger portion of the moisture evaporates in the air.

The particular features of atmospheric circulation over the territory of Northwest China which here has a typically anticyclonic character is concretely shown in the particular climatic indices. First of all here there are extremely great fluctuations in temperature. According to Chinese data (Ch'en Shih-hsiung, 1959), the mean temperature of the coldest month (January) is from -7, -9° in the south of the region (in Kashgar -7.4°, in Anhsi -9.0°, and in Yuling lying on the boundary with North China, -8.3°) down to -16° and more in the northern areas (Urumchi* -16.6°, in Hailar -28.3°); minimal temperatures drop from -20°, -30° in the south (in Kashgar -20.5°, in Anhsi -29.3°, in Yuling -32.7°) down to -40, -50° in the north (in Urumchi -38.3°, in Hailar -49.3°). The mean temperature of the warmest month (July) is 20-26° (in Hailar 20.8°, in Urumchi 23.8°, in Yuling 24.4°, in Anhsi 26.1°, in Kashgar 25.1°), with maximum temperatures rising up to 38° and even more (in Hailar 40.1°, in Urumchi 38.1°, in Yuling 40.0°, in Kashgar 40.0° and in Anhsi 43.0°).

The hottest point of the region is Turfan which lies in the deep intermontane depression, where the mean July temperature is 33.4°, and the maximum rising up to 47.6°.

Thus, the annual amplitude in the fluctuations of the mean monthly January and July temperatures is approximately 30-50° (in Kashgar 32.5°, in Anhsi 35.1°, in Yuling 32.7°, in Urumchi 40.4°, and in Hailar 49.1°), and the amplitude of fluctuations in the absolute minimums and maximums reaches the very great amount of 70-90° (in Anhsi 72.3°, in Yuling 72.7°, in Urumchi 76.4° and in Hailar 89.4°); only in Kashgar is it somewhat less: 60.5°. The amplitude of daily temperatures is also significant, and on the average is 12-17°.

---

*For the more northern points of Sinkiang we do not have data available.

The amount of atmospheric precipitation in Northwest China is extremely slight. In the interior portion of the region occupying a very large area, less than 100 mm. falls per year (in Anhsi 55.5 mm., in Kashgar 72.7 mm.), and in individual areas such as the Takla-Makan there are years when no precipitation at all falls. Close to the borders the annual amount of precipitation increases up to 100-200 mm., and only in individual areas such as the western portion of the Eastern Tien Shan, the Chinese slopes of the Mongolian Altai, the Barga and along the eastern boundary of the Ordos does it reach and even surpass 300 mm. (in Urumchi 293.8 mm., in Hailar 324.6 mm., in Yuling 409.9 mm.). Everywhere in the region the evaporability is very high and significantly exceeds the amount of precipitation falling. The distribution of precipitation over the seasons here, as in other parts of China, is very uneven and is also characterized by a maximum in the summertime and a minimum during the winter and spring. In various years the amount of falling precipitation will also differ greatly and in two years it will sometimes change by two to four times.

Another climatic feature of the region is the sharply expressed seasonal character of the winds. During the winter they, as we have already noted, are northerly, and during the summer westerly, southern and southeastern. The wind velocity is very high, and the spring winds are particularly strong when they blow every day and frequently exceed 20 meters per second, i.e., reach storm force. For example, in the period 1951-1956, in Huheta'o in April they recorded a wind velocity of 24.5 meters per second, in Hailar in May 27.5 meters per second, and in Urumchi in March 44 meters per second (Ch'en Shih-hsiung, 1959).

Virtually the entire territory of Northwest China is in the area of interior drainage. Only the rivers along the southwestern slopes of the Mongolian Altai, the Barga (the right-bank part of the Amur Basin) and the edges of the Ordos (the Hwang Ho Basin) drain to the ocean. In line with the small amount of atmospheric precipitation, there are extremely few permanent rivers in the region. Besides rivers belonging to the designated basins they also include only the rivers in the eastern portion of the Ili Basin lying in the west of the Eastern Tien Shan, and also Suliehho and Edzin-Gol flowing off the Nanshan where the amount of precipitation is

somewhat greater. The exterior submontane portions of the
region in general have the greatest amount of water but this,
however, in no way can be compared with the more easterly
regions of the land; the piedmont regions have concentrated
in them rather many small rivers, lakes and mineral
springs. However, the interior basic portion of it is almost
completely without water. We have already pointed out that
even the large rivers such as the Tarim and Khotan do not
have water year-round over the entire course, and all of the
small rivers in emerging from the mountains, as a rule,
disappear in the sands. Individual lakes encountered in the
deserts of the region such as Lobnor, the Edzin-Gol lakes
and certain others are very shallow and are subject to strong
fluctuations in the level, and to one degree or another are
mineralized. Many small lakes in general are temporary.

A typical feature of the territory in Northwest China
is the presence of a dense network of dry channels where water appears only very rarely, after heavy downpours and then
only for several hours. Regardless of this, individual dry
beds are very long and have a large water-collecting area.
They come together in individual enclosed basins and in the
centers lakes frequently develop which lie in the lowest portions of the plains.

Under the arid conditions of Northwest China, groundwaters assume a great importance in the formation of the
landscapes. The reserves of these waters to a significant
degree are determined by the regional climatic features.
Thus, according to V. M. Sinitsyn, the peripheral mountains of the region such as the ranges of the Eastern Tien
Shan and the Eastern Nanshan which receive up to 300 mm.
of atmospheric precipitation a year, have significant reserves of underground water. On the contrary, the mountains and elevations lying in the interior dry portion of the
region are poor in underground waters. Large reserves of
underground waters are also concentrated in the Mesozoic
and Meso-Cenozoic basins. Here over many geological eras
water has accumulated received from surrounding elevations
and at present these depressions are artesian basins.

The predominant portion of underground waters in
Northwest China is mineralized which has been caused by
the abundance of salts in the rock forming the mountains and

plains of this territory and by the intensive evaporation.
There is a predominance of salty chloride and chloride-
sulfate waters; fresh hydrocarbonate and hydrocarbonate-
sulfate waters are encountered chiefly only close to the bordering mountains (V. M. Sinitsyn, 1959).

The specifics of the climatic and hydrological conditions in the given territory have caused the sharply expressed aridness in all of the physical-geographic processes
occurring here, and thus the aridness of the landscapes. Of
the physical-geographic processes a very important and leading role is played here by the physical weathering processes
and the work of the wind. Also important within Northwest
China are the processes of salt accumulation. The latter
are due to the intensive evaporation of groundwaters emerging on the surface in the low areas. The lowest portions of
the plains and intermontane depressions are the centers of
salt accumulation as these areas for a long geological time
have been areas of water and salt drainage.

All of these conditions are extremely unfavorable for
the development of the soil-vegetation cover. The sharp
continental climate seen in the large amplitude of annual
temperatures and the sharp changes in the seasons of the
year, the extreme dryness of the air, the brevity of the vegetation period and unfavorable combinations of heat and
moisture have greatly impeded the growing of plants. Under
such conditions only a few very drought-resistant perennial
shrubs and subshrubs can survive and this leads to the extreme homogeneity in the specific composition of the vegetation and the shallowness of the soils. The latter is also
helped by the great deflation of the fine particles which is
particularly intense during the spring with the hurricane
winds.

One of the basic soil-forming processes in Northwest
China is the process of carbonate accumulation, and on the
predominant area of the region one will find desert limestone crusts (gray-brown desert soils). In the border parts
of the region such as the Barga, the Chinese portion of the
Mongolian Altai, the mountains of Border Dzungaria and in
the western portion of the Eastern Tien Shan which have
more water and therefore a richer vegetation, of

predominant significance in soil formation is the sod process and chestnut soils are formed.

The paucity in the specific composition of the flora and fauna of Northwest China can also be explained by the protracted existence of drought conditions here which not only did not help to develop a large number of floristic and faunistic species on the spot, but also did not favor the migration of them from neighboring regions. The Tarim Depression is marked by the particularly small number of species, and this area is surrounded by high mountains and has an extra-arid climate. At the same time it has a very large number of endemic species which in general is true for the region being described and particularly for the central desert parts. In the peripheral areas of the region where the climate has become particularly arid only in the postglacial times, the specific composition of the plants and animals is richer and is marked by a certain mixing of species. Thus, for example, in the southeast of the region (in the eastern part of the Nanshan), one can strongly feel the influence of the Eastern Asiatic and Eastern Tibetan floras and faunas, and in Dzungaria there is a marked influence of Mediterranean elements which have come here from Middle Asia.

At present over a larger part of Northwest China there exist exclusively xerophyte species of plants and animals. Among the plants there is a sharp predominance of perennial xerophyte shrubs and subshrubs which have the fewest requirements on the habitat under the conditions of the waterless stony and sandy deserts. Annual plants are found only in individual areas and then only during the years which are relatively abundant in precipitation. With the general sparseness of the vegetation cover, the distribution of vegetation over the territory of the region is extremely uneven and is very closely linked with the character of the soil, parent rock, with the degree of wetness and thus with the topography. Therefore the specific composition of the plants will change here very frequently and sometimes sharply.

The animal world is also represented by desert forms. Although the specific composition of the fauna is not rich, the number of individual specimens is very great. Here ungulates are dominant as well as rodents and reptiles; the bird fauna is relatively homogeneous and poor. The distribution of animals over the territory of the region is also very uneven; the greatest number of them is found in the northern semidesert portion of the region and in the oases of the interior part.

From all that has been stated above, it is clear that the landscapes of Northwest China are extremely specific and differ sharply from the landscapes in the other regions of the nation. Strictly speaking, in Northwest China there are three latitudinal-geographic zones--the steppe zone, the semidesert zone and the desert zone. However, in essence the predominant portion of the region which is much more extended along the latitude than along the longitude lies in the desert and semidesert zones; only the border parts of the region are part of the steppe zone. Vertical zonality can be seen in the individual mountain systems of Northwest China in differing degrees. The location of the mountains in the various latitudinal geographic belts has a very great influence upon the general character of the landscapes and the subsequent shift of them along the vertical.

The most deserty region is the southern most isolated, hot and dry part of the region including the Tarim, Alashan and partially the Ordos plains, the Kashun Gobi and the Peishan Uplands. The dominant landscapes are sandy and stony deserts. Significant areas are covered here either by shifting sands or the rocky mantle of the hammadas where the soil-vegetation cover has developed extremely weakly, and they are almost completely uninhabited. Only on individual desert areas with a somewhat better ground wetting-- in the channels of temporary runoffs and the depressions-- do individual specimens of very hardy desert vegetation begin to appear.

Thus, in the hammadas on the desert limestone crusts grow basically only extremely suppressed and sparse clumps of haloxylon, nitraria, Russian thistle and Ephedra Przewalski. On the sandy deserts there is basically tamarisk which is encountered in individual clumps among bare sands, having taken hold on the slopes of the barkhans or ridges. In areas where the groundwater is close to the surface, aside from tamarisk, there is also calligonum, and along the edges of the desert there is reaumuria and kharmik. In the north

of the region in the sandy deserts haloxylon will grow. In
the dry channels and particularly in oases along the feet of
the mountains where the level of the groundwater rises close
to the surface, the vegetation is much more diverse. Here
there are typical groves of Populus diversifolia, with an admixture of jida (Elaeagnus moorcroftii), tamarisk shrubs,
willow, caragana, reed thickets, chiy, licorice and camel's
thorn. The landscapes in the valleys of the Tarim, Yarkend, Khotan and other major rivers show a completely different picture where true poplar forests grow under the conditions of sufficient surface and ground wetting.

In the northern and eastern parts of the region, in the
northwest of Dzungaria, in the southeastern portion of the
Gobi and in the east of the Ordos where all of the indices for
the temperature regime are lower than in the south and the
amount of precipitation is somewhat greater, since this territory experiences a certain although very slight influence
of the oceanic air currents, semidesert landscapes predominate. The soil-vegetation cover is more developed. The
soils are basically brown desert-steppe, frequently alka-
line and rocky. The vegetation is represented by various
subshrubs, more rarely by shrubs and by relatively diverse
Russian thistles; of the trees, in the west one encounters the
poplar and in the east the elm.

The mountains lying in the described latitudinal-
geographic zones are also marked by a predominance of desert and semidesert complexes although, as in general in the
mountains, the landscapes here are somewhat more diverse
and the change in them occurs more frequently and sharply.
Depending upon the position of any mountain system relative
to the prevailing winds and the direction of the slopes, the
vertical zonality of the landscapes is marked by its own particular features.

In the desert and semidesert zone, according to
A. G. Bannikov (1953), of the ungulates one will most widely
find the Middle Asian gazelle and the onager, of the rodents
jerboas, and of the reptiles the Phrynocephalus lizards. Of
the birds the common Syrrhaptes paradoxus is typical.

Only the extreme parts of the region--the eastern and
the northwestern--lie in the steppe zone.   The steppe

landscapes occupy the largest area in the east where they are characteristic for the plains of Inner Mongolia. This is the sole place in the region where one can observe all stages of the gradual transition from the relatively moist gramen-meadow steppes on dark chestnut soils through a series of intermediate steppe landscapes to the Southern Gobi semideserts. The boundary between the steppes and semideserts here does not have such a strictly latitudinal direction but rather follows from northeast to southwest, being deflected by the influence of the Pacific monsoon.

In the northwestern portion of the region, the steppe landscapes occupy a very small area of piedmont plains in the Chinese section of the Mongolian Altai and are represented chiefly by dry steppes on light-chestnut and chestnut soils. The boundary of them with the semideserts can be followed here basically along a latitudinal direction, being deflected only by the topography.

Regardless of the great commonness in the landscapes prevailing in Northwest China, individual areas of it have certain and sometimes very basic physical-geographic features. First of all this is due to the degree of aridness in the territory, because the greatest differences here can be observed between the interior parts of the region and its western and eastern borders. Moreover, this is related to the topography although we cannot observe here such a close dependency of the landscapes upon the particular features of the topography as occurs in the eastern part of the nation, for example, in Northeastern and Northern China. Many mountainous and plain areas lying in the interior portions of Northwest China, regardless of the sometimes significant elevation difference, have a greater similarity in the landscapes than differences. Thus, while as a whole Northwest China precisely corresponds to the Central Asiatic geomorphological area, the intraregional physical-geographic units do not always coincide with the geomorphological.

It seems to us that the soundest physical-geographic units or subregions of Northwest China where the landscapes are characterized by a presence of their own particular specific features and at the same time are rather significantly distinct from the landscapes of neighboring territories would be the following:

1) The plains of Inner Mongolia and the Yinshan Mountains;
2) the Ordos and Alashan plains, the Alashan Range;
3) the plain of the Kashun Gobi and the Peishan Uplands;
4) the Tarim Plain;
5) the Dzungarian Plain;
6) Eastern Tien Shan;
7) the mountains of Border Dzungaria and the Mongolian Altai.

THE PLAINS OF INNER MONGOLIA
AND YINSHAN

As we have already pointed out, the territory of Inner Mongolia is characterized by a significant evenness in the topography. Here predominate flat or gently-undulating elevated plains among which in certain areas one will encounter low, flat-topped elevations and flat-bottomed depressions. The plains lie on the average at an elevation of 900-1,000 meters above sea level, with peaks rising to a maximum of 1,500 meters, while the depressions lie at a level of 600-700 meters, so that the relative excesses within this region are generally not great. An exception is the southwestern area where the Yinshan Mountains are found rising up to 2,000-2,500 meters, with individual peaks somewhat higher. These mountains separate the plains of Inner Mongolia from the Ordos plains, and consist of four ranges with a predominantly longitudinal strike. The chief ones of them are the Tach'ingshan (the highest range with the altitude reaching 2,850 meters above sea level), the Wulashan, the Sheyten-Ula and the Hara-Narin. These ranges lie like windbreaks and are separated by longitudinal tectonic valleys. There is a characteristic asymmetry in the slopes of this mountain system caused by the disjunctive tectonics with the northern slope being gentle and the southern steep and abrupt.

In terms of the character of the topography within the plains of Inner Mongolia, one can separate the southern portion which is sometimes called the Chahar Plain, the northern portion or the Barga Plain, and the volcanic area of Darigang. The topography of the Chahar Plain is an alternation of large basins covered by salt swamps and salt lakes and plateaus scattered with hills, ridges and many sand areas. The topography of the Barga is characterized by the

presence of flat and gently-undulating plains which occupy a
large portion of it and low residual flat-topped mountains,
particularly found in the north and west.

The predominant portion of the described territory is
composed of Cretaceous deposits covered by a shallow mantle of sandy-clay or gravel deposits of the Quaternary Age.
The latter, in being a product from the decomposition of local rock, cover not only the plains but also the low elevations.
The Cretaceous of the region are not rich in minerals. According to the data of V. M. Sinitsyn (1959), only in certain
places over small areas will one encounter solitary beds of
rather low-quality brown coals.

The depressions of the present relief have been filled
by Tertiary deposits, frequently of lacustrine origin. The
largest depressions are the Barga which occupies the central portion of the Barga, and the Wuchumuch'i which lies
further to the south. In the Barga, more accurately in the
surroundings of the town of Chalainor, there are rich deposits of brown coal. In the Barga, moreover, in the Cretaceous deposits oil has been discovered.

The Yinshan Mountains are basically composed of
ancient metamorphic rock and they are particularly rich in
minerals, chiefly metallic. Among the latter are basically
iron ores. Here lies the major ore deposit of Bainobo which
is of great industrial significance. Moreover, here in the
Carboniferous, Permean and Jurassic deposits in the Tach'-
ingshan and Wulashan Mountains there are deposits of hard
coal with rather significant reserves, particularly in the
diggings near the town of Shihkuaikou.

Recently in Inner Mongolia they have also discovered
a number of chromite deposits, but as yet they have not been
studied (P. Ya. Antropov, 1958).

In the landscape sense, the region of Inner Mongolia
rather sharply differs from the territories lying further west.
This is one of the wettest regions in Northwest China and is
predominantly steppe. The geographic position of the region
which is greatly extended along the meridian leads to a situation whereby basic changes in the landscapes here are due
to the phenomena of latitudinal zonality and are expressed in

the gradual transition from the gramen steppes with a solid grassy cover developing on dark chestnut soils to the gramen sage steppes with a sparser covering on chestnut soils, and then to the subshrub sage-gramen steppes on the light chestnut soils and then to the Southern Gobi semideserts. The wet monsoons have a certain influence here as they partially cross the Greater Khingan and Jehol Uplands, and this is expressed in the intensification of xerophyteness in the landscapes as one moves to the west. In addition, the relief also influences the distribution of the landscapes as the relief, although not fundamentally changing the general dependency in the change of landscapes from north to south, frequently introduces particular alterations in the individual areas of the territory.

Thus, the sharpest differences in the natural conditions of Inner Mongolia can be observed in the transition from the northeast to the southwest. The Barga stands out particularly here as within this area the greatest amount of precipitation falls, and all of the chief rivers of the region cross it--the Border Argun' with tributaries, the Lower Kerulen, the Orchungol--and it has one of the largest lakes in China, the Dalainor. This lake is virtually undrained since the Cloudy Channel which links it with Hailar does not have a permanent current and is a chain of meadows, lakes and swamps overgrown with water-loving vegetation. During the rainy periods its channel is filled with water, and depending upon the water level at Hailar and in the lake it flows in either direction. The other rivers of the Barga are also characterized by an unstable regime and this is due to the sharp fluctuations in the amount of falling precipitation over the seasons of the year and over the individual years which, as we have noted, is a property of many territories of China. For example, in Hailar, of a total annual amount of 324.6 mm., 3.7 per cent falls in the winter, 11.8 per cent in the spring, 65.5 per cent in the summer and 19.0 per cent in the autumn. This leads to a situation whereby in the dry period, the most of the Barga rivers dry up completely, while in the period of summer rains and spring flooding the water level in the rivers and lakes rises and in certain years so significantly that the waters overflow the banks and inundate the neighboring plains.

In the northern and eastern portions of the Barga where the amount of atmospheric precipitation is approximately 300 mm. per year and sometimes somewhat more, gramen-motley grass and tansy steppes predominate on dark chestnut and chestnut soils. They occupy the high river terraces, the piedmont valleys, and the slopes and peaks of the low mountains. In the intermontane basins and along the dry valleys there have developed typical bistort-Cleistogenes and Elymus-Cleistogenes steppes with a predominance of hair feather grass, while along the river floodplains there are reedgrass-sedge, swampy meadows with shrubs of willow on meadow and meadow swampy soils.

For the southern and western portions of the Barga, where the annual amount of atmospheric precipitation fluctuates within limits of 200-300 mm., there is a characteristic combination of bistort-Cleistogenes and Elymus-Cleistogenes which have developed on chestnut and light-chestnut soils. The most widely found species here are bistort, tansy, feather grass, meadowgrass, Elymus and burnet. To the south the amount of sage increases. Along the shores of the salt lakes and on the salt swamps various Russian thistles are typical as well as reeds and goosefoot. In the low-mountain areas to the south of the Manchurian Station one can observe a vertical zonality and there is the following regular shift in the vegetation groupings.* The peaks of the low mountains are covered by a sage association (Artemisia frigida Willd.) with motley grass. In the upper parts of the slopes there is a typical feather grass association (Stipa baicalensis Roshev) with tansy (Tanacetum sibiricum L.). In the middle portion of the slopes the feather grass disappears and motley grass appears in association with the tansy. The lower parts of the slopes are an association of Stipa baicalensis with Elymus and motley grass. Where bedrock crops out, along the foot of the rocks one will encounter clumps of Siberian apricot (Prumus sibiricus).

The areas of aeolian sands in the Barga are usually retained by vegetation which is represented by the typical

---

*An oral statement by Chinese geobotanists.

sand-dwellers such as caragana, chiy, Agriophyllum arenarium, etc., and also willow and sage. In certain areas one
will encounter pine, elm, evonymus, although to a certain
degree felled. In general we noted that at present there is a
process of a return of the sands.

In comparison with the Barga, the remaining more
southerly portion of Inner Mongolia is much more arid. The
amount of atmospheric precipitation falls sharply here, and
in the southwest of the region only about 100 mm. fall a
year. There are virtually no rivers here, and those which
do exist are very small and have broken courses, usually
drying up in swamps and salt bogs.

The salt swamps and the small bitter-salt lakes are a
characteristic feature in the landscape of the given territory
since here, under the conditions of strong evaporation which
significantly exceeds the amount of precipitation falling, the
salt accumulation processes occur very intensively. This
has led to a situation whereby with the passage of time thick
salt beds have accumulated which are a specific mineral of
the region and are of industrial significance. Salts of the
Quaternary Age are widely found and these have accumulated
in the lakes; in terms of composition Glauber's salt and
cooking salt. Salt accumulation is one of the most important
present physical-geographic processes for the given territory and plays a significant role in the formation of its landscapes.

As one moves south of the Barga, the vegetation cover
becomes more and more spares. Here more widely one will
find the subshrub sage-gramen steppes and southern semideserts on the light-chestnut soils which are encountered
only in spots in the Barga. Chinese researchers have drawn
a boundary between the dry steppes and semideserts approximately along the line of Peilemiao--Undurmiao--Pailing-
miao.

In general the landscapes of the plains in the southern
portion of the region are extremely homogeneous and here
predominates a semidesert with a gradual increase in the
desertiness towards the west. The zonality of the landscapes can be traced here poorly, in being manifested only
in a gradual shift in the quantitative ratios of the dominant

species. For example, in the southeastern wetter portion
of the region on the dark-brown soils where the vegetation
is still relatively dense, gramen are most widely found such
as feather grass (Stipa gobica, etc.) and bistort. Of the
shrubs and subshrubs one will frequently encounter caragana
(Caragana mana), tansy (Tanacetum trifidium), winterfat
(Eurotia ceratoides) and certain others. Of the halophytes
very typical are the Russian thistle Salsola passerina and
Anabasis brevifolia. In the lowlands one will widely find
chiy and suaeda.

In the southwestern more arid portion of the region on
the light-brown soils the vegetation is significantly sparser.
Here predominate the above-named Russian thistles and the
gramen such as the Stipa gobica and bistort as well as the
wild onion occupy a second place. In the south of the region
of Inner Mongolia, in contrast to the northern part, one will
already encounter large areas of barren sands with a relief
of barkhaned chains extended, as a rule, in a northeast direction.

The landscapes of the Yinshan Mountains are somewhat
more diverse than the plains surrounding them and this is
basically explained by their higher hypsometric position.
The most diverse are the landscapes in the eastern and central portions of the Yinshan which to a certain degree have
been subjected to the moist monsoons. In truth, here there
are virtually no constantly running water courses, although
the slopes of the mountains have been broken up by narrow
and deep valleys; only on the southern slopes of the mountains will one encounter individual small streams which flow
into the Hwang Ho. According to Chinese sources, in the
lower and middle belts of the mountains here dry steppes
predominate, and at elevations of 1,900-2,600 meters there
appear landscapes of the forest-steppe with the presence of
elm, birch and certain other trees, while at elevations
above 2,600 meters meadow-steppe complexes have developed. The extreme western part of the Yinshan which is
also in the desert zone is characterized by typically desert
landscapes.

In economic terms, the territory of Inner Mongolia is
a region of livestock raising which is of national significance.
Regardless of the arid climate, here there are extensive

natural pastures with the chief ones confined to the steppe
zone. The natural steppe covering has been well preserved.
In the moister areas, i.e., in the northern part of the
Barga and along the western slopes of the Greater Khingan,
tall-grass steppes have developed, and to the south they
change gradually into low-grass, but the fodder qualities for
the majority of grasses in both areas are very fine.

In contrast to the western portions of the Chinese Gobi,
the groundwater supply in Inner Mongolia is comparatively
good.

In individual areas, for example, along the eastern
boundary of the region, the groundwater lies very close to
the surface and is virtually not mineralized, and therefore
one will frequently find springs and slightly-salined lakelets
which is also favorable to the development of pasture livestock raising. As one moves to the west, the stratification
depth of the groundwaters and the degree of their mineralization increase.

Farming in Inner Mongolia is little developed, regardless of the fact that the dark-chestnut and chestnut soils in
terms of their properties are marked by rather high fertility.
Here the climatic conditions are the chief impediment to the
development of farming, and more precisely, the insufficient
amount of precipitation. It has been established, for example, that for developing farming in the surroundings of Manchuria Station each year they lack some 185 mm. of moisture (Yen Jenchang, 1950). Even the best-watered river and
lake sections of the plains covered by meadow-swampy soils
are little suitable for plowing since they are subject to periodic droughts and inundations which develop as a result of
the overflowing of Lake Dalainor, the Orchun-gol and Hailar
rivers as well as the other rivers draining the plains.

Only in the extreme north of the Barga area, in the so-
called Three-River Plain, the population also farms along
with livestock raising. This flat plain is composed of alluvial deposits from the Khaula, Derbula and Kenho on which
black earth soils have developed. The plain is well irrigated, and the population successfully raises spring wheat,
barley and vegetables here.

THE ORDOS AND ALASHAN PLAINS,
THE HOLANGSHAN RANGE

The high plains of the Ordos and Alashan divided by
the Hwang Ho River and the Alashan Range have a great
deal in common both in terms of the character of the topography and in terms of the landscape features. The absolute
elevations of the surface of the Ordos and Alashan are on the
average 1,100-1,200 meters, and individual elevations rise
up to 1,500-2,000 meters, and rarely more. The characteristic feature in the topography of this territory is the alternation of flat extended depressions and gentle elevations.

In the Ordos there are the Alapusushan elevations in
the north and the Ts'akang-Ch'ilot'u in the central part. The
Alapusushan elevation extends from the southwest to the
northeast and is a sort of connecting link between the Alashan and Wulashan. The larger portion of it has low relative elevations and a hilly surface, and only in the west assumes the appearance of ridges--the ridges of Arbiso and
Kantegeri with dentiform rocky peaks with an absolute elevation of 3,015 meters, and a relative elevation of about 1,000
meters. The Ts'akang-Ch'ilot'u elevation has a flatter surface. The designated elevations are separated by a gentle
undulating plain with cumulose sands--the so-called Kuzup-
chi Desert. An analogous plain lies also to the south of the
Ts'akang-Ch'ilot'u between it and the Loess Province.

In the Alashan, the number of elevations and low areas
is greater and the orientation of them is more homogeneous.
Due to this, the surface is divided into a number of strips
where the low elevations made up of groups of small rocky
ridges and hillocky areas alternate with depressions covered by sand areas, salt swamps, salt lakes and takyrs.
The largest elevations of the Alashan are the Khongordza
elevation extending in a latitudinal direction along the state
boundary, the Arykshan and Ts'ungnaishan-Yablaishan elevations of the same direction which cross the entire desert
and reach in the Yablaishan Ridge 2,200 meters absolute
elevation (the highest marker of the Alashan), and finally,
the Bayan-Ula elevation with a northeast strike. The lowest
area of the Alashan is the depression zone lying in the north
between the Khongordza and Arykshan elevations including

the basins of the Edzin-Gol lakes, the Goytso basins and the
Shantang basins which are separated by groups of hillocky
areas or sand areas. The most extensive plain of the Alashan stretches between the Bayan-Ula elevation and the Holangshan Range. The southern more elevated portion of it
is covered by a solid area of barkhan sands which has been
given the name of the Tengri sands, and the northern part is
covered by individual sand areas and salt bogs, while closer
to the mountains are areas of rocky desert.

The Holangshan Range which separates, as we have already mentioned, the Ordos from the Alashan, has a narrow
dentiform ridge reaching in its chief peak 3,230 meters
above sea level, with asymmetrical slopes, the western gentle and the eastern very abrupt, rocky and very rugged. The
latter gives the Holangshan the typically alpine appearance,
although eternal snows are missing on the peaks.

The geological structure of the Ordos and Alashan
plains is very different and this is due to the different history of their pre-Neogene development. The Ordos plains
which generally represent, as we have noted, a platform
syneclise, are composed of thick beds of Upper Paleozoic
and Mesozoic sandstones and sandstone shales. The Carboniferous and Jurassic deposits of the syneclise include intercalations of coal and oil-bearing layers. The area where
the coal beds are found here (i.e., not only in the given region but also further south in the Loess Province which is
also part of the syneclise) is very great and at present in
terms of the coal reserves, this geological basin is considered one of the richest in the nation. According to geological data, coal accumulation can be seen particularly
abundantly along the periphery of the syneclise; within the
described region the hard coal deposits lying on the eastern
slopes of the Holangshan Range and in the southeastern part
of the Ordos are also of industrial significance.

The oil deposits are confined here basically to the
monoclinal and anticlinal structures. In the northern part
of the described region there is located a large monocline
which falls gently towards the northwest and west, and here
are known numerous outcroppings of oil (Chang Keng et al.,
1958). As we have already pointed out, Chinese geologists
assume that the oil-bearing zone in the Ordos syneclise may

cover a significant area, but this territory has been far from sufficiently prospected. On the Mesozoic deposits of the syneclise in certain areas are Tertiary sandstones and clays which are concentrated chiefly in the lower portions of it, and subsequently they were covered either by a thin mantle of eluvium or a thicker layer of sands.

The geological structure of the Alashan Plain is more complex. The central portion of it was composed of ancient pre-Sinian deposits which were gradually overlaid by a mantle of Quaternary sands, but crop out on the surface in the elevations. The northern part is composed of Paleozoic and Mesozoic (chiefly Cretaceous) sediments while the southern piedmont portion (i. e., the Hohsi Corridor) was filled by beds of Paleozoic sedimentary and Meso-Cenozoic continental deposits which reach particularly great thickness in certain depressions such as the Chiuch'uan, Kanchou and Chaoshui.

In these basins are concentrated major deposits of coal and oil. The Carboniferous, Jurassic and Cretaceous deposits are coal-bearing, but, as geological data indicate, only the Jurassic deposits are of industrial significance. Oil accumulation has been observed here among the Tertiary, Jurassic and Permean deposits, and most frequently they are found in the anticlinal structures. Geologists feel that the oil deposits in the Hohsi Corridor are among the most promising in China (V. M. Sinitsyn, 1959).

On the plains, as throughout all of Inner Mongolia, there are numerous salt deposits and in the Ordos soda deposits.

The Holangshan Range, the Arbiso elevation and many elevations of the Alashan are composed of pre-Sinian rock which evidently should be the source of a number of metallic minerals. According to the presently existing data, in the Holangshan Range there are known deposits of chromites which are related to the masses of ultrabasic rock.

Typical for the area of the Ordos and Alashan is the broad development of sands which give this territory a unique coloring. The sands are found, as a rule, on the low plain areas between elevations, thus forming, in accordance with the topography, individual strips and within them they comprise large areas. Sands are usually absent on elevations since they are blown off by the constant strong winds.

In line with the broad development of sands and virtually the complete absence of water courses which is, of course, due to the insignificantly small amount of atmospheric precipitation, the vegetation of the Ordos and Alashan is very sparse, while the soil cover is very thin. As a whole, deserts predominate on the predominant area of the region. However, with a more detailed study of these deserts, one can note that they are not always of the same type. This is due both to the climatic features of the region and to the topography, the stratification depth of the groundwaters and also to the character of the soil-earths.

The greatest diversity is characteristic for the Ordos which lies in essence within two climatic zones, the semi-desert and desert. The first includes the extreme southeastern and smallest part of the Ordos where some 100-200 mm. of atmospheric precipitation fall per year, and in certain areas up to 300 mm.; it is crossed by small streams, the tributaries of the Hwang Ho, and dark-brown soils predominate. In the second belongs the entire remaining portion of the Ordos where less than 100 mm. of precipitation fall per year, where permanently active rivers (with the exception of the Hwang Ho which is only transient here) are missing, and the dark-brown soils are replaced by the gray-brown desert soils. Thus, the Ordos in landscape terms is a transitional region where, in the first place, one can see a gradual transition of certain landscape types into other ones and, in the second place, the landscapes in the southeastern and northwestern parts of it differ rather sharply.

The Alashan plains as a whole lie in the desert zone, and the climatic conditions in the various parts of this territory differ slightly, and therefore as a whole the difference in the landscapes here is less sharp than in the Ordos. However, due to the fact that the shift in the plain and elevated areas occurs more frequently here than in the Ordos, and in line with this the moisture conditions and the character of the soil also change, the microlandscapes here are more diverse.

M. P. Petrov who studied the desert vegetation of
Central Asia has established within this territory various
types of deserts, and describes their basic vegetation
groupings (1959a, b, c). In the desert portion of the Ordos,
the designated researcher has established: gravel-sandy
deserts, sandy deserts and saline-soil deserts. Here the
most widely found are the sandy deserts with a predominance
of hummocky and rich-hummocky sands overgrown by green-
sage thickets (with a predominance of Artemsia ordosica
Krasch.) which, as M. P. Petrov writes, determines the character of the landscape in this part of the Ordos. Here there
are also frequent shifting barkhaned sands on which one will
from time to time encounter sparse growths of psammophile
shrubs such as hedysarum (Hedysarum mongolicum Turcz),
caragana (Caragana korshinskii Kom or C. microphylla
Pall.), sages (Artemisia ordosica Krasch.), etc. The
gravel-sandy deserts are found on the piedmont plains of the
Arbiso and Kantegeri; they are characterized by a mixed
subshrub and shrub vegetation represented by reaumuria
(Reumuria soongorica), caragana (Caragana tragacanthoides,
C. tibetica), Russian thistle (Salsola laricifolia), etc. In
the mountains the basic vegetation grouping is a mixed-
shrub feather grass dry mountain steppe consisting of almond
(Amygdalus mongolica), caragana (C. tragacanthoides, C.
stenophylla), bindweed (Convolvus tragacanthoides), feather
grass (Stipa bungeana, S. glareosa), etc. The salt-soil deserts predominate on the salt swamps of the lake basins and
along the bottoms of the dry channels which are periodically
filled with water during the summer; here predominate
small-shrub halophytes such as Russian thistle (Kalidium
gracile Fenze, K. foliatum Pall.), nitraria (Nitraria tangutorum), etc. In the lower parts of the slopes of lake basins,
salt meadows have developed with sparse motley grass with
a clear dominance of sedges (Carex duriuscula) and chiy
(Lasiagrostis splendens).

For the desert-steppe portion of the Ordos which is
transitional from the dry steppe of the Loess Province to the
deserts, according to the data of M. P. Petrov, there is a
characteristic combination of solid ridge-hummocky sands,
barkhaned sands almost completely devoid of vegetation, and
broad lake depressions covered by thick vegetation. On the
overgrown and semi-overgrown sands predominate steppe
green sages, and on the barkhans one will encounter the

mesophilous shrub vegetation with the participation of green
sages. The flat lake depressions and the stream valleys,
where the groundwaters lie close to the surface are covered
with stepped gramen-motley grass meadows consisting of
bentgrass (Agrostis alba L.), Polygonum lutosus Pov, Ar-
thraxon hispidum Manino, etc., and thickets of mesophilous
shrubs such as willow (Salix cheilophila, S. flavida) and sea
buckthorn (Hippophae rhamnoides). The more salty areas
are covered by stepped salt meadows of sedge (Carex duriuscula), chiy (Lasiagrostis splendens) and anemones; the banks
of the fresh lakes are covered with meadow-swamp vegetation.

M. P. Petrov has pointed out that in the Ordos the
change of desert xerophile associations into the stepped or
mesophile ones occurs very gradually.

In the Alashan, as in the Ordos, the basic type of desert is sandy. However, the Alashan vegetation differs from
the Ordos in the greater xeromorphic halophile features and
this will be explained by the greater continentality and aridness of this territory as well as by the greater salting of the
surface deposits. On the barkhaned sands which are clearly
predominant one will encounter solitary shrubs of hedysarum (Hedysarum scoparium), caragana (C. korshinskii, C.
microphylla), Atraphaxis frutescens, Agriophyllum arenarium. On the semi-overgrown sands there is a denser
shrub psammo-halophile vegetation consisting of: tamarisk
(Tamarix ramosissima), nitraria (Nitraria tangutorum),
sage (Artemisia sphaerocephala, A. ordosica), and also
sparse growths of Zaysan haloxylon (Haloxylon ammonden-
dron) with an undergrowth of nitraria (Nitraria tangutorum).

Aside from the sandy deserts in the Alashan one will
also find rocky-gravel, sandy-pebble (Gobi) and salt deserts.
According to the data of M. P. Petrov, the rocky-gravel
deserts are confined to the above-listed low-mountain ranges
and are characterized by the presence of desert-steppe vegetation groupings. This is a mixed shrub and subshrub vegetation with sympegma (Sympegma regeli), Russian thistle
(Salsola laricifolia), caragana (Caragana stenophylla), Zygophyllum xanthoxylon with an admixture of feather grass
(Stipa bungeana, S. glareosa, etc.). The sandy-pebble deserts are characteristic for the elevated plains and are

covered by a very sparse shrub and semi-shrub vegetation with the chief representatives being reaumuria (Reaumuria soongorica), bindweeds (Convolvulus tragananthoides, C. gortchakovii), nitraria (Nitraria sphaerocarpa), and Russian thistle (Salsola passerina). The salt deserts are found in the depressions and on the bottom of them, as we have already mentioned, there are frequently lakes. In these depressions, due to the close stratification of the groundwaters, there has developed a swampy, meadow-salt swamp and salt swamp vegetation. The shores of the lakes are covered by dense thickets of reeds, cattail, rush, and above grow salt meadows with chiy and a subshrub salt desert of Russian thistles (Kalidium foliatum, K. caspicum and K. cuspidatum). These salt wastes are marked by the thickest vegetation cover for the desert. Here usually are population points which are basic livestock centers of the Alashan.

The landscapes of the Holangshan Range, due to its significant elevation, are much more diverse, and in the northern highest portion of the range, there is a clearly expressed vertical zonality. In the lower stage of the mountains, approximately up to an elevation of 1,900 meters above sea level, the landscapes differ little from the surrounding deserts. On the piedmont plains, up to an elevation of 1,600 meters above sea level, they are represented by sage-reaumuria desert with feather grass and sparse motley grass; on the higher foothills there is a mountain feather grass-shrub dry steppe. In the middle stage of the mountains, approximately between 1,900 and 2,100-2,500 meters, one will encounter thickets of sparse shrub vegetation such as honeysuckle (Lonicera sp.), rose (Rosa sp.), cinquefoil (Potentilla fruticosa), ephedra (Ephedra sp.), etc., with a sparse motley grass, and above, up to 3,000 meters, until recently there were spruce-pine forests. At present these forests have been heavily felled, and on the site of them there usually are small groves of aspen and Asian white birch or open glades with rich motley grass. At elevations above 3,000 meters, which are very few in the Alashan, there are alpine meadows of bistort, saussurea, dianthus, buttercup, etc., among which one will occasionally encounter shrubs of caragana, spirea, willow and cinquefoil.

The landscapes of the valleys of the major rivers--the Hwang Ho and the Edzin-Gol--are also distinct from the desert landscapes which are dominant in the region. The Hwang Ho Valley within the described region is characterized by an alternation of narrow areas with broader terraced ones where one can usually trace three terrace levels. The first or floodplain terrace is covered by flooded meadows where the vegetation is represented by gramen-motley grass formations with a predominance of chiy (Lasiagrostis splendens), reedgrass (Calamagrostis preudophragmites), sedge (Carex duriuscula); on the saltier areas there usually are associations of Russian thistle (Kalidium gracile) and annual Russian thistle (Salsola collina, etc.). This terrace is used for pasturing livestock. The second terrace is covered by cultivated lands and the natural vegetation has been completely destroyed; for the third nonirrigated terrace there is a typical sparse desert vegetation.

The cultivated vegetation in the oases of the middle courses of the Hwang Ho is particularly rich. Aside from all sorts of field and vegetable crops, here there are numerous orchards and groves of poplar, willow, white acacia, elaeagnus, paulownia, etc.

The vegetation of the Edzin-Gol Valley is much more halophilic and, as was pointed out by M. P. Petrov, in terms of its composition is close to the vegetation of the river valleys in Middle Asia and Kazakhstan. Here are found large-grass meadow salt swamps consisting of karelinia (Karelinia caspica), camel's thorn (Alhagi kirghisorum), etc., and the remains of the tugaic arboreal-shrub vegetation in the form of small thickets and groups of Populus diversifolia, elaeagnus, tamarisk and small shrubs such as wolfberry, nitraria, false-tamarix (M. P. Petrov, 1959b). In economic terms, the Edzin-Gol Valley has been developed much less than the Hwang Ho Valley. Here due to the lack of water supply and also to the sparse population, there are large areas of virgin lands.

In general, the natural conditions in the region of the Ordos and Alashan have not helped in its extensive economic utilization. They have basically used only the better irrigated piedmont areas of the region (in particular, its southern Nanshan portion), the Hwang Ho Valley and in part the

Edzin-Gol Valley. A major impediment both in developing the lands and in industrial and railway construction is the presence of shifting sands which, as we have pointed out, are widely found in the region. The formation of them, particularly in the more eastern portion of the region, where all conditions exist for the self-growth of the sands, to a great degree has been a heritage from the past irrational economic activity of man. In recent years in the Chinese People's Republic in general and in the desert and semi-desert portions of the region in particular, they have done certain work on reinforcing and reforesting the shifting sands.

THE PLAINS OF THE KASHUN GOBI AND THE PEISHAN UPLANDS

Between the Alashan and Tarim plains there stretches an extensive but relatively insignificant elevation which connects the Kashun Gobi and the Peishan Uplands. The absolute elevations of the Kashun Gobi are 1,200-1,400 meters, and the elevation of certain ridges in the Peishan Uplands reaches almost 2,800 meters.

The Kashun Gobi is basically a gently undulating plain which has been greatly but shallowly broken up by a complex network of broad ravines between which lie flat elevations and rocky crests some 50-100 meters high which have developed in the relief as a result of selective denudation. The ravines are either similar to the inland basins occupied by salt swamps or descend in the form of slightly incised gulleys and in places gorges, towards the Khami Basin, and the drop of it relative to the surface of the Kashun Gobi is about 1,000 meters. In the topography of the Peishan one can establish five chains: the Ch'ikech'ingtse in the north, the Machungshan, the Hsiaomachungshan and the Yingwangshan in the center, and the Pohsiangtse in the south. Each chain, in turn, consists of a number of elevations usually with rocky crests, sometimes individual and sometimes connected in groups. As a whole the topography of the Peishan is a combination of relatively low ranges separated by intermontane depressions. The ranges are composed of ancient metamorphic rock and also Carboniferous and Cretaceous deposits, while the depressions have been filled with a thin

mantle of Tertiary and Quaternary rough-fragmentary deposits. Along the edges stretch the sandy-pebbly plains which
shift directly into the plains of the Kashun Gobi.

The geological structure of the Kashun Gobi and the
Peishan has not been sufficiently studied. It is known that in
the metamorphic rock of the Kashun Gobi there are indications of iron mineralization, and in the sandy-shale stratum
on the Lower Paleozoic there is optical quartz. In the Jurassic sandy-argillite bed of the Peishan they have found two
deposits of hard coal and of them one is being worked. According to the data from reports of the first researchers, in
the Paleozoic bed of the Peishan they have encountered polymetallic ores and in the metamorphic rock gold (V. M.
Sinitsyn, 1959).

The Kashun Gobi, the Peishan, like the nearby sections
of the Tarim and Dzungarian plains and the piedmont plains
of the Nanshan known in Chinese literature under the name of
the Hohsi Corridor, is the driest part of Central Asia. Over
the year only several millimeters of precipitation fall, and
therefore here there is no permanent water course, and
springs are encountered also very rarely with a small discharge and heavily mineralized water. The surface is cut
up by a dense network of dry channels which head towards
the low areas where extensive undrained basins form. The
largest of them are the Shonanor Basin lying in the northern
part of the Peishan and the Kashun Gobi, the Edzin-Gol
Basin, the Lobnor Basin, and the basin of the Suleho River
lying along the southern boundary. In contrast to the Ordos
and Alashan, water will not be found each year in the dry
channels.

In this part of Central Asia where the temperature
fluctuations are very great, the physical weathering processes are exceptionally strong. Material is moved basically
only by the wind since the erosion processes here are minimal as a consequence of the extreme aridness. The wind
blows and carries off only the fine particles, while the
coarser material remains on the spot, and it gradually
forms, as we have already pointed out, a rocky mantle.
Such areas of stony deserts (hammadas) occupy an enormous
area in this territory. The vegetation cover is extremely
sparse. The soil profile due to the aridness of the climate

has developed very slightly. The water regime of the soils is chiefly of the sweating type. On the surface or in the upper parts of the profile, a varnish is formed, as well as a salt crust or a calcareous illuvial horizon, and a gravel mantle is widely found. The basic soil type is brown desert limestone crusts.

Generally within the Peishan and Kashun Gobi there is a dominant almost lifeless landscape of a barren surface of bedrock covered by rock rubble with a black film of desert varnish. The sandy deserts which are so widely found in the Ordos and Alashan are extremely rare here. In the Peishan there are virtually no salt deserts but in the Kashun Gobi they will be found, frequently occupying undrained basins which are extensive in terms of the area. Within the hammadas the vegetation is encountered extremely rarely, usually in small groups or even individually; of all the Central Asiatic plants they are the most xerophilic. Among them is the ephedra (Ephedra przewalskii), beancaper (Zygophyllum xanthoxylon), nitraria (Nitraria sphaerocarpa), Russian thistle (Salsola arbuscula), sympegma (Sympegma regeli), iljinia (Iljinia regeli), etc. Only along the dry channels and particularly close to the springs is the vegetation cover somewhat thicker and more diverse. Aside from the above-named plants, here one will encounter the large-shrub caragana (Caragana leucophloea), wolfberry (Lycium ruthenicum), calligonum (Calligonum mongolicum), tamarisk (Tamarix ramosissima), Populus diversifolia, elaeagnus (Elaeagnus moorcroftii), camel's thorn (Alhagi sparsifolia), Zaysan haloxylon and certain others (M. P. Petrov, 1959b).

It is interesting to note that in this exceptionally arid region, the Matsungshan Range which is the highest and therefore receives a somewhat greater amount of precipitation has a forest vegetation. According to the data of Grumm-Grzhimaylo, here there are spruce forests with an admixture of birch, mountain ash, buckthorn and Juneberry.

The region of the Kashun Gobi and Peishan is almost completely uninhabited.

THE TARIM PLAIN*

The Tarim Plain occupies one of the greatest intermontane depressions of Central Asia with a very great area, 530,000 sq. km. The plain is surrounded by a virtually complete ring of high mountains and only in the east comes into direct contact with the plains of the Hohsi Corridor which connect it with the Alashan Plain. The absolute elevations of the Tarim Plain are 800-1,400 meters above sea level, the surface of it slants to the northeast where Lake Lobnor lies. The plain is composed on the surface by Quaternary predominantly alluvial deposits which almost completely overcover its initial relief and among them only in the northwest can one establish two interior ridges composed of bedrock. The basic relief-forming factor at present is the aeolian.

Within the aggradation Tarim Plain, one can establish areas which differ in terms of the relief and the lithology of the friable beds comprising it. A larger portion of the plain is occupied by the Takla-Makan Desert which is covered by loose paleoalluvial sands where various aeolian landforms have achieved exceptional development. Along the foot of the mountain systems surrounding the plain there stretches a belt composed of proluvial-alluvial deposits of fused detritus fans. These piedmont trains comprising a gravel-stony desert are particularly well developed along the foothills of the Kunlun. Between the stony desert and the sandy Takla-Makan Desert lies a strip of loess-like sandy loams with a badland topography where the groundwater level is relatively close to the surface, and therefore among them in certain places one can encounter vegetation. Aside from the actually

---

*In the description of this and the subsequent regions we have used Trudy Sin'tszyanskoy kompleksnoy ekspeditsii 1957-1959 gg. (Transactions of the Sinkiang Multi-Field Expedition, 1957-1959), and in particular the works by N. T. Kuznetsov, V. N. Kunin, E. M. Murzayev, V. A. Nosin, B. A. Fedorovich and A. A. Yunatov.

plain sections in the Tarim Plain one will also encounter the yardangi which are individual elevations composed of bedrock (for example, the Mazartag Range lying between the Khotan and Yarkend rivers, and the Maralbashi elevations along the northern edge of the plain where the altitude reaches 1,500-1,700 meters absolute elevation) and low areas which are extensive salt wastes with large areas of hillocky sands. The latter include, for example, the Lobnor lowlands with the lowest point--Lake Lobnor--with an elevation of 780 meters above sea level, and depressions lying along the Tarim River.

The geological structure of the interior largest portion of the Tarim Plain has been little studied, and therefore data on the minerals of this region are far from complete. According to the geological materials, important deposits of minerals have been found in the young tectonic troughs in the border areas of the region. These deposits include the coal basins and the oil accumulations of the Kuchar and Yarkend troughs, the polymetallic ores, the copper-bearing sandstones and sulfur (V. M. Sinitsyn, 1959). The majority of these deposits as yet has been little studied and in fact is not worked.

The particular geographic position of the Tarim Depression and more specifically its position in the interior of the continent a significant distance away from the oceans (its center is more than 2,000 km. away from the sea) and the framing by very high mountain structures have created extremely unique conditions for the climatic and hydrological regime of this territory, and this, in turn, has had a direct influence upon the formation of the entire physical-geographic process. A characteristic feature of the natural conditions is, as we have pointed out, the exceptional aridness.

The climate of the Tarim Plain is characterized by extreme aridness. According to Chinese data, the annual amount of precipitation on this territory is less than 70 mm., and in individual areas is scarcely 30 mm. (Cherchen, Charklyk), and in the central portion of the depression in some years there is not a drop of rain (Li T'ao, 1958). The evaporation here is 20-25 times above the average annual precipitation norm. The winter for these latitudes is

relatively cool, the mean January temperatures are -8, -11°,
with minimums dropping down to -20, -27°, but on sunny
days the temperature frequently rises above 0°; snow rarely
falls and usually lasts only several days; the rivers and lakes
are covered with ice for three months (December-February).
The summer is hot and the mean July temperature exceeds
25°, with maximums rising up to 40°. Spring is characterized by strong winds predominantly northeastern which blow
the sands intensely. In certain areas of the plain, the winnowing process occurs very actively, for example, in Cherchen and Charklyk they have counted more than 100 days a
year when the sands shift.

The Tarim Plain is one of the largest undrained basins
of the world and the largest depression of Central Asia. It
receives rivers which begin in the Kunlun and Tien Shan
Mountains, but the majority of the rivers is small, and in
travelling a short distance from the mountains, they disappear into the sands. As we have already pointed out, only
several of the largest rivers such as the Tarim (Yarkend),
Khotan and Konchedar'ya cross the desert, but even their
current is not constant and they have water over the entire
extent only during the flood period. The basic water artery
of the Tarim Plain--the Tarim--begins in the Kunlun Mountains (the Raskemdar'ya River), crosses the plain from the
southwest to the northeast (the Yarkend River), and then, in
turning east, flows along the northern boundary of the Takla-
Makan Desert and empties into Lake Lobnor. The chief tributaries of the Tarim are the rivers flowing off the Eastern
Tien Shan, the Aksu, Musart and Konchedar'ya; the reverse
flowing off the Kunlun, as a rule, do not reach the Tarim,
and therefore do not play a basic role in its regime. Regardless of the fact that a portion of the Tarim waters is lost in
filtration and irrigation, they still reach the Lobnor.

The rivers of the Tarim Basin have a large load and
form a broad alluvial plain. The Tarim, like all plain
rivers, with much debris, flows in an elevated and very unstable channel. Almost in every flood season there are various changes in the contour of its channel and floodplain
parts, and this, in turn, has a strong effect upon the entire
appearance of the Tarim Valley, and also upon the formation
and development of its landscapes.

The rivers of the Tarim Basin are fed by snow in glaciers and by groundwaters. The highwater time occurs in July and August, at the time when there is the most intensive snow thawing; during the autumn the rivers are fed by underground water. The water regime of the rivers flowing off the Tien Shan and Kunlun Mountains is not the same. In the Kunlun Mountains, the amount of annual precipitation is less than in the Tien Shan, and therefore the amount of thaw water is greater here; moreover, the elevation of the snow line in the Kunlun is higher than in the Tien Shan, and due to this the thaw period begins later. As a consequence of this, the highwater period on the rivers of the Tarim Basin begins at different times, for the rivers flowing off the Eastern Tien Shan, the maximum discharge will be found in July, and in the rivers of the Kunlun, in August.

During the flood season in the valleys numerous temporary lakelets are formed, and several of them will sometimes exist for several years. The largest lake of the Tarim Basin, Lobnor, is a shallow nomadic body of water which does not have fixed dimensions or a permanent location. It has no clear shoreline and the lakewaters gradually shift into the bordering salt swamps which, depending upon the fluctuations in the influx of water and the seasonal changes in the evaporation intensity, constantly change.

The greatest number of rivers is thus concentrated in the piedmont belt of the alluvial-proluvial plains which receives water from the many small rivers in the surrounding mountains. In the upper portion of the piedmont train composed of large-fragment material, there is the filtration of surface waters and the formation of groundwater. In the lower portion composed of finer deposits, these waters come close to the day surface or are forced out on the surface. Oases are found in these spots.

Thus, the hydrological conditions of the Tarim Plain are characterized by a rather large amount of water supplied by surface water in the piedmont areas and a very slight amount of water in the interior parts which are supplied basically only by underground waters. According to recent data, the groundwaters here lie in a bed of aggradation deposits at a depth of from 1 to 10 meters and more. The groundwaters of the Tarim Plain to one degree or another are salty and this has been caused, in the first place, by the salt content of the rocks comprising the surrounding basin, and, in the second place, by the influx of salt solutions from the deposits filling the depression. The speed of the ground flow is very slight (hydrologists feel that it is practically stagnant), and this has caused the presence of a great discharge of groundwater in evaporation and transpiration. This, in its turn, has led to the intensified migration of salts from the groundwaters, even those lying at a significant depth, into the surface layers of the soils, and this is a distinguishing feature of the given territory.

The aggregate of the above-described climatic and hydrological conditions in the Tarim Plain creates within it such a sharply expressed desert regime that the normal growth of plants and the formation of a soil-vegetation cover itself are extremely difficult. On the predominant portion of the plain the chief vegetation elements are subshrubs. The existing flora is exceptionally poor in species: according to the data of Chinese scientists there are not more than 500 here. Widely found are relics of the Paleogene and Upper Cretaceous flora and this can be explained by the very protracted existence of extra arid conditions here. Botanists have pointed out that this circumstance has extremely limited both the process for developing new forms and species of plants, and the possibility of a more or less extensive migration from outside (A. A. Yunatov).

The meagerness of the vegetation cover here has sharply reduced the role of the biological factor in the soil formation process and thus has increased the influence of the geological conditions. In the latter the greatest significance is to be found in the broad distribution of rock deposits here, the extremely broad development of fine-grained predominantly dusty and always calcareous overburden and the presence of salt-bearing, Tertiary and Mesozoic rock which, as we have pointed out, forms the mountains surrounding the basin. On the predominant portion of the Tarim Plain, primitive desert soils have developed. The uniqueness of the hydrological regime has also had a great influence upon the character of soil formation, or more precisely, the intensive evaporation of groundwater which has brought about a strong development of hydromorphic soil formation phenomena against a background of the general desert bioclimatic regime. These phenomena are expressed in the broad distribution of meadow and swamp soils. Here frequently in line with the salinization of the groundwaters, the meadow regime of soil formation is combined with processes of salt accumulation, and as a result of this salt swamps are formed.

Thus, the basic landscapes of the Tarim Plain are sandy deserts, rocky gravel-pebble deserts, the hammadas, the valley landscapes, and the landscapes of salined expanses. The sandy deserts which within the plain occupy the greatest area are barren sands almost completely devoid of vegetation. Only very rarely in the depressions between the barkhans and along the old channels will one encounter solitary specimens of tamarisk, haloxylon and "tograk" (Populus diversifolia).*

The stony deserts which occupy the piedmont alluvial-proluvial areas of the plain are also marked by an extremely sparse vegetation cover and primitive desert soils. The larger portion of them is barren, and only in the gulleys and ravines will one encounter sparse vegetation. The latter is represented here by individual specimens of such strongly xerophilized shrubs such as ephedra (Ephedra Przewalskii), nitraria (Nitraria sphaerocarpa), bean-caper (Zygophyllum xanthoxylon), calligonum (Calligonum kaschgaricum), and subshrubs such as iljinia (Iljinia Regelii) and sympegma (Sympegma Regelii).

The valley landscapes, on the contrary, are marked by a rich (for the desert) soil-vegetation cover. These landscapes have extensively developed along the Tarim Valley, and also in the low portions of the piedmont plains composed of loess where the groundwater level is relatively high and which during the flood period are inundated. Here, as we have pointed out, are concentrated the large oases and the areas of arboreal vegetation. Very characteristic is the landscape of tugaic forests consisting of "tograk" (Populus diversifolia and P. pruinosa), and in places of Chinese elm with the participation of elaeagnus (jida--Elaeagnus

---

*Here and below from A. A. Yunatov.

angustifolia), thickets of tamarisk (Tamarix Glycyrrhira glabra) and reed found along the lowlands. Beneath the tugaic forests have formed the so-called tugaic soils which differ from the meadow soils in the fact that in them due to the virtually complete absence of grassy vegetation a humus horizon of the sod type has not formed.

Researchers who have worked in these regions write that some 1,500 years ago similar poplar-tamarisk forests skirted the Takla-Makan Desert in a solid ring. At present, as a consequence of the drop in the groundwater level, many of these forest areas have died and they have lasted only on individual better irrigated plain areas (V. M. Sinitsyn, 1959).

On the heavily wetted areas of the floodplains with stagnant waters, reed meadow swamps are formed in which peat frequently accumulates. Here there are few true floodplain meadows; in them predominate complex associations of lycium, salttree, licorice, dogbane, reed, reedgrass and in places chiy, with varying participation of Russian thistle. Here under the conditions of a shallow groundwater depth (2-6 meters), under the strong effect of the shrub-grassy vegetation, meadow soils have formed. In terms of the hydrological regime, the soil scientists here have distinguished two categories of meadow soils--sazov (on slightly flowing groundwaters forced out on the side) and alluvial (fed by a permanent ground flow and periodically inundated by river flooding).

In the Tarim Plain the landscapes of the salined expanses are very widely found. As we have already pointed out, ground feeding under the conditions of intense evaporation leads to the significant development of salined soils with their own halophyte vegetation. Among the latter a leading place is held by several species of tamarisk, Halostachys Belangeriana, Russian thistle (Kalidium foliatum) karelinia (Karelinia caspica), and lycium (Lycium ruthenicum). Depending upon the degree of salinization here the plants distinguish the meadow salt swamps which are relatively less salty and in varying degrees overgrown by shrub-grassy vegetation, the typical salt swamps which are saltier than the former and overgrown by the more resistant halophytes, and the salina salt swamps, i.e., drying-up salt lakes and muds.

In the Tarim Plain for agriculture they can use only the oases where the population is employed in farming and livestock raising. The latter has developed particularly along the Tarim Valley. Here also are significant areas of virgin lands which after certain measures in improving them can be successfully used for cotton planting (Yang Chi-ch'eng, 1958).

THE DZUNGARIAN PLAIN

The Dzungarian Plain is a large intermontane depression composed of thick beds of Paleozoic and Meso-Cenozoic deposit which lie horizontally over the larger area of the plain. Many of them are rich in minerals, chiefly hard coal and oil. The basic coal-bearing layers are found here in the Jurassic deposits, and it has been pointed out that the greatest thickness of the Jurassic coal beds is in the piedmont areas of the Eastern Tien Shan. The coal deposits stretch in the form of a virtually unbroken belt for 400-500 km., and the total thickness of the strata frequently exceeds 100 meters. In terms of coal reserves, the Urumchi deposit should be noted; its reserves have been estimated at several billion tons. The oil deposits stratigraphically are found in the complex of rock from the Upper Triassic to the Tertiary inclusively and are enclosed in large asymmetrical anticline structures. There are numerous outcroppings of oil on the surface. One of the largest oil deposits in China, the Karamay, is located here. A large deposit being worked is also located at Tushantse in the southern part of the basin to the southeast of Shihho.

In recent years in the Dzungarian Depression they have discovered new oil deposits, with an important one at Urhe lying 100 km. from Karamay. In this regard, the oil-bearing area prospective in industrial terms here to a significant degree has been enlarged. In general the Chinese geologists assume that a whole series of structures in the Dzungarian Depression is oil-bearing and that the prospects for finding oil here are very great (Chang Keng et al., 1958). Besides coal and oil in the Dzungarian Basin there are also numerous outcroppings of asphalt and bituminous rock. For example, in the middle portion of the depression there are more than 20 asphalt hills; the Jurassic coal-bearing suite is rich in asphalt-bearing rock.

The Dzungarian Plain covers a large area, but is

certainly much smaller than the Tarim Plain. The surface of the
plain is flat with a general slope to the southwest. The larger
portion of the plain lies at an elevation of 300-500 meters above
sea level, and in the lower southwestern portion the elevation
drops down to 189 meters (the level of Lake Ebi-Nur), and in
the higher eastern part it rises up to 1,000 meters and more.
In the topography of the Dzungarian Depression there are three
major parts: the southwest, the northwest, and the northeast.
The southwestern part is a flat aggradation plain composed in
the interior parts of alluvial deposits, in the west lacustrine and
in the foothills alluvial-proluvial. In the northern part of the
depression which recently has undergone uplifting there predominate denudation plains. In the northwest these are bedded plains
or plateaus composed of horizontally lying deposits of Tertiary
Age which are very thick; in the northeast there are socle plains
with more ancient rock emerging on the surface. In general
the relief of the eastern portion of the Dzungarian Plain is very
unique and close to the relief of the Kashun Gobi. Here, as in
the Gobi, there is a combination of hummocky elevations and
basins separating them with a rocky surface and salt wastes.
The extreme western portion of the plain stands out in its lowest
absolute elevations and the abundance of lakes. All of the major
lakes of the Dzungarian Plain such as Ulyungur, Baga-Nur, Ebi-
Nur and also a number of smaller ones, are concentrated here.
According to the paleogeographic data, these lakes are relics
of significantly larger bodies of water.

In general the basic area of the Dzungarian Plain is
covered by a broad desert with the landforms being basically
barkhans and only in certain areas retained by vegetation.

The surface of the Dzungarian Plain is rather significantly
broken up, but due to the small amount of atmospheric precipitation as a whole this has been done by aeolian processes and not
water. Aeolian processes have formed here both deep enclosed
depressions and an extensive area of semi-loose rich sands
called the Dzotosyn-Elisu. Close to the mountains where the
rivers appear the ruggedness has been caused by erosion. The
largest rivers of this territory are the Black Irtysh, the Urungu
flowing off the mountains of the Mongolian Altai, and also the
Manass and Kuytun flowing off the Eastern Tien Shan. All of
these rivers, with the exception of the Black Irtysh, are related
to the interior drainage basins, flowing into the above-listed
lakes, but none of them crosses the plain.

In general the amount of water on the Dzungarian Plain is low. This territory, being extremely distant from the oceans and closed off by high mountains from the moist west winds, receives not more than 200 mm. of precipitation in its western parts and less than 100 mm. in the eastern. Regardless of the fact that the mean monthly temperatures in the coldest months on the piedmont plains are approximately -20° with winter absolute minimums dropping to -40, -43°, there are frequent instances when the winter temperature rises above 0°; this brings about the intensive evaporation of the snow, reduces its thickness, and consequently the reserves of water. The southwestern portion of the Dzungarian Plain receives the most amount of water, as the rivers here are fed by the thaw water of the alpine glaciers in the Eastern Tien Shan; there is least water in the central and eastern portions which receive an insignificant amount of atmospheric precipitation (50-80 mm. per year), and the fall has an episodic character. There are no permanently running water courses in this portion of the Dzungarian Plain, and the basic element in the hydrographic network here is the dry channels (sayrs) cutting the surface of the plain.

A characteristic feature of Dzungarian rivers, like the other rivers in the desert areas, is the marked drop in their discharge further down the current, and the smaller rivers in emerging onto the plain gradually disappear in the sands. The reason for the water loss is above all the strong infiltration of the water in the river channels and also the losses in evaporation which several times exceeds the amount of atmospheric precipitation. The river waters which filter through become the abundant sources for feeding groundwater. According to the data of the Sinkiang Expedition, over virtually the entire territory of the western part of the Dzungarian Plain, there has developed a solid water table. An insignificant amount is forced out on the day surface, feeding the rather numerous "karasu" or swampy localities. As one advances to the low areas of the Dzungarian Plain, the freshwaters become salty, turning into the more mineralized sulfate and chloride waters.

The river system of the Dzungarian Plain is certainly not homogeneous. The rivers flowing off the Eastern Tien Shan Mountains, which, as we have already pointed out, are basically fed by the thawing of the alpine snows and glaciers, have a summer high-water period (the end of June to the beginning of August), and to this basic wave of salt waters is added several rain floodings. During the winter, the rivers, as a rule, do not freeze and have a slight runoff as they are fed by groundwater.

All of the remaining rivers flowing into the Dzungarian Depression where the basic mass of runoff is formed from thaw waters of seasonal snows, have a spring high-water period. During the summer there is the low period sometimes interrupted by rain floods, but during the dry years the surface runoff ceases. During the winter the volume of runoff for these rivers is not great and on several rivers as a consequence of the exhaustion of the groundwater, the runoff ceases altogether.

A hydrographic feature of the Dzungarian Plain, like the other arid plains, is the meandering in the low areas of the rivers and lakes. The direction of the rivers, the size of the lakes, their depth, and the degree of water mineralization change constantly. An example of such changes in the hydrographic network can be seen from the rebirth of Lake Ikhekak and the disappearance of the neighboring Lake Ayrik (Tellinur). At the same time there has been a change in the landscape of the surrounding territories which can be observed once again from the example of the mentioned lakes. Thus, according to the materials of the Sinkiang Expedition, the shift of Lake Tellinur brought about the mass drying-up of reed thickets along its banks and caused a sharp drop in the groundwater level over extensive expanses, and this, in turn, brought about the death of the tamarisk and haloxylon over large areas.

The vegetation cover over the predominant portion of the Dzungarian Plain has a xerophyte appearance and is extremely sparse; over large areas vegetation is completely absent. Annual ephemers which are so widely found on the neighboring plains of Middle Asia do not have basic significance in the vegetation cover of the Dzungarian Plain, and this is due to the shift of the precipitation maximum from early spring to the summer. The gray-brown desert soils are the zonal soils for the given territory. Here the most widely found are the common and saline gray-brown desert

soils and, in addition to them, one will encounter different
varieties of this soil type.

Thus, within the Dzungarian Plain lying much farther
to the north of the plains described below, the zonal landscape type is deserty. However, the latter is not always the
same in different parts of the plain. Depending upon the climatic and orographic conditions, and thus upon the underground water regime, here one can set up several types of
desert landscape. The broad central portion of the plain
where surface runoff is absent and the barkhaned sands are
widely found is a haloxylon desert with a predominance of
Haloxylon persinum in the west and Haloxylon ammodendron
which is typical for the Central Asiatic deserts in the east,
and sparse clumps of this plant are scattered along the barren sands. Takyrs have developed in the depressions between the barkhans. In the most arid eastern portion of the
Dzungarian Plain, there is a predominance of rocky deserts
with extremely sparse vegetation consisting of ephedra
(Ephedra Przewalskii), stunted very meager haloxylon, Anabasis brevifolia and bean-caper (Zygophyllum xanthoxylon).
Extensive areas of the Nomin-Gobi are barren outcroppings
of bedrock and are devoid of a vegetation-plant cover, and
clumps of saksaul appear only in certain places along the
dry channels. On the piedmont plains of the Eastern Tien
Shan one will find a predominance of sage and biyurgun
(Nanophyton erinaceum), and in areas with a shallow stratification of the groundwaters, reaumuria deserts with a subshrub of Dzungarian reaumuria (Reaumuria soongorica). In
the lower portion of the detritus fans and on the proluvial
trains in the zone where there is subfeeding and the emer-
gence of groundwater, there have developed meadow,
meadow-swamp and peat-swamp soils on which one will encounter sparse elm groves and tograk forests alternating
with reed swamps and chiy patches. But where the groundwater level lies below 10 meters, the typical landscape is
salt swamp characterized by diverse Russian thistle, small
tamarisk and rush. On the takyred depressions, on the saline gray-brown soils, haloxylon-reaumuria and tamarisk-
reaumuria deserts have developed. In the western and northwestern parts of the plain, where the amount of atmospheric
precipitation is somewhat greater than in the east, one will
find landscapes of semideserts and dry steppes with a dominance of sage-Russian thistle or sage-gramen complexes.

The predominant portion of the Dzungarian Plain, like the remaining deserts of Northwest China, is virtually not used in economic terms. The basic farming areas are concentrated on the piedmont plains within the oases; the basic fodder lands are found in the steppe zones. The latter within the Dzungarian Plain occupy a small area in comparison, for example, with the plains of Inner Mongolia, and therefore livestock raising here is on a relatively smaller scale.

In general in Northwest China, regardless of the limitation on the amount of land suitable for plowing, they have maintained large areas of virgin lands which could be planted with the corresponding measures. In line with this, here under the conditions of the dry climate, farming is almost exclusively irrigated, and a very important measure for developing the virgin lands is the full and rational utilization of the resources of surface and groundwaters.

THE MOUNTAINS OF THE
EASTERN TIEN SHAN

The Dzungarian and Tarim plains are separated by a large system of mountains known as the Eastern (Chinese) Tien Shan stretching in a latitudinal direction. The Chinese portion of the Tien Shan is a complex system of ranges and depressions in which one can orographically establish two basic groups of ranges--the northern and southern; they are separated by a strip of intermontane depressions which are broken up by the interior ranges. The height of the main chains of the Eastern Tien Shan is 4,000-5,000 meters above sea level, and the interior chains reach up to 4,500 meters, with the elevation of the depressions running from 2,500 meters above sea level down to 154 meters below sea level. Individual peaks of the Eastern Tien Shan exceed 5,000 meters.

In the structure of the Eastern Tien Shan one will find a whole complex of rock from the Precambrian metamorphic to the friable deposits of the Cenozoic which lie basically zonally, and this has been caused by the unique history in the geological development of this territory. Thus, the ancient metamorphic rock comprises the larger portion of the ranges in its interior zone, Paleozoic sedimentary and

igneous-sedimentary beds form its northern and southern
chains, while Meso-Cenozoic sandstones and conglomerates
fill the intermontane depressions in the interior zone of the
Eastern Tien Shan and comprise the foothill ridges of this
mountain system.

Geomorphologically the Eastern Tien Shan can be divided both in a zonal-latitudinal direction which fits well
with its geological structure, and in a direction from west
to east which to a significant degree has been caused by the
climatic factors. In the western portion, the ranges and
depressions are sharply expressed; in the north these are
the Borokhoro, Iren-Khabirga and other ranges, in the south
the Kakshaal-Tau which runs along the border with the USSR,
the Khalyktau, etc., and in the center are the large intermontane depressions which form the upper course of the Ili
River, etc. In this portion of the Tien Shan, there are high
mountains either with sharp outlines, eternal snows and glaciers, or with a broad levelled peak, and frequently asymmetrical structure. Here the landforms of ancient glaciation are widely found and the ruggedness of the mountains is
great. In the eastern portion of the Chinese Tien Shan one
can clearly note only the northern group of ranges--the
Bogdoshan, Barkul'tag, Karlyktag, and the southern group is
poorly expressed. In contrast to the western portion, here
are mountains with flat peaks and gentle slopes; an exception
is the Bogdoshan Range having an alpine outline.

The extensive alpine system of the Eastern Tien Shan
has been subjected to the influence of air masses from various directions. First of all it is a clear climatic boundary
between the temperate climate of the Dzungarian Plain and
the very hot and dry climate of the Tarim. Moreover, in the
western part, particularly in the interior intermontane basins
open to the west, the moist winds freely enter from the At-
lantic, while the eastern portion of these mountains has been
subjected to the influence of the dry winds from the Central
Asiatic deserts. All of this leads to a situation whereby the
climate in the various parts of the Eastern Tien Shan in general is rather different. There have not been sufficient meteorological observations for the Eastern Tien Shan, and
therefore information on the climate of this mountain system
is very approximate and one can judge it only from indirect
features. The winter here is protracted and rather cold; the

summer is short and not hot; the annual and daily amplitudes
in temperature fluctuations are very significant. The annual
amount of precipitation increases with altitude, and also as
one moves towards the north and particularly towards the
west. In the uplands of the western portion of the Eastern
Tien Shan, the amount of atmospheric precipitation is significant enough so that large glaciers are formed here reaching a length of more than 30 km. As has been pointed out,
the basic glaciation centers are the Iren-Khabirga and the
Bogdo-Ula.

The western portion of the Eastern Tien Shan, respec-
tively, is better watered. The large rivers with much water
such as the Upper Ili with its tributaries and the Khadyk-Gol
are formed here, in the alpine plains. The first flows to the
west into the USSR, emptying into Lake Balkhash, and the
second to the east towards Lake Bagrahkul'. The northern
slope of the Eastern Tien Shan is cut by numerous although
short and undrained rivers, while the southern slope is virtually without water, and the formation of runoff occurs from
both surface water and groundwater and the dispersion is
consequence of losses in filtration, evaporation and irrigation. The formation of runoff occurs chiefly in the upper
portions of the mountains, but it may partially occur lower
down--in the lower portions of the slopes, on the detritus
fans and piedmont plains where there are mud flows and
"karasu" which are unique groundfed streams.

The feed of the rivers in the various portions of the
Eastern Tien Shan differs and is very diverse. Hydrologists
here establish areas with a predominance of rivers: glacier-
snow-fed, snow-glacier, snow, snow-rain, rain-fed and
ground.

The particular features of the climatic regime have
also caused the great uniqueness in the exogenic processes
which can be seen here. In the upper belt of the mountains
this is basically nival and glacier processes, the processes
of the mechanical destruction of rock and the mass development of gravitational slope movements. In the medium
mountain areas there are strong processes of river erosion,
and in the low-belt mountains, arid processes. The great
intensity of the physical weathering processes which are particularly characteristic for the southern slopes of the

Eastern Tien Shan creates very favorable conditions for the development of mud flows and the formation of purely pro-luvial detritus fans which are very short and steep.

Here, as elsewhere in Northwest China, everywhere there have developed very intensive processes of salt accum-ulation in the soil earths and groundwaters. The ground-waters are particularly heavily salined in the southern por-tion of the Eastern Tien Shan (where the salinity of the bed-rock is great), and this leads to the formation of extensive salt wastes in the piedmont plains and intermontane depres-sions.

The soil-vegetation cover on the individual parts of the Eastern Tien Shan differs sharply and also changes basically from west to east and from north to south. Best of all it is developed on the wetter intramontane plains of the west, less solid and diverse on the northern mountain slopes and com-pletely insignificant on the southern slopes and in the east-ern dry area of the Eastern Tien Shan. The same changes can be noted in the soil types, the specific composition of the vegetation and animals and in the structure of the verti-cal zonality of the landscapes, and for this, besides every-thing else, there is the characteristic feature that the geo-graphical belts do not occupy a strictly determined altitude position here.

According to the data of Chinese research, the mate-rials of the Sinkiang Expedition and certain sources in liter-ature, one can compile the following scheme for the land-scapes in the Eastern Tien Shan.

In the nival zone above 3,600 meters absolute eleva-tion where barren rock and rock streams predominate and on the more stable areas of the talus, primitive mountain meadow soils have been formed on which grow the alpine cushion plants, for example, Arenaria diapensiaides and Sibbaldia tetrandra.

At elevations of 3,600-2,700 meters, in the western extremity of the northern ranges and on the slopes facing north in the more southerly ranges which to a certain degree experience the effect of the humid western winds, on the mountain meadowy, usually shallow rocky, soils will be found

alpine meadows. These are composed chiefly of xerophile
sages, for example, Cobresia filifolia, and there are sedges
(Carex sp.--Alchemilla vulgaris) as well as gramen such as
brome (Bromus inermis), poa (Poa pratensis) and certain
others. In the southern ranges of the Eastern Tien Shan
which are much drier than the northern, this subalpine
meadow belt is changed into a subalpine steppe and its
boundary is shifted to higher levels.

At elevations from 2,600 down to 1,600 meters in the
northern ranges of the Eastern Tien Shan there grow coniferous forests on the mountain forest soddy soils. Here, in the
upper portion of this belt (above 2,300 meters), the alpine
meadows will descend, but the dry steppes extend into the
lower portion. The specific composition of these forests is
extremely homogeneous, an undergrowth is absent, the
grass cover is shallow and mosses have developed. The
basic strain is spruce (Picea Schrenkiana and P. sinhiangen-
sis). The coniferous forests occupy, as a rule, the shadowy
northern slopes of the ranges, while the southern slopes are
virtually completely stepped. In the warm and moist mountain valleys one will encounter areas of leafy forests of
apple (Malus sieversii) and apricot (Ameniaca vulgaris). On
the southern ranges of the Eastern Tien Shan forests are virtually absent and only in certain areas along the shadowy
slopes will one encounter very small forest areas. Thus,
there are no solid forest belts in the mountains of the Eastern Tien Shan, even within its northern part.

In the northern ranges at elevations below 1,600 meters above sea level, there have developed steppes with a
predominance of feather grass (Stipa capillata) and sheep's
fescue (Festuca sulcata) on the black earths and chestnut
soils, and in this area along the valleys one will frequently
find the desert Central Asiatic landscapes. These landscapes are represented usually by subshrub Russian thistle
deserts with Anabasis salsola, Salsda rigica and Nanaphyton
erinaceum. At the same time on the southern ranges of the
Tien Shan there predominate typical desert complexes which
rise here up to an absolute elevation of 1,700-2,000 meters
coming into direct contact with the subalpine steppes. The
intermontane basins of all the altitude levels are greatly
deserted and in the landscape hammadas are dominant.

The landscapes in the eastern portion of the Chinese Tien Shan such as the Choltag, Kuruktag and other ranges, are typically desert. Here one will find sympegma-stepped and bean-caper ephedra and nitraria deserts, rarely the feather grass and Russian thistle-feather grass steppes and the Nanophyton erinaceum-Agropyron cristatum dry steppes. Along the bottoms of the intermontane basins are found salt meadows, tamarisk shrubs and lush Russian thistle deserts.

The southern slopes of the Kokshaal-Tau Range are also marked by a great degree of desertiness. The alpine cobresia meadows are encountered here only in the axial portions of the range up to an elevation of 2,900-3,000 meters. Below, down to 2,500 meters, there is a dominance of xerophyte varieties of subalpine steppes such as sage-gramen steppes and cushions. Below, down to 2,000 meters are the deserty sage-feather grass steppes; the entire lower belt of the mountains and the intermontane plains is a typical Russian-thistle steppe--reaumuria-Russian thistle or sympegma-Russian thistle, or it is completely void of vegetation.

The border ranges in the southern part of the Eastern Tien Shan, as a rule, have been heavily eroded and show an extremely meager vegetation. The piedmont gravel-rocky plains with gypsum soils are covered by Russian thistle deserts, and only along the river valleys composed of loess material will one find thickets of tamarisk and floodplain meadows.

The landscapes of the wettest portion of the Eastern Tien Shan--the Chinese portion of the Ili intermontane depression--are completely different. Here predominate meadow steppes and sage deserts which in terms of their composition are closer to the Middle Asiatic. The leading species of vegetation on the steppes are feather grass (Stipa kirghisorum), species of oat and the unique beard grass steppes with Andropogon ischaemum found in the Soviet portion of the Tien Shan. The basic species of desert vegetation are the sand acacia (ammodendron sp.), the sand astragalus and Carex physocles, also typical for the more western deserts but not encountered in the deserts of Central Asia.

Proceeding from this, the botanists have concluded
that here, as along the ranges of Border Dzungaria, there is
a major botanical-geographic boundary between Middle and
Central Asia (A. A. Yunatov).

The natural resources of the Eastern Tien Shan as yet
have been little developed. The minerals have virtually been
unstudied. According to the data of V. M. Sinitsyn (1959),
at present they know deposits of hard coal, lead and zinc,
tin and molybdenum, copper and iron. The hard coal is
found in the Jurassic deposits of the intermontane depressions in the interior zone of the Eastern Tien Shan, the Kun-
ges, the upper reaches of the Tekes and the Turfan-Khami,
each of which is an independent coal basin. The lead and
zinc deposits have been discovered in many ranges of the
Eastern Tien Shan, and, as V. M. Sinitsyn writes, are evidently the most economically promising. They are encountered in the deposits of different systems of the Paleozoic,
and, as a rule, are found in the fault zones. Manifestations
of lead and molybdenum have been found in the northern
slopes of the Borokhoro Range and in the western portion of
the Khalyktau.

The ore manifestations are related to the contact
zones of granite intrusions; as yet they do not have practical
significance. Ore manifestations with copper are encountered in the Eastern Tien Shan everywhere and are basically
confined to the igneous rock, but as yet they have not found
deposits of industrial significance. Iron mineralization has
been found in the interior zone of the Eastern Tien Shan. It
is of two types: skarn which is encountered in the contact
points of granite intrusions with Carboniferous limestones
and sedimentary confined to the Jurassic deposits of the depressions. V. M. Sinitsyn has pointed out that the latter
type is encountered in the Eastern Tien Shan more frequently
and economically it is more valuable.

In agricultural terms, only the northern ranges of the
Eastern Tien Shan and the intermontane depressions of its
interior zone are used as these have rather rich fodder lands
and nomadic livestock raising has been developed. Lumbering is also found but the scale is not comparable with lumbering in Northeast China.

THE MOUNTAINS OF BORDER DZUNGARIA
AND THE MONGOLIAN ALTAI*

The mountains of Border Dzungaria which frame the Dzungarian Plain on the west consist of a number of short ranges running northeast (the Maili, Barlyk, Dzhair and Urkashar ranges) and latitudinally (the Saur and Tarbagatay ranges). The latter lie on the border between the USSR and the Chinese People's Republic and are only partially in China. The elevation of the listed mountains fluctuates from 2,000 to 3,000 meters, and the highest peak located in the Saur Range (3,085 meters) lies on the border with the USSR. The mountains are divided by three large intermontane depressions--the Irtysh, the Dyam-Emel in the center and the so-called Dzungarian Gates in the south. These intermontane depressions connect the Dzungarian Plain with the plains of Eastern Kazakhstan in the Soviet Union. The mountains of Border Dzungaria are characterized by a combination of level surfaces and deep valleys and in the alpine portions narrow ridges and rocky peaks appear. On the highest peaks, as we already have pointed out, glaciers can be found. The mountains are composed of igneous-sedimentary rock of the Paleozoic and granites; the depressions lying at elevations of 400-700 meters are filled predominantly with proluvial deposits from the detritus fans. The mountains of Border Dzungaria, particularly in the Dzhair Range, are rich in deposits of vein and placer gold. The vein gold is found basically in the igneous-sedimentary rock of the Lower Paleozoic and has been widely worked. The placer gold is found in the friable deposits from the various valleys of the Dzhair, but it does not have particular economic significance (V. M. Sinitsyn, 1959).

---

*The Mongolian Altai in China occupies a small area, entering only in its southwestern slope, and the landscapes generally do not stand out so sharply from the landscapes of the mountains in Border Dzungaria. In considering this, we have combined the mountains of Border Dzungaria and the Mongolian Altai in one region, although perhaps this is somewhat artificial.)

The mountains of Border Dzungaria lie on the path of
the western air currents and are an important climatic
boundary. The northern and northwestern slopes lying predominantly in the USSR receive relatively abundant precipitation, the amount reaching 300 mm. per year, while the
southern and southeastern slopes of these mountains are dry,
and in Dzungaria the amount of atmospheric precipitation,
as we have already noted, does not exceed 200 mm. The
rivers flowing off the mountains of Border Dzungaria are fed
basically by snow water and have a spring flood season, and
during the summer the runoff is maintained due to groundwater. In the piedmont belt--in the zone where groundwater
comes to the surface--are found springs and sources which
are particularly numerous in the western portion of the
mountains.

The Mongolian Altai which is the southeastern continuation of the Altai Mountain System of the Soviet Union consists of a number of parallel ranges and intermontane tectonic troughs running southeast. The range has an asymmetrical profile and a sharply expressed step-like structure
which has been caused by the fault dislocations of the Cenozoic. The latter have had a particularly great influence upon
the character of the present relief of the Mongolian Altai.
These faults, for example, have frequently been the cause
for the direction of the rivers, and they can also explain the
changes in the direction of the rivers, in particular, the
sharp turns of the Urungu and Black Irtysh rivers where
they emerge on the piedmont plains, etc. Along the border
of China and Mongolia stretch the highest ranges 3,200-
3,500 meters absolute elevation, and on their plateau-like
surface rise sharp peaks covered by eternal snows and glaciers. The tallest peak of the Mongolian Altai, Mount
Tabyn-Bogdo-Ola (4,356 meters) lies in Mongolia. The
slopes are broken by deep trough-like valleys. The middle
portions of the slopes are marked by a steep descent and by
strong and deep erosion cutting. Here in the upper belt of
the mountains the frost weathering processes have been
strong. The lower portions of the slopes are smooth,
plateau-like and slightly broken up. The foothills are undulating plains with groups of hills. The piedmont aggradation
plain, as a particular plain belt (like the ones which have
widely developed along the foothills of the Eastern Tien Shan
and Kunlun), here is absent.

The mountains of the Chinese portion of the Mongolian Altai are composed basically of ancient crystalline rock and sedimentary beds of the Paleozoic which, as in the Eastern Tien Shan, lie zonally. In the structure of the southwestern slope of these mountains there are sandy-shale and igneous Paleozoic deposits which form the divide part of the range and the lower portion of the slopes, and also metamorphic shales and gneisses, and intrusive granites which have developed between them. According to the geological data, each of these three structural zones has its own complex of minerals. Thus, in the divide zone in the contact points with the granite intrusions they have established several deposits and ore manifestations of rare minerals such as wolfram and molybdenum. The crystalline zone is an area of rare-element mineralization related to the pegmatite veins. For the lower sedimentary zone there are characteristic copper mineralization and deposits of piezoquartz. Here in the Carboniferous deposits they have also found hard coal deposits. Between these structural-metallogenic zones, along the faults, are scattered small deposits of lead and zinc. Moreover, in the Chinese portion of the Mongolian Altai they have frequently encountered deposits of gold. As of yet these have been found only in placers which recently have been intensively worked. The richest placers are located in the upper tributaries of the Irtysh (V. M. Sinitsyn, 1959).

The mountains of the Mongolian Altai which are marked by significant altitude capture the greater portion of the moisture brought in by the northwest winds, and these mountains are noted for a greater amount of precipitation than in the lower mountains of Border Dzungaria. For the various points of the Mongolian Altai, the amount of atmospheric precipitation fluctuates from 130 up to 630 mm. per year, in places reaching as high as 750-800 mm., increasing with altitude and towards the west. Winter precipitation predominates and this is caused by the frequent incursion of cold northern air masses. Snow will be found during four and a half to five months in a layer up to 50 cm. thick, and in the high northern parts, up to 80-90 cm. and more.

In general the climate of this territory is cold. The mean January temperatures are -18°, minimums drop down to -50°; the mean July temperatures are 21° (at elevations around 1,000 meters).

The mountains of the Mongolian Altai are part of the area of exterior drainage. The predominant portion of the rivers in the southwestern or Chinese slope belongs to the Irtysh Basin, and only the rivers in the extreme eastern portion flow into the Urungu River which terminates on the Dzungarian Plain in the undrained Lake Ulyungur.

The rivers flowing off the Mongolian Altai are basically snow-rain-fed. However, for the rivers which are formed in the various altitude belts of these mountains, there is a characteristic predominance of different feed sources, and this causes the character of their flooding. Thus, in the alpine zone of the Chinese portion of the Mongolian Altai, where glaciers and snowfields are widely found, the basic source of the rivers is the snow thaw water. Below, in the zone of medium-elevation mountains, the basic source of the rivers is the thaw water from seasonal snow; in the zone of the low mountains and in the foothills, a rain feed predominates, chiefly due to the intensive summer downpours. The greatest discharges of the rivers occur in the beginning of the summer; during this time the intensive thawing of the snows coincides with the falling of rain, and this frequently leads to inundation on the piedmont plains. During the winter the rivers freeze.

In line with the difference in the climatic features and the hydrological regime in the mountains of Border Dzungaria and the Mongolian Altai, the landscapes generally are not at all alike. For the mountains of Border Dzungaria there is a characteristic altitude zonality which is inherent to the mountains of the subboreal sharply continental dry areas. According to materials from recent research, in the belt of the piedmont trains here predominate desert landscapes--the teresken, nannophyton and keurek deserts. These desert complexes frequently rise up the slopes of the mountains and the valleys. In the lower and middle belts of the mountains, one will widely find steppe landscapes with dry tyrs and desert bistort or sage-sheep's fescue steppes on chestnut soils which higher up turn into sheep's fescue and sheep's fescue-feather grass steppes on chestnut and black-earth soils. In the upper belt of the mountains there are common meadow steppes with a predominance of sedge on the subalpine mountain-meadow soils. The forests are found only along the slopes of the Saur Range where they are represented by the grass larch (Larix cetaherbosa) which is combined with the meadow steppes and subalpine motley grass meadows, and in the upper belt change into cobresia wastes.

According to the geobotanical data, the mountains of Border Dzungaria form that boundary where the Middle Asiatic landscapes meet. In these mountains one can observe a direct intertransition of one landscape into another. For example, along the trains and slopes of the mountains, and also along the bottoms of the intermontane valleys, the Central Asiatic deserts will rise very high, while along the valleys exposed to the west (Chuguchak, etc.) one will encounter sage steppes which are a zonal landscape type for the plains of Central Asia and Kazakhstan.

The landscapes of the Mongolian Altai are more diverse than the mountains of Border Dzungaria. Here over a relatively small area of the abrupt narrow southern slope there is a consistent change in the altitude belt--from the deserty belt of the piedmont plains, through the steppe and forest, to the alpine meadow belt of the uplands. As one moves from the northwest to the southeast, the boundaries of these altitude belts, in line with the increase in the aridness of the climate, gradually rise, and thus there is an increase in the degree of desertiness in the landscapes and the natural appearance of these mountains changes.

In the foothills below an elevation of 550 meters in the northwest and 1,200 meters in the southeast, true deserts have developed--the nannophyton or Russian thistle (with a predominance of Anabasis aphylla). Higher up they change into sage-gramen semideserts which have developed on the brown desert-steppe and chestnut soils. The grass cover here is sparse, and typical are fescue, sage and feather grass (Stipa effusa). At an elevation of 800 meters in the northwest and 1,450 meters in the southeast the dry steppes begin which have developed on the chestnut soils. Here spiraea (Spiraea hypericifilia) is dominant along with sage (Artemisia frigida) and fescue (Festuca ovina), and among them there are sparse xerophyte shrubs such as caragana

and ephedra. The upper boundary of these steppes runs at
an elevation of 1, 300-1, 700 meters, and it is also the lower
boundary of the forest. The upper boundary of the forest
runs along an elevation of 2, 300 meters in the northwest and
an elevation of 2, 600 meters in the southeast.

The forests of the Chinese portion of the Mongolian
Altai are basically coniferous with an admixture of birch and
aspen on gray forest soils. In the forests of the northwestern part of this mountain system there predominates Siberian larch (Larix sibirica) and Siberian fir (Abies sibirica),
and beneath the crown have extensively developed spiraea
and sedges. Somewhat higher where the climate is colder
and wetter on soddy-podzolic soils grow forests of Siberian
pine--pine-foxberry associations (Pinus sibirica--Vaccinium
vitis-idaea)--and these form the southern section of the Siberian tayga which extends into China. The chief tree of the
coniferous forests in the southeastern portion is the Siberian
larch, but it grows rather poorly; the xerophyte sedges are
very numerous. In general as one moves to the southeast,
the forests gradually thin out and have been felled on individual areas.

Above the forest boundary lie subalpine meadows with
a predominance of sage, Anthoxanthus and fescue (Festuca
rubra). In the uppermost belt of the mountains are found
motley grass alpine meadows with various gramen, cobresia
and sedges, and among them close to the snow peaks appear
the tundra low shrubs. In the northwestern portion grasses
are predominant such as Poa alpine, timothy (Phleum al-
pinum) and oats (Helictotrichon tibeticum), and of the shrubs
there is birch (Betula roundifolia). In the southeast the lion's
foot (Alchemilla vulgaris) and cinquefoil (Potentilla sp.) are
dominant.

CHAPTER 9

THE TSINGHAI-TIBETAN REGION

N. M. Kazakova
USSR Academy of Sciences
Institute of Geography

The Tsinghai-Tibetan Region, like the region of Northwest China, has a very large area and rather clear boundaries in the form of mountain ranges. Its surface is a complex combination of various elevation ranges, individual mountain areas and plains. In terms of the character of the relief, here one can make out the western part where high plains predominate, and the eastern part with a clear predominance of ranges, and this, as we have already pointed out, is due to the particular features in the tectonic development of this territory. The plains in the western portion of the uplands have a somewhat different surface and are separated by ranges with a predominant latitudinal strike. The largest of them are the Tangla and Kangtissushan Mountains. The absolute elevations of these mountains are very high (individual peaks more than 6,000 meters), but their soft and smooth outlines, the slight ruggedness and, relatively speaking, their not so high elevation over the surrounding plains gives them the general appearance of relatively low mountains. The ranges in the eastern portion of the uplands lie northwest and meridionally; they are deeply cut and in the topography of the uplands they stand out significantly sharper.

The border mountains of the region are even higher, with individual peaks rising up to 7,000-8,000 meters. As has already been pointed out, typical for them is also a sharp asymmetry in the slopes--more precisely, the interior slopes of the mountains, as a rule, are gentle, and the exterior are very steep.

Thus, the Tsinghai-Tibetan Region lies at enormous absolute elevations many times exceeding the elevations of the neighboring territories, and here the highest mountain ranges are located along its periphery. All of this creates the complete isolation of the region against the external influences and has caused the unique course in the development of all the physical-geographic processes occurring within it, and this, in turn, explains the existence of completely unique landscape complexes.

The distinguishing features of the climate in the Tibetan Uplands are the low mean annual temperatures and the great air dryness, and this is a consequence of the great air rareness, the paucity of water vapor in it and the related strong winds. Over a predominant portion of the uplands, the climate is severe, very dry, sharply continental, with great amplitudes in the fluctuations of the annual and summer day temperatures and extremely strong winds frequently turning into storms. The amount of precipitation is low and drops from the southeast to the northwest. The basic mass of precipitation is brought in by the monsoons from the Indian Ocean and in the extreme northeastern part from the Pacific, and therefore most of the precipitation falls in the summer. Winter precipitation is insignificant and is due to the penetration of Mediterranean cyclones into Tibet. The climatic conditions of the various altitude belts and individual portions of the broad Tibetan Uplands are not the same.

In terms of the altitude feature, the sharpest difference can be observed between the semi-arid climate of the river valleys lying at an elevation of 3,000-3,900 meters above sea level, the belt of mountain-steppe climate within 3,900-5,000 meters, the belt of the mountain climate at elevation from 5,000 meters and above up to the snow line, and finally, the nival belt lying above the snow line, i.e., approximately above 5,800 meters (Ku Shen-hsiu, 1955). According to the territorial feature they have established the Sikang, Kam, Changtan and Southwestern Tibetan climatic regions, and each of them has its own particular features.

In hydrological terms, the Tibetan Uplands are, on the one hand, an area where major Asiatic rivers are born such as the Hwang Ho, Yangtze, Mekong, Salween, Indus and Tsangpo (Brahmaputra), and, on the other hand, the interior portion of the uplands is completely landlocked. An enormous area lying between the Kunlun and Altyntag Mountains in the north and the Kangtissushan in the south does not have an egress to the ocean. For this area there is a characteristic presence of many isolated enclosed basins lying at different levels. The river network here has developed slightly and does not have any definite orientation; rivers are short, have little water and flow into undrained lakes. On the other hand, there are many lakes which lie in shallow basins among the plains or in the intermontane valleys. The dimensions of the lakes and the degree of mineralization differ, but salt lakes of relatively small size predominate.

The southern portion of the Tibetan Uplands is drained by the rivers in the basins of the Tsangpo and the Upper Indus, and the eastern portion by the rivers in the basins of the Hwang Ho, Yangtze, Mekong and Salween. The river network here is dense, particularly in the southeast, and the rivers have a steep long profile, a rapidy channel and a narrow, frequently canyon-like valley. The large rivers carry a great deal of water, and the processes of regressive erosion are very intensive, and due to this the headwaters of the rivers advance rather rapidly to the west and thus the area of interior landlocked Tibet is gradually being reduced. The rivers in the southern and eastern portions of the Tibetan Uplands are fed by the rain (the monsoon type) and by glaciers and snow.

The physical-geographic processes under the conditions of a cold and dry climate are not marked by diversity. In the interior landlocked and relatively even portion of the Tibetan Uplands, they are basically reduced to the processes of frost weathering, salt accumulation and wind activity. On the peripheral areas with a steeper relief and a wet climate, erosion processes acquire great significance, particularly channel, and in the southeast where the air temperature rises sharply, the biochemical processes begin to play a significant role.

In line with the particular features of the topography, the climate and the entire course of the physical-geographic processes, the landscapes are very unique and, it must be said, differ little for such an enormous territory. Over a larger portion of the Tibetan Uplands there predominates a landscape of the cold alpine desert. The climatic and soil

conditions here in general are little favorable for the growing of plants. Due to the limited amount of heat and warmth,
the soil formation processes occur slowly; the soil cover is
shallow and therefore, as Ku Shen-hsiu (1955) writes, the
root system of the plants reaches the parent rock. The
plants which have adapted to the existing conditions are
rather meager and have a number of specific features. Usually these are perennials with hard leaves close to the
ground, usually of a cushion shape. The plants are marked
by an exceptional frost resistance and a very short vegetation period. The specific composition is extremely poor;
chiefly they belong to grassy vegetation.

For the vegetation of the Tibetan Uplands also there is
a virtually complete absence of relic forms. This is explained, in the first place, by the geological youth of the
given territory, and, in the second place, by the glaciation
which occurred in the Quaternary Age when the preglacial
vegetation was basically destroyed. According to geobotanical data, the return of vegetation after the disappearance of
the glaciers occurred chiefly from migration of species from
neighboring territories.

The postglacial Tibetan flora owes its origin to the desert flora of Central Asia and to the mesophyte flora of Eastern Asia.

The animal world of the uplands is also poor in species, but on the other hand, the number of specimens is very
great here. Ungulates predominate which are aided by the
open expanses, as well as rodents. Thus, the majority of
animals dwelling within the uplands is representative of the
steppe and desert-steppe fauna which, according to the zoo-
geographic data, like the flora, owes its formation to the
Central Asiatic desert fauna. Naturally, the present fauna
of the high cold Tibetan Uplands and the lower hot plains of
Central Asia itself is not the same. According to data of
A. G. Bannikov, in Tibet there is a particular alpine faunistic complex.

The physical-geographic zonality of the landscapes
within the predominant portion of the Tibetan Uplands is expressed extremely poorly. This applies both to the latitudinal geographic zonality and to the altitude zonality which

might seem paradoxical for such an extensive and high territory as the Tibetan Uplands. However, regardless of the
enormous difference in the absolute elevations which reach
4,000-5,000 meters and in places even more, one will not
observe a consistent shift in the landscapes according to
elevation. As a rule, a number of the altitude-geographic
belts either does not stand out at all or they are extremely
reduced and are merely individual fragments of a varying
landscape belt.

Predominant here are desert complexes and deserts of
the piedmont plains frequently change into the desert landscapes of the uplands. The latter are dominant over the entire extent of the interior relatively level portion of the uplands which stretch along the meridian for more than 1,000
km. The latitudinal-geographic zonality here, thus, is almost completely absent. The basic reason for such phenomena is to be found in the extreme aridness of the climate
over the given territory and in those areas where the climate
changes a little towards greater wetness, one can immediately note an increase in the number of landscape-
geographic belts.

Another picture can be observed in the southeastern
mountains of the Tibetan Uplands which are marked by extremely great ruggedness and a much warmer and moister
climate. Along the deep valleys which are open in the south
and southeast, moist sea winds penetrate and due to this the
soils, vegetation and animal world change sharply. Here for
the first time within the uplands dense forests appear in
which dwell all sorts of animals and birds. In the specific
composition of the flora and fauna in the mountains of Southeastern Tibet one can strongly feel the influence of the tropics. Many species of plants and animals which dwell here
and in the other mountains of South Asia are not at all known
in the Tibetan deserts. In the mountains of Southeastern
Tibet, in contrast to the remaining parts of the Tibetan Uplands the vertical zonality of the landscapes is better expressed, and it can be seen in the gradual transition from
grassy-shrub landscapes in the uplands with a predominance
of ungulates and rodents, through the subalpine coniferous
forests, to the forest landscapes of the warmly-temperate
and subtropical belts with a predominance of Himalayan and
Indo-Chinese fauna.

A more detailed description of the Tibetan Uplands can
be given according to the basic physical-geographic regions:
the Changtan Plain, the mountains of the Eastern Kunlun, the
Altyntag Range; the mountains of the Western Kunlun; the
mountains of Southern Tibet; the mountains of Eastern Tibet;
the Nanshan Mountains and the Tsaidam Depression.

THE CHANGTAN PLAIN, THE MOUNTAINS
OF THE EASTERN KUNLUN AND
THE ALTYNTAG RANGE

The alpine plain of the Changtan lying in the central
portion of the Tibetan Uplands between the Kunlun in the
north and the Kangtissushan Mountains in the south, occupies a significant area. Morphologically, the Changtan is a
flat or slightly undulating surface which includes a number
of broad slightly inclined plains which stretch over large
distances and are separated by relatively low mountain
ranges. Rock trains have developed greatly here and these
cover the slopes of the mountains and fill the intermontane
plains. The plains are thus composed of a large amount of
friable deposits, either stony or gravel-rocky and greatly
compacted.

The Kunlun--the longest mountain system of Asia--is
one of the basic orographic units of China. The maximum
altitude of the mountain system--Mount Ulugmuztag--reaches
7,723 meters. The Kunlun includes a number of mountain
ranges which over a significant extent (from 74 to 102° e.
long.) have a latitudinal or almost latitudinal strike. Approximately at 100-102° e. long. the ranges make an arc-like
bend and turn sharply to the south, taking on a meridional
strike. This change in the direction of the Kunlun ranges is
due to a major turn in the strikes of their structural elements. Contrasting to the Kunlun direction is the Russian
Range stretching from the southwest to the northeast. The
Cherchen River separates the Russian Range from the more
northerly range, the Altyntag. The latter, according to the
data of V. M. Sinitsyn (1958), is not a part of the Kunlun,
since the history in the development of these mountain areas
differs sharply. At the same time, Huang Po-ch'in (1952)
includes the Altyntag, like the neighboring Nanshan, in the
Kunlun System.

The Eastern Kunlun includes a series of parallel echelon-like mountain ranges of great extent separated by the longitudinal tectonic troughs. The largest are the ranges of the Kukushili, their eastern continuation, the Bayan-Khara-Ula, the Arkatag (the Przheval'skiy Range) and the Bokalyktag (the Marco Polo Range). For this territory there are also characteristic small relative elevations, with absolute elevations of 6,000-7,500 meters, flat dome-shaped peaks which stand out little in the relief, gently sloping slightly broken-up slopes covered by a mass of fragmentary material. Only the northern slopes of the Eastern Kunlun which rise over the Tsaidam Depression are steep and very rugged.

The mountains of the Altyntag which lie between the Tarim and Tsaidam plains, on the one hand, and between the Kunlun and Nanshan, on the other, are a group of ranges and ridges running northeast. In the relief of the Altyntag one can distinguish the southwest, northeast and central portions. The southwest part bordering on the Kunlun is a large mountain system consisting of two parallel chains, the Toguz-Davan Range in the west and the Yusupalyktag Range in the east separated by an intermontane tectonic trough. The ranges are high, in places above 6,000 meters, rocky, and the peaks are covered with eternal snows, and the slopes are very rugged. The mountains in the northeast portion of the Altyntag bordering on the Nanshan, on the contrary, consist of a number of short ranges and those of them lying in the continuation of the Nanshan ranges are higher, reaching 5,000 meters and more, with the peaks covered in places by snow; those ranges which lie along the line of intermontane depressions of the Nanshan, as a rule, are low and river valleys run along them. The central portion of the Altyntag drops sharply and is narrow, and the elevations here rarely exceed 4,000 meters.

As has been pointed out already, the enormous absolute elevation of this region leads to the great air thinness and the air cannot concentrate and maintain a large amount of heat and moisture, the blocking on the west and south by even higher mountain structures impedes the penetration of humid air masses from outside. All of this, taken together, causes the high degree of continentality and the extreme aridness of the Changtan, the Eastern Kunlun and the

Altyntag. The climate of this territory is characterized by
very low air temperatures, aridness, strong winds, intense solar radiation and great amplitudes in the day temperatures. The amount of precipitation annually is less than
100 mm., and is confined, as we have pointed out, basically
to the summer months. The summer is brief (not more than
three months) and cold with the mean July temperatures not
reaching 10° which is typical for the climate of the poles.
During the day in this season of the year the temperature
will rise up to 10-15°, sometimes up to 30° and above,
but at night it falls below 0°, and sometimes down to -10,
-15°; the mean daily temperature fluctuations reach 24°
(B. V. Yusov, 1958). The winter is long with severe frosts
and strong winds. The minimum temperatures drop down to
-35°, and the wind speed exceeds 20 meters per second, and
since the amount of precipitation is insignificant and the
snow which falls evaporates instantaneously, there are frequent dust storms.

In line with the air dryness, the eternal snows and glaciers here lie at a very high elevation. As is pointed out in
the book Zarubezhnaya Aziya (Foreign Asia), the boundary
lies at 5, 700-6, 000 meters above sea level, and in places
even higher, and this is more than 1, 000 meters higher than,
for example, on the southern slopes of the Himalayas.

In the region, particularly in the Changtan, under the
conditions of the low temperatures and the weak evaporation,
as we have pointed out, an enormous amount of small, enclosed, and usually salt lakes is formed. The lakes are
found along the low areas of the plains and lie at an elevation of 4, 500-5, 000 meters, with the largest lakes of Tibet
being the Namtso (Tengri-nur) and Selling. The Tibetan
lakes are relics of onetime significantly larger bodies of water and the traces of them can be observed in the relief in
the form of ancient shorelines. Certain lakes have already
become salt swamps, others are flowing and connected by
small streams. In general, the river network in the Changtan, as in the other portions of this region, is little developed. The undrained basins not only do not have an external
runoff, but do not even interconnect--so weak are the erosion processes here. The rivers are fed basically by the
thaw waters of the snows and glaciers. The runoff is
slightly influenced also by the groundwaters and (even less)

by rainwater. During the winter all of the rivers, with rare exceptions, freeze down to the bottom and the groundwaters reaching them form large icings. The river drainage is confined, thus, almost exclusively to the summer months, the amount of runoff is significantly small, and the runoff module in the center of the Changtan equals approximately 3.2 liters per second per sq. km. (B. V. Yusov, 1958). In the Altyntag Mountains, there are very few rivers. The largest of them, the Cherchen and Yusupalyk, are located in the southwestern portion of the mountains; individual small water-carrying channels are encountered in areas in the northeast, but the central portion of these mountains next to the Tsaidam is completely waterless.

The extremely strong processes of physical and in part frost weathering lead to the formation of those colossal accumulations of friable material which, as we have already pointed out, have gradually levelled the relief. The arid processes are very intense here, in particular the winnowing of the fine particles, and due to this in this area there remains basically the coarser gravel-pebble material which is gradually compacted and polished, becoming a unique shiny mantle which is no longer subjected to further deflation.

As within Central Asia, the salt accumulation processes play a large role in this region, particularly on the Changtan plains. As was pointed out already, here there are numerous salt swamps and in places the thickness of the salts is so great that they form entire beds which, as a result of the aeolian working have acquired unique and strange shapes of pyramids, spheres and cones.

A significant portion of the described territory is sterile, stony, gravel-rocky or salt expanses.

According to Chinese sources, here there are only 53 species of plants belonging to 23 families. The greatest amount of species is related to the families of the Gramineae, Compositae and Cruciferae, and one will also encounter Leguminosae and Chenopodiaceae (Ch'ien Ch'ung-shu et al., 1957). There is a predominance of stony tundra landscape.

Regardless of the relative homogeneity in the nature of this region, within it there are still several different types of landscapes. The northern portion of the Changtan and the Eastern Kunlun is marked by the greatest desertiness where there is a predominance of rock-gravel stone deserts, either completely sterile or having an extremely sparse vegetation cover. On the relatively well-drained areas of the plains and mountain slopes, on the mountain-meadow soils there will grow creeping shrubs of teresken (Eurotia ceratoides), among which one will also encounter acantholimon (Acantholimon diapensoides), capsella (Capsella Thomsonii), astragalus (Astragalus Malcolmii, A. Arnoldii), thermopsis (Thermopsis inflata), sage (Artemisia Wellbyi), saussurea (Saussurea tridactula) and certain others. Along the shores of lakes where there is drainage, there will be a dominance of sedges (Carex Moorcroftiana, etc.) which usually have a cushion shape; on poorly drained swampy areas the main place is occupied by the hard Tibetan cobresia (Ch'ien Ch'ung-shu et al., 1957). Such a landscape of hilly swamps is very typical for the Changtan. In places along ravines protected against the wind one will encounter poa, sheep's fescue and reaumuria.

The landscape of the southern and particularly the southeastern portion of the Changtan is more diverse, where one begins to feel the influence of the Indian monsoon and the amount of annual precipitation somewhat increases, being a little above 100 mm. Here there appear extensive steppe areas with poa (predominantly Poa alpina and P. nemoralis), sheep's fescue, feather grass (Stipa pennata), and sometimes quack grass (Agropyrum Thoroldianum). The vegetation is still low but forms almost a solid grass cover which is rather good pasturing. In these alpine steppes at great elevations (up to the line of the eternal snows, i.e., approximately up to 5,800 meters elevation), chiefly in the passes, one will encounter the giant sandwort (Arenaria holosteoides), two species of delphinium (Delphinium Brunonianum, D. glacialis), several species of sage, astragalus, saussurea (particularly Saussurea tridactilis, S. glandulipera) and several other plants usually of a cushion shape (Yusov, 1958). On the shore of Lake Namtso on the low hills for the first time one will encounter the tree juniper (Juniperus squamota). This is the sole relatively large tree plant of the

Changtan, and it forms small shrub thickets with a flattened shape.

In general there are few shrubs in the Changtan, and they are chiefly creeping. Aside from the above-mentioned teresken, one will encounter nitraria which grows on the most sterile salty soils, caragana (Caragana pygmaea) growing in spots on the dry slopes of the hills and in the more protected valleys, and also myricaria (Myricaria prostrata), ephedra (Ephedra gerardiana) and tansy (Tanacetum tibeticum). Extensive areas of the region, particularly in the Changtan, are covered by salt swamps which are frequently completely devoid of a vegetation cover. The mountains of the Altyntag are also completely sterile; as V. M. Sinitsyn writes, only in the valleys and gorges will one encounter individual specimens of ephedra, small bushes of haloxylon and tamarisk, rush and several species of Russian thistle.

THE MOUNTAINS OF THE WESTERN KUNLUN

This region, including the entire western portion of the Kunlun and a portion of the Northern Chinese slopes of the Karakorum, occupies, in comparison with the other regions of the Tibetan Uplands, a small area. A particular feature of the region which separates it from the nearby eastern territories is the great ruggedness of the topography and the rather significant scale of glaciation.

The Western Kunlun is narrow, consisting of a series of parallel chains running northwest, greatly broken up by river valleys and narrow intermontane depressions. These chains include a number of very high mountain ranges such as the Kingtau, Kongur, Muztag, etc., and the highest elevations (more than 7,000 meters) are concentrated in the western and eastern parts of the Western Kunlun, and the central part is relatively low (5,500-6,000 meters).

Here, as a rule, there are no extensive enclosed plains with a number of landlocked lakes which are so widely found in the interior portion of the Tibetan Uplands; the rivers drain off to the piedmont plain of the Tarim Depression.

A significant portion of the mountains in this region, with elevations of 6,000-7,000 meters and more, is exposed to the effect of winds. However, the air masses coming from the north and northwest, in crossing the Tien Shan, reach the Kunlun so dry that the amount of atmospheric precipitation here is very slight. Nevertheless, in the upper portions of the mountains, where there is a strong cooling of the air masses, the amount of atmospheric precipitation is greater than in the interior portions of Tibet, and in the Western Kunlun is more than 100 mm. per year, and in the Karakorum which is subject to the influence of the Indian monsoon, clearly even more. This is the cause of the much greater scale of glaciation in the Western Kunlun and particularly in the Karakorum, in comparison to the neighboring more easterly territories.

At elevations above 5,000 meters, the precipitation always falls in a solid state, but below it frequently snows even in the warmest month of the year (July).

In the middle and low portions of the mountains, the amount of precipitation drops sharply. According to approximate computations, in these portions of the northern slopes of the Western Kunlun, there falls all of 30-70 mm. per year, and in places even less. From observations in recent years, at the Shakhidulla Station lying at an elevation of 3,543 meters, in 1958 they recorded 38 mm., and in 1957, 24 mm. In the southern ranges of the Kunlun, the degree of climate aridness evidently is even greater, since moisture enters from the north in even smaller amounts, and the Himalayas and Karakorum prevent the incursion of the Indian monsoon.

In line with this distribution of atmospheric precipitation, the formation of river drainage on this territory occurs chiefly in the alpine zone. Here is born a large number of rivers, and some of them, such as the Yarkend, Karakash and Yurunkash are relatively large. The basic source of the rivers in the alpine zone (at elevations of more than 3,500-4,000 meters) is the thaw water from the seasonal and eternal snows and glaciers; the groundwaters also have a certain significance, but only partially the rainwater. The

groundwaters have accumulated here in the large-
fragmentary deposits such as the stone streams, talus and
moraines, and actively feed the rivers. However, this occurs basically only in the summer, since during the winter
a significant portion of the groundwater is forced into the
river valleys where it forms large icings. According to recent data, icings in the high mountains of the Kunlun are
widely found; usually they occupy the entire width of the
valleys reaching 1 km. and more and stretching several kilometers, and are 1.5-2 meters and even more thick.

The river network which is formed in the medium and
low mountain zones is already much sparser, and many of
the rivers have only a temporary flow. They are fed basically by rainwater; the role of groundwaters here is sharply
reduced, since in accumulating in the friable loess-like
sandy loams which cover in a thick mantle the middle and
lower portions of the northern slopes of the Kunlun, they
rapidly evaporate.

The river runoff of the Western Kunlun, although
greater than the neighboring eastern regions, is still generally small and only in the westernmost extremity of the
northern slopes of the Kunlun is there more water and the
runoff increases somewhat, but this leads immediately to a
general change in the landscape. The seasonal runoff is
marked by great unevenness. The greatest runoff will be
found in the winter when it is 5-8 per cent of the annual volume of runoff, and, as we have already pointed out, this
can be explained by the great expenditure of water on the
formation of icings in the river valleys. During the spring
when the icing begins to thaw, the runoff increases up to
5-20 per cent of the annual. The amounts of autumn runoff
are approximately the same. The greatest runoff is in the
summer, 55-75 per cent of the annual, and on certain
rivers even up to 83 per cent, when the maximum amount of
precipitation falls and at the same time there is a thawing of
the alpine snows and icings.

As a consequence of the slight amount of atmospheric
precipitation falling within the region and the location of the
rivers basically in the alpine zone, the landscapes in the
Western Kunlun are also marked by a sharply expressed desertiness which can be clearly seen from the foothills up to

the alpine belt. The forest and steppe zones here in essence
are absent. In the interior chains of the Kunlun, the desertiness of the landscapes is even sharper as significant areas
are completely sterile, and fragments of hot deserts reach
almost up to the high-mountain areas.

Thus, the structure of vertical zonality in the landscapes of the Western Kunlun in general is very simple. According to the observations of V. A. Nosin, it is as follows:
In the foothills and lower portions of the slopes, desert complexes have developed. On the desert soils which are primitive "crusts" on a rough-stone substrate and thicker on the
loesses, there grow chiefly associations of sympegma with
the participation of Kalidium, reaumuria, ephedra, nitraria
and certain other plants. These landscapes frequently rise
even higher, covering areas of the medium mountain elevations. In the western portion of the northern slopes, the
mountain deserts reach up to 2,400-2,600 meters elevation,
and in the east up to 2,600-2,800 meters.

In the middle belt of the mountains there predominate
semidesert (desert-steppe) landscapes. The vegetation here
is either almost pure sage areas with a small admixture of
sympegma, ephedra, teresken and solitary gramen, or
steppe sage areas in which, in addition to the sage, there is
a large amount of feather grass, poa, regneria, sheep's
fescue and other gramen. The soils are brown mountain-
desert, analogous to the soils in the southern slopes of the
Eastern Tien Shan.

This landscape belt is particularly well developed
along the northern border ranges of the Kunlun, but in the
interior portions it is reduced in area and becomes broken.

In the western portion of the northern slopes, the
semidesert belt lies approximately between 2,400-2,600 and
3,000-3,100 meters absolute elevation, and in the eastern it
is higher, between 2,600-2,800 and 3,200-3,300 meters.

In the upper portion of the medium-elevation mountains
and in the beginning of the alpine zone, at an absolute elevation of 3,300-3,500 meters, one will encounter fragments of
mountain steppe and meadow steppe. They occupy, as a rule,
the areas which are the best protected against the wind and

the wettest. The vegetation cover is here predominantly
gramen such as fescue, poa, etc., with a significant participation of sage, crazyweed, iris and large cushions of rock
jasmine. The soils of these fragmentary steppes are similar to the mountain-steppe soils of the Eastern Tien Shan
and have been determined by the soil scientists in the Sinkiang Expedition as mountain chestnut calcareous.

In the alpine belt there predominate cold deserts
which form one of the basic landscape belts of the Kunlun.
Here a solid soil-vegetation cover is missing. On the most
even elements of the relief, there have developed very
sparse cryophilic associations of hard, small cushion
shapes of teresken, Acantholimon, Brachanthemum, etc.,
on primitive soils with a crusty surface extending up to the
nival zone. On the wetter (due to the thawing of snow banks)
areas one can observe fragments of mountain alpine meadows with humus-sod and peat-sod soils, usually surface-
gley and salt swamp. Extended areas of the river valleys
are covered by wet cobresia-sedge meadows. Frequently
the meadow soils are salined, and sometimes the degree of
salting is so great that true crust meadow salt swamps are
formed. Moreover, in the alpine belt one can ubiquitously
observe traces of surface salt accumulation and this is a
clear indication of the climate dryness in the Kunlun.

As in the above-described mountains of the Eastern
Tien Shan, in the Kunlun there is a clearly expressed tendency for a rise in the degree of aridness in the landscapes
as one moves from the north to the south, and particularly
from west to east. Botanists with the Sinkiang Expedition
have pointed out that in the extreme eastern portion of the
Kunlun bordering on the Pamir-Alay, the structure of vertical zonality is still rather similar to the Tien Shan.* On the
piedmont trains and in the intermontane valleys one will also
find dominant the rocky deserts--the hammadas--which in
the lower belt of the mountains (up to 2,500-2,700 meters)
are regularly placed by sage and partially Russian thistle
deserts. In the middle belt of the mountains steppes appear,
initially also heavily deserty, and then one can note

---

*Below taken from the materials of A. A. Yunatov.

individual areas of forests consisting of spruce (Picea
Schrenkiana) with an admixture of creeping or tree juniper
(Juniperus turkestanika) and alpine elements in the grass
cover such as cobresia, edelweiss, meadowrue (Thalictrum
alpinium), etc. Then comes a narrow belt of subtropical
juniper groves, and above, right up to the nival area, cobresia wastes are dominant.

To the east, the structure of the vertical zonality is
significantly simpler. The Russian thistle deserts climb
higher, occupying the site of the sage deserts, and the latter,
in turn, occupy almost completely the area of the destroyed
forest belt. Along the northern slopes of the deep valleys,
one will encounter individual small areas of sparse spruce
groves and juniper thickets. Higher up one will find only
small spots of cobresia which are replaced by barren rocky
slopes and placers.

In the interior portions of the Western Kunlun, the
number of landscape zones becomes even less. The sage
areas here rise into the alpine area, where at elevations on
the order of 4, 000 meters they are replaced by the teresken
deserts in which the cushion form of teresken is dominant
(Eurotia ceratoides s.l.). At elevations of 5, 100-5, 200 meters, along the border of the nival belt, very sparsely one
will encounter associations of Tanacetum xylorhizum and
species close to it.

THE MOUNTAINS OF SOUTHERN TIBET

The natural boundary between the northern extremely
dry and southern more moist portions of the Tibetan Uplands
is the Kangtissushan Mountains. These mountains include
three major ranges: the Kaylas, Nienchen-Tangla and Aling-
Gangri, as well as a number of smaller ones. The Kaylas
which lie in the west and the Nienchen-Tangla in the east
form a southern and generally more or less unbroken chain
in this mountain system. The Aling-Gangri is the northern
range, and it is not as long and dies out to the east. The
mean elevation of the Kangtissushan is 5, 500-6, 000 meters,
and the highest point, Mount Aling-Gangri, is 7, 315 meters.
A characteristic feature of the Kangtissushan is the fact
that in the relief one can clearly see only the southern chain

which, in particular the Kaylas Range, shows sharp alpine
landforms and heavy glaciation. This chain is the watershed
between the Indian Ocean and the landlocked area of Northern Tibet, and this makes a particular impression on the
nature of the northern and southern parts of these mountains.
The northern branch of the Kangtissushan is marked by flat
peaks, low relative elevations, little ruggedness, and the
intensive development of physical weathering processes,
i.e., it has a typical Northern Tibetan appearance. The
southern branch, and particularly the southern slopes, experience the influence of the Indian monsoon. The amount of
atmospheric precipitation here increases, the surface is
broken up by deep gorges in which flow the rivers of the
Tsangpo and Upper Indus basins which are short but have a
lot of water and heavily eroded slopes. In general the southern slopes of the Kangtissushan are marked by steepness,
great fluctuations in the relative elevations, and by sharper
landforms.

The climate of the Kangtissushan as a whole is severe
and in the northern portion little differs from the climate in
the south of the Changtan. Similar conditions of the topography and climate have caused an analogous course in the
development of the physical-geographic processes prevailing on this territory, and this, in turn, has led to the formation of landscapes which are very reminiscent of the above-
described landscapes in the southern portion of the Changtan.
In both places there are stony deserts, semideserts or
steppes with lakes, salt bogs and swamps (a landscape
called by the Tibetans "tan").

At the same time, the physical-geographic processes
and landscapes in the southern slopes of the Kangtissushan,
particularly the lower parts, have fundamentally altered.
First of all this is due to the significant warming and wetting of the climate. A certain idea on the climate in this
territory can be gained from the climatic indices for Lhasa
lying at an elevation of 3,650 meters above sea level. In
truth, one cannot mechanically extend these data for the entire territory in the southern slopes of the Kangtissushan,
since Lhasa is in an intermontane depression. According to
the data of Chinese scientists, the climate in Lhasa is characterized by the following indices: the January temperature
is 0.3°, with minimums falling down to -14°, fluctuations in

the daily temperatures are more than 15°; the mean June temperature (the warmest month) is 16°, and maximum reaching 30°. The annual amount of precipitation is 1,462 mm., and of this almost 90 per cent falls during the summer and in the beginning of autumn (July-September) with a maximum in July; at the end of autumn and during the winter, precipitation is virtually absent (Ch'en Shih-hsiun, 1959).

In other places along the southern slopes of the Kangtissushan, as was pointed out, the climatic indices are somewhat different. This is particularly true of the amount of precipitation, since a distinguishing feature in the climate of this territory is the extreme variability in precipitation from place to place. For example, while on the slopes with a southern exposure which are favorably situated in terms of the monsoon, as in Lhasa, there are more than 1,000 mm. of precipitation per year, on the slopes with a northern exposure and in the enclosed valleys less than 300 mm. falls. The precipitation over the years also is variable, and this depends upon the development of the Indian monsoon. As in all areas with a monsoon type of climate, during certain years such a small amount of precipitation falls that a drought begins, while in other years, conversely, the precipitation is so abundant that there are very significant floods.

The southern boundary for the described region is the Himalayas. The Northern Chinese slope of the Himalayas which borders the high dry Tibetan Uplands is more gentle and significantly less rugged than the southern; in landscape terms it is also much more homogeneous. Thus, while the southern slopes of the Himalayas which are subject to the Indian monsoon are marked by a sharp change in the vertical belts--from the cold deserts of the alpine belt to the tropical landscapes of the foothills--on the predominant area of the northern slopes there are meadow-steppe landscapes.

The Himalayas are separated from the Kangtissushan by the valley of the Tsangpo River which occupies an enormous tectonic depression. The slopes of these mountain systems facing the Tsangpo are drained by the rivers of its basin. The direction of the rivers here is subordinate to definite patterns. The main rivers--the Tsangpo and Upper Indus--flow in a latitudinal direction, while their tributaries which cut through the slopes of the Himalayas and the

Kangtissushan have a current which is usually close to meridional. The rivers are of the mountain type and begin in
the glaciers. The feed of the rivers, as has been pointed
out, is mixed--rain and glacier-snow. The amount of runoff, in comparison with the territory in the northern portion
of Tibet, sharply increases here. According to the data
given in the book by Yusov entitled Tibet, the runoff module
for the rivers on the northern slope of the Himalayas during
the summer is 9. 6 liters per second per sq. km., on the
southern slopes of the Kangtissushan 9. 5 meters per second
per sq. km., and in the Lhasa Valley from 16 to 19 liters
per second per sq. km., while the runoff module for the
rivers in the central portion of the Changtan is, as we have
pointed out, only 3. 2 liters per second per sq. km. In
truth, these figures are not accurate since due to the lack of
data we have not given corrections for evaporation, and
therefore they can be viewed as merely comparative.

Within the northern slopes of the Main Himalayan
Range which, as is known, is not over the entire extent the
watershed range of the Himalayas, one will also find the
headwaters of several rivers of the southern slopes. While
these rivers flow here they have the same hydrological features as the rivers flowing to the north, to the Tsangpo.

In physical-geographic terms, the northern slopes of
the Himalayas have a great deal in common with the southern
slopes of the Kangtissushan, and this can first of all be explained by the similarity of the relief and the very similar
climatic conditions. Precise climatic data for this portion
of the Himalayas are not available to us, but judging from
the indirect indications and, more precisely, from the character of the landscapes, one might assume that the climate
here is distinct from the climate in the southern slopes of
the Kangtissushan, perhaps, only slightly less arid, and this
is due to the great possibilities for the penetration of the Indian monsoons.

Regardless of the generally better climatic conditions
in the mountains of Southern Tibet, in comparison with the
northern parts, nevertheless the general low air temperature, the sharp daily temperature fluctuations and the protracted dry winter with strong winds are unfavorable for
the normal growth of trees. At the same time, the high

relative humidity over the entire year, the presence of a
snow cover and sufficient moisture in the soil create proper
conditions for the growth of perennial grasses. This, in
turn, has caused the good development of a soil cover here.

On the southern slopes of the Kangtissushan one can
trace rather clearly the vertical zonality of the landscapes.
In the upper parts of the slopes (approximately above 4, 000
meters above sea level), on the mountain steppe soils one
will find a predominance of alpine steppes with a specific
composition close to the alpine steppes on the northern
slopes of this mountain system, but marked by great diversity. Thus, in particular, here there is a significant increase in the amount and size of the shrubs and among them
there is shrub juniper (Juniperus incarva), barberry, honeysuckle (Lonicera quinquelocularix), and in places cotoneaster and dog rosa. In the wettest areas exposed to the
monsoon winds, on mountain-meadow soils, one will encounter alpine meadows composed of numerous various gentians,
cinquefoils, buttercup, edelweiss, saxifraga, primrose,
onion, etc. The lower portions of the slopes are covered by
a meadow-steppe vegetation and are good natural pastures.
According to B. V. Yusov, here there are numerous representatives from species of sweetclover, dandelion, cinquefoil, tansy, iris (Iris cumaonensis), and also bistort, crazyweed, fescue, wood betony, poa and, as always, sedge
Moorcroftii. In the wet areas grow chiefly sedge and meadow
foxtail (Alopercus pratensis).

On the predominant portion of the northern slopes of
the Himalayas, there is a dominant landscape of meadow
steppes with very diverse vegetation analogous to the landscape on the lower slopes of the Kangtissushan, and only for
the highest areas is there a typical desert landscape.

Within the described territory, as in the more northern
portions of the Tibetan Uplands, one can note a general tendency for a change in the climate and thus in the landscapes,
as one moves from west to east. This can be traced best of
all along the Indus-Tsangpo intermontane depression, since
this portion of Southern Tibet has been the more studied.

The western portion is a territory where the headwaters of the Indus and Satlej are found, and is marked by

the greatest dryness and the lowest temperatures. Thus, for example, in Gartok, lying at an elevation of 4,600 meters above sea level, the annual amount of precipitation, as in the Changtan, is less than 100 mm., and the mean January temperature is -12° frost. Naturally the landscapes in these areas are close to the landscapes in the northern ranges of the Kangtissushan, and here also alpine steppes predominate. To the east the alpine steppes are replaced by alpine meadows with cobresia, sedge, poa and other grasses from the families of Cyperaceae and Gramenae. Along the valley of the Upper Tsangpo, among these meadows, there appear shrubs and rarely dwarf trees of willow and poplar. True forests begin growing only in the basin of the middle course of the Tsangpo, approximately on the meridian of Lhasa, where, as we have noted, the climate is already much warmer and moister. Coniferous forests cover the mountain slopes in thick areas. Here and further down the river, at an elevation of 3,000-4,000 meters grow the pure fir stands (Abies spectabilis, A. Webbiana) with an undergrowth of rhododendron. At elevations of 2,500-3,000 meters one will find hemlock (Tsuga dumosa) and spruce (Picea spinulosa). On the dry slopes at elevations of 2,500-3,500 meters one will encounter larch (Larix Griffithii); at elevations from 1,500-2,500 meters the basic tree is the pine (Pinus insularis and P. Griffithii). On the wet slopes there are various species from the family of Lauraceae and Fagaceae. Below 1,500 meters are found the humid-tropical or monsoon forests.

The subalpine coniferous forests are also encountered in areas on the northern slopes of the Himalayas, occupying a series of mountain passes. Here the climate is drier than in the Tsangpo Valley, and therefore in the upper portion of the relatively wet slopes there is a predominance of spruce (Picea Morinda) and fir (Abies Pindrow); on the dry slopes there is larch (Larix Griffithii). In the lower portions predominate deodar cedar (Cedrus Deodara) and pine (Pinus longifolia).

THE MOUNTAINS OF EASTERN TIBET

The landscapes of the Changtan and the Eastern Kunlun to the southeast gradually change into the landscapes of Eastern Tibet (the so-called Kam area) which in comparison with them present an even more amazing contrast than do the landscapes in the southern portion of the uplands. As has already been pointed out, the eastern portion of the Tibetan Uplands is very rugged mountain area consisting of a number of mountain ranges (the range of the Russian Geographical Society, the Woodwill-Rockhill Range, the Dalai-lama Range, etc.), which extend from north-northwest to south-southeast and are broken up by very deep gorges. The absolute and relative elevations here are very great, and due to this the topography has a clearly expressed alpine character. The ranges are narrow, rocky, with steep slopes and sharp ridges and the peaks are covered by glaciers. Erosion landforms have developed greatly here; the rivers Yangtze, Mekong, Salween and their numerous tributaries, in cutting deep into the mountains, have cut narrow steep valleys and deep gorges. The latter are such a characteristic element in the topography of this territory that it is frequently called the "area of river gorges."

As a whole the climate here is milder than in the western portion of Tibet, since the monsoon winds bringing precipitation can penetrate here, but due to the great ruggedness of the topography, the climate is marked by great diversity. Thus, for example, in Yushu lying at an elevation of 3,700 meters, the mean January temperatures are -8°, with minimums falling down to -27°, while at Huangheyang, at an elevation of 4,400 meters, the mean January temperatures are -17°, with minimums down to -34°. In the winter little precipitation falls, but during the summer it is very abundant, and, as the climatologists have pointed out, it rains here almost every other day. The annual amount of precipitation in the various areas of Eastern Tibet differs greatly, but usually it fluctuates within limits of from 500 to 1,000 mm. (Chien Ch'ung shu et al., 1957).

The vertical zonality in the landscapes of the mountains of Eastern Tibet can be traced, as we have already pointed out, rather clearly. The basic territorial changes in the landscapes here occur from north to south and from west to east, i.e., from the areas of dry climate to the humid monsoon areas. In the northwestern and more even and driest portion of the mountains next to the Changtan, the typical landscapes are alpine steppes and meadows on alpine meadow or rock soils.* Here predominate cobresia (particularly Cobresia Royleana) and sedges; one will always find rock jasmine (Androsace Tapete), arenaria (Arenaria musciformis), rhubarb, gentian, buffalo pen, saussurea, astragalus and certain other plants. Below along the mountain slopes lie shrub thickets formed by rhododendron (Rhododendron fastigiatum), willow (Salix Biondiana, S. variegata), cinquefoil, spirea and juniper (Juniperus squamota).

As one moves southeast where the annual amount of precipitation increases almost up to 500 mm., the landscapes of alpine steppes and meadows give way to the landscape of the forest-steppe. At elevations of 3,000-3,900 meters, the chief varieties of trees are the Balfour spruce (Picea Balfouriana) and the purplecone spruce (P. purpurea); one also encounters fir (Abies squamata) which reaches the upper boundary for the spread of tree vegetation (4,300 meters above sea level), and in the northwestern portion of the region it extends into the area of the shrub steppe. In the southern part, the Balfour spruce is gradually replaced by larch (Larix Mastersiana). On the dry slopes lie either subalpine meadows or forests of juniper (Juniperus convallium and J. squamata); below are shrub thickets of oak (Quercus semicarpifolia) and pine groves (of Pinus densata).

Over the remaining area of the mountains in Eastern Tibet lie landscapes of subalpine coniferous forests on podzolic soils. In the northeast they turn into landscapes of summer-green and mixed forests of the temperate and subtropical zones of Central China, in the southeast and south into landscapes of evergreen (laurel) forests of Southwest China. In the upper belt of the subalpine coniferous forests there is a predominance of shade-requiring coniferous varieties, chiefly various species of fir and spruce, and the fir is dominant in the relatively humid areas while the spruce is found in the relatively dry ones. In the forests

------

*Here and below from Ch'ien Ch'ung-shu et al., 1957.

shrubs are numerous, various species of grass are in abundance, and mosses are widely developed everywhere. In
general the specific composition of these forests is very diverse and changes sharply from place to place, and this is
due to the extreme diversity in the natural conditions on this
territory. For example, in the extreme northern part of the
region, where the winter is rather cold and dry, one will
find mixed forests of pine and oak. Further to the southeast,
in the Sino-Tibetan Mountains, where the climate is already
wetter and the annual amount of precipitation exceeds 2,000
mm., at elevations of 2,000-4,000 meters one will find coniferous forests chiefly of fir (Abies Faberi), and more
rarely spruce (of Picea brachytula, P. complanata), and in
the second story of these forests also grow such warmth-
loving and moisture-loving varieties as hemlock (Tsuga
sinensis and T. junnanensis). At elevations below 2,000-
2,500 meters grow mixed forests consisting of false hemlock (Pseudotsuga sinensis), lithocarpus (Lithocarpus cleis-
tocarpa) and castanopsis (Castanopsis platyacatha). In the
secondary birch-aspen forests there is a predominance of
China paper birch (Betula albo-sinensis), remarkable birch
(B. insignus), Himalaya birch (B. utilis var. Praftii) and the
Szechwan poplar (Populus szechuanica). At elevations of
2,000-2,600 meters in large amounts one will encounter
sinarundinaria (Sinarundinaria szechuanica). Further south,
on the slopes of the Chinshakiang (Yangtze) Valley which is
open to the south, in the upper belt of the mountains (at elevations of 4,200-4,400 meters) there appears the yew
(Taxus chinensis Behd.), and on the slopes with a southern
exposure this tree grows lower, frequently with Yunnan hemlock. The chief trees at elevations of 2,800-4,200 meters
are the spruce (Picea likiangensis) and fir (Abies Forrestii,
A. Georgi, A. Ernestii), among which at elevations of
3,000-3,400 meters are widely found pine (Pinus densata)
and the alpine oak. Below 2,800 meters grows the Yunnan
pine which occupies a rather broad belt, and in the upper
portion of the belt on the wetter areas one will also encounter the Armand pine, and in the lower part shrub thickets
or low forests of various species of alpine oak (Quercus
monimotrica, Q. semicarpifolia, Q. pannosa). The latter
change directly into evergreen subtropical forests consisting of laurel, magnolia, michelia, Indian pine and other
southern trees.

Thus, as has been pointed out, on the territory of Eastern Tibet one can clearly trace the transition from the grassy-shrub landscapes with the alpine Tibetan appearance to the forest landscapes of the warmly temperate and sub-tropical belts. Analogous changes may also be observed in the animal world which from the northwest to the southeast and southwest becomes more and more diverse and in its specific composition is continuously enriched with representatives of the Himalayan and Indo-Chinese tropical faunas. There is a sharp drop in the number of ungulates and rodents, and here appear badgers, lynxes, several species of cat, monkeys, tigers, the giant panda and many other southern species.

THE MOUNTAINS OF THE NANSHAN AND THE TSAIDAM DEPRESSION

The northeastern extremity of the Tsinghai-Tibetan Uplands is the region of the Nanshan Mountains and the Tsaidam Depression. The Nanshan Mountains include a number of major rather narrow mountain ranges running predominantly northwest and intermontane tectonic troughs which separate them and which are covered by the river valleys and lakes. The mean altitude of this mountain system is 4,000-5,000 meters, with maximum elevations reaching and exceeding 6,000 meters. The mountains which are most significant in extent and elevation are the following ranges: the Richthofen, Tkholoshan, Ch'ingshihling, Humboldt, the Southern Kokonor and the highest chain of the Nanshan, the Seuss Range, which has the highest peak of the Nanshan rising up to an elevation of 6,346 meters above sea level. Aside from these ranges the Nanshan System includes a whole series of shorter but no less high ranges. According to the materials of Chinese researchers, in the general picture of the present relief of the Nanshan, one can establish the zone of alpine ranges which is an alternation of narrow folded-block ranges and deep valleys occupying the syncline troughs and grabens; areas of also high but slightly rugged block elevations with soft rounded contours; large intermontane depressions, frequently with lakes and swamps, lying in the central portion of the Nanshan, and the largest of them is the Kokonor Depression (Chang Jen-p'u, 1955).

For the relief of the Nanshan as a whole, there is a greater altitude and grandiose nature to the ranges of the western portion in comparison with the eastern. In the western portion the number of ranges is greater, they are higher, and, regardless of the great aridness of the climate and the higher position of the snow line, they are covered with snows and glaciers. In the eastern portion of the Nanshan there is a certain drop in elevation, and the snow cover on the glacier remains only on the individual high peaks.

The Tsaidam Plain lying between the Nanshan, Altyntag and Kunlun ranges is an extensive landlocked depression lying at a high elevation above sea level. The northwestern broad portion of the plain lies at an elevation of 2,700-3,000 meters, and is, as has been pointed out, basically denudation; on its surface in certain places one can trace low elevations and ridges composed of bedrock. The southeastern narrow portion of the Tsaidam lies at an elevation of 2,600-2,700 meters and is composed of thick beds of Meso-Cenozoic deposits, and is aggradation.

Over the predominant portion of the described territory the prevailing weather is of the Central Asiatic type, and only in the eastern extremity of the Nanshan does it become significantly milder. There is extremely little meteorological data for this territory, and therefore for the climate of the larger portion of the region at present we have only the most general idea. It is known that in the western part of the Nanshan, as in the neighboring Altyntag Mountains and in the Tsaidam Depression, the amount of atmospheric precipitation is very low, on the order of 100-150 mm. per year. The winds are dry and blow predominantly from the western and northwestern deserts. Regardless of the fact that snow and glaciers are to be found in the mountains, there are relatively few rivers here. They are all related to the area of interior drainage and a portion of them flows into the interior lakes of this mountain area such as the Kokonor, Khara-Nur, while others flow off the mountains and empty into the lakes and salt swamps of the Tsaidam, the Edzin-Gol lakes of the Alashan Desert, being lost in the detritus of the Hohsi Corridor. The largest rivers here are the Heiho, Linshui and Suliehho. They begin in the upper belt of the mountains and flow in longitudinal valleys where they have a slow current and break up into channels. The character of them changes where they cross the mountain ranges before emptying onto the plain of the Hohsi Corridor, and here they flow in narrow gorges, usually using the areas of tectonic disturbances, and form rapid currents. These and the other alpine rivers are almost exclusively fed by snow and glaciers.

Thus, in the western portion of the Nanshan and within the Tsaidam Plain, arid conditions prevail and this is reflected in the landscapes which little differ from the landscapes in the Central Asiatic deserts and desert mountains.

As everywhere in these areas, the vegetation here is extremely sparse, and extensive expanses on the mountain slopes are barren.* In the Nanshan up to an elevation of 3,000 meters above sea level, one will find deserts with tamarisk, haloxylon, kharmyk, reaumuria and other plants of the desert type. Above, up to an elevation of 3,300-3,500 meters, they are replaced by the dry steppes with feather grass, chiy, white willow, etc. At elevations of 3,300-3,800 meters, one finds subalpine meadows with a predominance of crazyweed, astragalus, gentian, cinquefoil, allium (on the wet portions of the slopes). At elevations of 3,800-4,400 meters, there has developed a mountain tundra where among the rock trains one will encounter shrub thickets of cushion plants such as saussurea (Saussurea sorocephal), stonecrop (Sedum guadrifidum), sandwort (Arenaria formosa), rhubarb (Rheum spiciforme), etc. Above 4,400 meters there are only individual specimens of plants.

As one moves to the east, the landscapes of the Nanshan become richer and more diverse, and the boundaries of the vertical zones gradually drop. Thus, for example, along the northern slopes of the western portion of the Southern Kokonor Range one will find spruce forests; on the moist slopes the meadows rise up to the very peaks, but in the intermontane valleys there are desert landscapes.

Within the Tsaidam Plain there is a predominance of gravel, sandy and clay deserts, semideserts, and salt

-----

*Below was taken basically from the materials of Ch'ien Ch'ung-shu (1957) and V. M. Sinitsyn (1959).

wastes. Particular desertiness marks the northwestern virtually waterless portion of the plain. As V. M. Sinitsyn
writes, only along the dry channels which sometimes ac-
cumulate an insignificant amount of rainwater, will one encounter solitary clumps of crazyweed, white willow, budar-
gana and reaumuria. In the depressions between the ridges
there are common salt lakes and salt swamps where Russian thistle grows as well as hallogeton, and other Russian
thistles. The southeastern portion of the Tsaidam has a
little more water. A rather large number of streams flow
off the Kunlun Mountains and these either dry up in the foothills emerging below as springs or penetrate into the interior of the depression and form salt lakes. Here the landscapes are more diverse than in the northwest. In the
piedmont belt where freshwaters emerge and the soil is
wetted well, there is reed in abundance as well as sedge and
certain gramens; on the less wet areas there are thickets of
tamarisk, nitraria, kharmyk and low reed, calligonum and
sugak (V. M. Sinitsyn, 1959).

The eastern portion of the Nanshan Mountains is
marked by a different climate and landscape. Here the top-
ographical features play a significant role, and more precisely the drop in the elevation of the mountains, as one
moves to the east, and the presence of intermontane valleys
open in the same direction. The latter reach rather far into
the Nanshan and this helps in the penetration of the humid
and warm monsoon, while the high mountains in the peripheral parts of the Nanshan, in turn, retain the dry and warm
winds coming from the surrounding deserts. An illustra-
tion of this would be the climatic indices for the town of
Hsining. The mean January temperature here is -7°, with
minimums falling down to -27°, the mean July temperature
is 18°, with maximum rising to 34°. The annual total of
precipitation is 366 mm., with the largest amount falling in
the period from July through September, with a maximum in
August; during the winter precipitation is virtually absent
(according to Ch'en Shih-hsiun, 1959).

The eastern portion of the Nanshan is greatly broken
up by rivers, and they all are a part of the Hwang Ho Basin.
An exception are the rivers of Lake Kokonor which, as we
have already pointed out, at present is landlocked. The

rivers in the eastern portion of the Nanshan have almost exclusively a rain and ground feed.

In landscape terms, one can note certain changes in
the interior portion of the Middle Nanshan where among the
desert expanses there are mountain steppe landscapes. A
fundamental break occurs basically to the east of Lake Kokonor. The low temperature and sufficient moisture help in
the relatively good development of coniferous forests here
which grow on elevations of approximately 2, 400-3, 000 meters, and, spreading south, form a solid line with the forests of Eastern Tibet (Ch'ien Ch'ung-shu et al., 1957). The
northern slopes are the most forested; the basic tree here
is the dragon spruce (Picea asperata). In the lower portion
of the forest belt one begins to encounter the Chinese pine
(Pinus tabulaeformis var. glacilifolia var. leucosperma),
and in the upper portion on felled areas secondary forests
with a predominance of birch (Betula albo-sinensis) and aspen (Populus tremula var. Dividiana), ferns (Pteridium
aquilinum) are also numerous. In the undergrowth, particularly on the dry slopes, there are relatively few shrubs,
and among them an important place is held by the sea buckthorn (Hippophae rhamnoides) and the evonymus (Evonymus
Przewalski), one will also find the southern species of rhododendron and caryopteris (Caryopteris tangutica).

Above 3, 000 meters an alpine belt has developed. In
the lower portion, at an elevation of 3, 000-3, 600 meters,
one will widely find shrubs and on the northern slopes there
is a large amount of caragana (Caragana pygmaea) and
cinquefoil (Potentilla fruticosa); on the southern slopes one
will find various species of rhododendron, barberry, goose-
berry, dog rose, honeysuckle, evonymus, cotoneaster and
many others. According to Chinese data, in terms of the
specific composition these shrubs are close to the shrubs
found in the undergrowth of the mountain coniferous forests
in North China, on the one hand, and the subalpine coniferous forests in Eastern Tibet, on the other.

In the upper portion of the alpine belt, at elevations of
3, 600-4, 000 meters, subalpine meadows have developed
which contain a very large amount of species, also close to
the North Chinese and Eastern Tibetan.

At elevations of 4, 000-4, 300 meters, there is a mountain tundra and in the vegetation cover one will frequently encounter globeflower (Trollius pumilus), allium (Allium cyaneum), species of saussurea (Saussurea stella, S. Medusa), species of corydalis, etc.

Thus, the landscapes of the Eastern Nanshan can no longer be called Central Asiatic. The specific composition of the vegetation and in part the animal world shows that this territory has undergone and evidently continues to undergo a significant influence from the Eastern Asiatic and Eastern Tibetan landscapes.

Research on the Tsinghai-Tibetan Uplands in essence is just beginning, and therefore many of the questions dealing with the particular features of nature in this region are still far from clear. The natural resources of the region are thus poorly known, although according to preliminary data one might assume that they are very significant.

Thus, for example, according to the data of Chinese researchers, on the Tibetan Uplands a preliminary survey has discovered a number of valuable minerals both metallic and nonmetallic. The basic accumulations of ores are found in the folded zone stretching from the west to the east from the Karakorum to the Yunnan Province, where mineralization has been due to the intrusions of granites and igneous rock. Here they have discovered deposits of antimony, arsenic, molybdenum, copper, zinc and lead. In the Tangla Range they have discovered deposits of iron ore and hard coal, as well as graphite, asbestos and soapstone. In the eastern portion of the Tsangpo Valley they have found deposits of magnetite, and near Lhasa hard coal and talc. In Tibet there are extensive placer and vein gold deposits. The reserves of various types of salts are unlimited such as borax, gypsum, common salt, quartz, soda, and they are found both in the form of beds and in the solar lakes, as well as various construction materials (Li P'u, 1954; B. V. Yusov, 1958).

In the Nanshan Mountains, chiefly in the northern and southern ranges, they have found deposits and ore manifestations of iron, chromium, copper, lead with zinc, gold and also deposits of coal from the Carboniferous and Jurassic

ages. The interior ranges of this mountain system as yet
are virtually unstudied (V. M. Sinitsyn, 1959).

The minerals of the Tsaidam Depression have been
much better studied; in Chinese literature it is called the
"treasure house of natural riches for China." First of all
they have found large deposits of coal and oil here which are
partially being worked. The coals of the Tsaidam Basin are
basically of a Jurassic age. At present they are beginning
to work the coal deposit of Yukeh lying in the central portion
of the depression, where the seams are up to 15 meters
thick (Chang Keng et al., 1958). Oil shows have been noted
in a number of areas in the western portion of the depression and are confined to the Lower Tertiary sandstones. Of
great industrial significance is the oil-bearing structure of
the Yuchuan-tse which lies close to Lake Gazkul'. Geologists assume that besides this structure favorable conditions
for oil deposits may be found in neighboring structures such
as Hsiangshuits'an, Kaymilik, etc. In general the most
prospective are felt to be the structures lying in the western
and northwestern portions of the depression, where they
have recently obtained oil gushers with a great output. The
productive layers here are in the Lower Tertiary deposits
and lie at a depth of 300-600 meters. Besides coal and oil
in the Tsaidam Depression they have discovered rich deposits
of salt as well as gold, silver, copper, tin, borax and certain
other minerals.

In the mountains of the eastern, and particularly the
southeastern, portion of the Tsinghai-Tibetan Uplands rich
forest resources are to be found. According to the data of
Chinese scientists, the forest reserves here are very significant, and they are marked by very high quality. Such trees
as spruce, fir, larch, juniper and pine give valuable construction wood, and the spruce at the same time is a good
material for aircraft construction and a raw material for
making cellulose. Aside from the trees, the forests in
Eastern Tibet are also rich in various species of grass,
among which there is a large number of medicinal plants
such as rhubarb, species of fritillary, angelica, and many
others which are of significant importance (Ch'ien Ch'ung-
shu et al., 1957).

The alpine steppes and alpine meadows of the Tsinghai-
Tibetan Uplands are a rich fodder resource for the region.

The most important fodder grasses here are cobresia and
the various sedges which have high food qualities. Many of
the alpine regions of Tibet, with the exception only of the
most deserty northern portions, at present are widely used
for pasturing, and at the same time they are an important
base for the further development of livestock raising. As
Chinese scientists state, the most serious task at present is
to seek out the possibilities for rationally utilizing and improving the pastures, improving the quality of fodder
grasses, controlling plant freezing, discovering the resources of underground freshwater and thereby making new
pastures available.

The larger portion of the Tibetan Uplands lies at an
elevation above 4,000-4,500 meters above sea level, i.e.,
it lies above the boundary of possible farming. Only in the
low areas, chiefly along the Tsangpo Valley, are there individual farming sites. In the future, particularly with the
carrying out of the proper irrigation work, obviously there
can be a certain expansion in the plowed lands of this territory.

BIBLIOGRAPHY

BIBLIOGRAPHY*

Cyrillic Sources

Afanas'yev, V.A., "Forest Cultivation of Cunninghamia in China," Lesnoye khozyzystvo (Forestry), 1959, No. 10.

Alekseyev, V.P., Rastitel'nyye resursy Kitaya (Vegetation Resources of China), Leningrad, Publishing House of the All-Union Horticulture Institute, 1935.

An Tse-p'ing, "The Kuant'ing Reservoir in China," K'ehsueh huapao, 1954, No. 7, (in Chinese).

Antropov, P. Ya., "On Certain Achievements in the Geological Prospecting Service of the Chinese People's Republic," Sovetskaya geol. (Soviet Geology), 1958, No. 12.

Anuchin, V.A., Geograficheskiye ocherki Man'chzhurii (Geographical Essays on Manchuria), Moscow, Geografgiz (State Geographical Publishing House), 1948.

Atlas teplovogo balansa (Atlas of the Thermal Balance), Edited by M.I. Budyko, Leningrad, 1955.

Bakhtiyev, F. Kh., Ocherki po istorii i geografii vazhneyshikh kul'turnykh rasteniy (Essays on the History and Geography of Important Cultivated Crops), Moscow, Pedagogical Publishing House, 1960.

Bannikov, A.G., "The Animal World of Central Asia," Geografiya v shkole (Geography in School), 1953, No. 3.

_____ . Mlekopitayushchiye Mongol'skoy Narodnoy Respubliki (Mammals of the Mongolian People's Republic), Moscow, Izd. AN SSSR (USSR Academy of Sciences Publishing House), 1954.

Baranov, P.A., "The Potential of One Mu," Izv. AN SSSR, seriya biol. (News of the USSR Academy of Sciences, Biology Series), 1960, No. 1.

Bedarev, P.K., "Flooding in Northern Manchuria," Vestnik Man'chzhurii (The Herald of Manchuria), Harbin, 1934, No. 9.

*This bibliography prepared according to the original.

Beletskiy, Ye. A., "In the Mountains of Western China," Izv. Vsesoyuz. geogr. o-va (News of the All-Union Geographical Society), 1958, Vol. 90, No. 1.

Belousov, V. V., "Basic Features in the Tectonics of Central and South China," Izv. AN SSSR, seriya geol. (News of the USSR Academy of Sciences, Geological Series), 1956, No. 8.

Belyayevskiy, N. A., "New Data on the Geomorphology and Geography of the Western Portion of the Takla-Makan Desert," Izv. Vsesoyuz. geogr. o-va, 1947, Vol. 79, No. 4.

_____ . "On the Orography and Geomorphology of the Mountain Areas of the Western Kunlun," Izv. Vsesoyuz. geogr. o-va, 1948, Vol. 80, No. 3.

Berger, Ya. M., "The Development of Farming in the Sinkiang-Uigur Autonomous Region of the Chinese People's Republic," Voprosy geografii sel'skogo khozyaystva Kitayskoy Narodnoy Respubliki (Questions in the Geography of Agriculture in the Chinese People's Republic), Moscow, Izd. AN SSSR, 1959.

Berlyand, G. T., "The Thermal Balance in the Atmosphere of the Northern Hemisphere," in the book: A. I. Voyeykov i sovremennyye problemy klimatologii (A. I. Voyeykov and Present Problems of Climatology), Leningrad, Gidrometeoizdat (State Hydrometeorological Publishing House), 1956.

Bey-Biyenko, G. Ya., "The Results of the Sino-Soviet Zoological-Botanical Expedition of 1955-1956 in Southwest China. Blattoidea of Szechwan and Yunnan," Entomologicheskoye obozreniye (The Entomological Review), Vol. 36, No. 4, 1957; Vol. 37, No. 3, Leningrad-Moscow, 1958.

Bogdanovich, K. I., "Geological Research in Eastern Turkestan," Trudy Tibetskoy ekspeditsii 1889-1890 gg. (Transactions of the Tibetan Expedition of 1889-1890), Part 2, St. Petersburg, 1892.

_____ . "Northwest Tibet, the Kuen-Lun and Kashgaria," Izv. Russk. Geogr. Ob-va (News of the Russian Geographical Society), 1891, Vol. 27.

Borovskiy, V. M., "In Southeast China," Izv. AN SSSR, seriya biol., 1959, No. 5.

Borshchev, I. G., "Materials for the Botanical Geography of the Aralo-Caspian Area," Zap. Akad. nauk (Notes of the Academy of Sciences), 1865, Vol. 7, Book 1, Append. No. 1.

Chang Ch'ang-ling, "The Hydrography of the Hwang Ho and the State of the Work on Systematizing the Hydrological Materials," Kehsueh t'ungpao, 1953, No. 7, (in Chinese).

Chang Chia-ch'eng, "Certain Views on the Nature of the Chinese Monsoons," Tr. Gl. geofiz. observ., No. 90, Leningrad, Gidrometeoizdat, 1960b.

_____. "Mean Characteristics over Several Years for Certain Meteorological Elements and Circulation over China During the Winter Half-year," Tr. Gl. geofizich. observ., No. 90, Leningrad, Gidrometeoizdat, 1960a.

Chang Chi-chia, "Mean Characteristics of Atmospheric Circulation over a Number of Years and the Weather Regime over China during the Summer Half-year," Tr. Gl. geofiz. observ., No. 90, Leningrad, Gidrometeoizdat, 1960.

Chang Chung-yin, "Questions of the Geomorphology of the Yenshan Range in North China," Zap. Leningr. gornogo in-ta (Notes of the Leningrad Mining Institute), Vol. 32, No. 2-3; Voprosy gidrogeologii i inzhernernoy geologii (Problems of Hydrogeology and Engineering Geology), Leningrad, 1956.

Chang Chung-yin, et al., "The Geology of the Yenshan," Tichih lunp'ing, 1951, Vol. 16, No. 1, (in Chinese).

Chang Ch'un-lin, "The Most Important Fish Species of China," Shengwu-hsueh t'ungpao, 1955, No. 8, (in Chinese).

Chang Ch'un-lin, et al., Atlas naiboleye rasprostranennykh rub Zheltogo morya i Pokhayskogo zaliva (An Atlas of the Most Widely-Found Fish of the Yellow Sea and the Pohai Gulf), Shanghai, 1954, (in Chinese).

Chang Ehr-tao, "New Tectonic Movements in the Lishan Mountains (to the South of the Town of Lint'ung)," Tichih chihshih, 1957, No. 2, (in Chinese).

Chang Hung-tsu, "The Distribution of Mammals in China," Tili chihshih, 1955, No. 4, (in Chinese).

Chang Jen-chun, "Quaternary Glacial Phenomena in the Region of the Fanshan Mines," Tichih lunp'ing, 1951, Vol. 16, No. 1, (in Chinese).

Chang Jen-p'u, "The Mountain Region of the Chilienshan (Nanshan)," Tili chihshih, 1955, No. 4, (in Chinese).

Chang Keng, Cheng Ch'ing-ta, and P. P. Zabarinskiy, Neftyanyye i gazovyye mestorozhdeniya Kitayskoy Narodnoy Respubliki (Oil and Gas Deposits in the Chinese People's Republic), State Power Publishing House, 1958.

Chang Pao-sheng, "The Glacial Relief of the T'aipaishan," Quarternaria Sinica, 1958, Vol. 1, No. 2, (in Chinese).

Chang Po-sheng, "The Upper Boundary for the Spread of
Loess and the Development of the Hwang Ho Channel,"
Kehsueh t'ungpao, 1956, No. 3, (in Chinese).
Chang Wen-t'ang, "Weathering Products of the Tsaidam De-
pression," Tichih chihshih, 1957, No. 7, (in Chinese).
_____. "Young Volcanoes of Northern Manchuria," Voprosy
geografii, Coll. 35, Moscow, Geografgiz, 1954.
Chang Wen-yu, Tektonicheskaya karta Kitaya (A Tectonic
Map of China), Peking, Chinese Academy of Sciences
Publishing House, 1959, (in Chinese).
Chao Ch'i, "Geomorphological Features of the Alluvial and
Proluvial Plains of Sinkiang and the Conditions for De-
veloping Them," Tili hsuehpao, 1960, Vol. 26, No. 2,
(in Chinese).
Chao Yen-chi, "A Physical Geographic Outline of the Tsaidam
Depression in the Tsinghai," Tili chihshih, 1954, No. 8,
(in Chinese).
Chaykovskiy, V. K., "Basic Features of Metallogenesis in the
Western Slopes of the Greater Khingan from Data of
Work Done in 1956-1958," Tr. Tret'yey sessii ob''yedi-
nennogo sovetsko-kitayskogo uchenogo soveta po prob-
leme r. Amur, Vol. 2, Moscow, 1959, (mimeographed).
Chemekov, Yu. F., "Particular Features of Quarternary Gla-
ciation in the Sihote-Alin' Range," in the book: Voprosy
geologii Azii, Vol. 2, Moscow, Izd. AN SSSR, 1955.
Ch'en Cheng-hsien, "The Hohsi Corridor," Tsentr. un-t
geogr. otd. in-ta tochnykh i yestestv. nauk, 1943,
November, (in Chinese).
_____. "The Tarim Depression," Tsentr. un-t, geogr.
otd. in-ta tochnykh i yestestv. nauk, 1944, February,
(in Chinese).
Ch'en Chia-fang, "The Chemical Properties of the Yellow
Earths in the Mountain Region of the Northern Part of
Fukien Province," T'ujang hsuehpao, 1953, Vol. 2,
No. 3, (in Chinese).
Ch'en Chiao-i, Khuankhe (The Hwang Ho), Tientsin, "Ichi
shutien" Publishing House, 1953, (in Chinese).
_____. Reki Kitaya (The Rivers of China), Shanghai,
"Hsinchihshih" Publishing House, 1954, (in Chinese).
Ch'en Ching-shen and Ko Hsui-min, "The Natural Conditions
of the Lesser Tengri Sands in the Autonomous Regions
of Inner Mongolia," Tili hsuehpao, 1960, Vol. 26, No. 1,
(in Chinese).

Ch'en Ching-sheng and Chou Kuang-yu, Rastitel'nyy pokrov
srednego i nizh nego techeniya reki Sulehe v prov.
Kan'su (The Vegetation Cover in the Middle and Lower
Reaches of the Suliehho River in Kansu Province),
Peking, 1957, (in Chinese).

Ch'en Ko-ta, "The Problem of the Shoreline of China," Chungko kehsueh, 1950, Vol. 1, No. 2-4, (in Chinese).

Ch'en Shih-hsun, Klimat Kitaya (The Climate of China), Peking,
1959, (in Chinese).

Ch'en Shu-p'eng, Atlas perspektivnykh kart Kitaya (An Atlas
of Perspective Maps of China), 1954a, (in Chinese).

_____ , "The Karst Topography of Southwest China," Tili
chihshih, 1954b, March, (in Chinese).

Ch'en Shu-p'eng, Liu Jen-wei, and T'eng Chun, "Geomorphological Observations in the Ch'inho River Basin," Tili
hsuehpao, 1956, Vol. 22, No. 2, (in Chinese).

Ch'en Tao-ming, "The Development of the Deserts and Agriculture," Jenmin jihpao, November 16, 1962, (in Chinese).

Ch'en Yung-chung, "Neotectonic Movements and Certain Manifestations of Them in the Relief," Tili chihshih, 1957,
No. 3, (in Chinese).

Cheng Chao-hsuan, "The Climate of Taiwan," Tili hsuehpao,
June, 1954, (in Chinese).

_____ , "On the Problem of Present Fluctuations in the
Shore of the South China Sea," Tili hsuehpao, 1957,
No. 2, (in Chinese).

Cheng Chao-shun, "The Soils of the Northeast," Tili chihshih,
1953, No. 11, (in Chinese).

Ch'eng Po-chung, Yegorov, V. V., et al., "Soda Salting in the
Nonni-Sungari Depression," Tr. Tret'yey sessii ob"-
yedinennogo sovetsko-kitayskogo soveta po probleme r.
Amur, Vol. 3, Moscow, 1959, (mimeographed).

Cheng Tso-hsin, Ptitsy Kitaya (The Birds of China), No. 1,
1955a, (in Chinese).

_____ . Spisok promyslovykh ryb Kitaya (A List of the
Commercial Fish of China), 1955b, (in Chinese).

Chia Shen-hsiu, "The Nature of the Tibetan Uplands," Kehsueh
t'ungpao, 1953, No. 8, (in Chinese; in Russian published
in Priroda, 1955, No. 2).

Chiang Yan-wen, "The Bird Fauna of China," Tili chihshih,
1955, No. 1, (in Chinese).

Chiao Ta-k'ang, "On the Prospects for Developing Irrigation
Works in the Hwang Ho Basin," Tili chihshih, 1955,
No. 10, (in Chinese).

Ch'ien Ch'ung-shu, Wu Cheng-i, and Ch'en Ch'ang-tu, "A Draft
of the Geobotanical Zoning of China," in the book:
Fiziko-geograficheskoye rayonirovaniye Kitaya.

Ching Hsi-chi, K voprosu o kolebatel'nykh dvizheniyakh
beregovoy linii p-va Lyaodun (On the Question of Fluctuating Movements on the Shoreline of Liaotung Peninsula), Ch'angch'un, Tungpei Pedagogical Institute Publishing House, 1957, (in Chinese).

Ch'ing Shu-yuan, "Forest Belt Plantings in the Northeast of
China," Lesnoye khozyaystvo, 1956, No. 8, (in Chinese).

Ching Su, "The Ice Age in China," Tili, 1941, Vol. 1, No. 1,
(in Chinese).

Chou Li-san, "The Khami, A Typical Desert Oasis," Tili,
1948, Vol. 6, No. 1, (in Chinese).

Chou T'ing-ju and Liu P'ei-t'ung, Opisaniye rel'yefa i pochv
Kitaya (A Description of the Topography and Soils of
China), Peking, Sanlien, 1956, (in Chinese).

Chou T'ing-ju, Shih Ya-feng, and Ch'en Shu-p'eng, "A Draft for
the Geomorphological Zoning of China," in the book:
Fiziko-geograficheskoye rayonirovaniye Kitaya, No. 1,
translated from the Chinese, Moscow, IL, 1957.

Chu Chen-ta, "The Barkhan Landscapes of the Takla-Makan
Desert," Tili chihshih, 1960, No. 1, (in Chinese).
———. "The Lakes of the Kianghan Plain," Tili chihshih,
1955, No. 3, (in Chinese).

Chu Hsiao-ch'eng, et al., "Iron Ores in the Provinces of
Kiangsi, Chekiang, Kiangsu and the Direction for Pros-
pecting Them," Tichih yuehk'an, 1958, No. 11, (in
Chinese).

Chu Ke-chen, "Controlling Erosion--An Important Measure
for Raising Agricultural Production in Mountain Regions," Jenmin jihpao, December 22, 1955, (in Chinese).
———. "The Subtropical Zone of China," Kehsueh t'ungpao,
1958, No. 17, (in Chinese).

Chu Mei-tse, "The Advantages of Growing Green Fertilizers,"
Jenmin jihpao, October 19, 1961, (in Chinese).

Ch'u Pao-chien, "A Study of Climatic Features of Sinkiang,"
Priroda, 1958, No. 11.

Chu Ping-hai, "The Climate of the Tsinghai-Sikang-Tibetan
Uplands," Tili chihshih, 1954, (in Chinese).

Ch'u Shao-t'ang, Geografiya novogo Kitaya (The Geography of
New China), translated from the Chinese, Moscow, IL,
1953.

Chu Shih-mo, "A Discussion on Lateritization in China,"
Bull. of the Soil Soc. of China, 1948, Vol. 1, No. 1,
(in Chinese).

Chu Tse-fan, Feng Chung-wek, and Chu Chin-chiu, "The Con-
dition of the Forest Resources of the Right Bank of the
Amur within China and the Particular Problems of Study-
ing Them at Present," Sb. nauchnykh dokladov kom-
pleksnoy Amurskoy ekspeditsii, 1958, Vol. 1, (in Chinese).
Chu Tse-fan and Koldanov, V. Ya., "The Forest Riches of the
Northeast of China," Priroda, 1961, No. 3.
Chun Jen-ling and Su Pei-hai, "The Shift of Lake Lobnor,"
Tili chihshih, 1955, No. 5, (in Chinese).
Chung P'u-ch'iu, "The Vegetation of the Tibetan Uplands and
its Location," Shengwuhsueh t'ungpao, 1954, No. 10,
(in Chinese).
Dal'niy Vostok (The Far East), Moscow, Izd. AN SSSR, 1961.
Dil's, L., Botanicheskaya geografiya (Botanical Geography),
(Translated from German), Petrograd, 1916.
Dolgushin, L.D., "Basic Features in the Present Glaciation of
Central Asia According to Recent Data," Materialy
glyatsiologicheskikh issledovaniy Mezhdunarodnogo geo-
fizich. goda, khronika obsuzhdeniya (Materials of the
Glaciological Research of the IGY, Verbatim Report of
Discussions), No. 1, Moscow, 1961, (mimeographed).
_____. "Present Glaciation of the Nanshan (Ch'i-len-shan),"
Izv. AN SSSR, seriya geogr., 1959, No. 6.
Dylis, N.V., "The Forests of China and Their Study," Izv.
AN SSSR, seriya biol., 1958, No. 4.
Dzhordzhio, V.A., and Petrosyants, M.A., "The Summer Anti-
cyclone over Tibet," Dokl. AN Uzbeksk. SSR (Reports
of the Uzbek Academy of Sciences), 1950, No. 8.
Ekonomicheskaya geografiya avtonomnogo rayona Vnutrennyaya
Mongoliya, (The Economic Geography of the Autonomous
Region of Inner Mongolia), 1956, Peking, (in Chinese).
Fang Hsin-min, Tibet, Shanghai, 1954, (in Chinese).
Fang Wen-p'ei, "What I Know About the Omeishan," Ch'engtu,
1955, (in Chinese).
Fedchenko, B.A., "The Vegetation of Central Asia and the Role
of N.M. Przheval'skiy in Studying it," Izv. Vsesoyuz.
geogr. o-va, 1940, Vol. 72, No. 4-5.
Fedchenko, B.A., and Knorring, O.E., "Introduction to a Study of
the Vegetation of Chinese Turkestan," Tr. po prikladnoy
botanike, genetike i selektsii, 1930, Vol. 22, No. 5.
Fedorov, An. A., Linchevskiy, I.A., and Korpichnikov, M.E.,
"In the Tropics and Subtropics of China," Botanich.
zhurn., 1956, Vol. 41, No. 8.
Fedorov, An. N., "The Flora of Southwest China and its Significance for Knowing the Plant World of Eurasia," in

288 THE PHYSICAL GEOGRAPHY OF CHINA

yevicha Komarova (Ten Years Since the Death of Vladi-
mir Leont'yevich Komarov), Moscow-Leningrad, Izd.
AN SSSR, 1957, (Komarov Lectures, 10).
_____. "The Humid Tropical Forests of China," Botanich.
zhurn., 1958a, Vol. 43, No. 10.
_____. "In the Homeland of Tea," in the book: Voprosy
evolyutsii, biogeografii, genetiki i selektsii (Problems
of Evolution, Biogeography, Genetics and Selection),
Moscow-Leningrad, Izd. AN SSSR, 1960.
_____. "On the Floristic Links of Eastern Asia with the
Caucasus," in the book: Materialy po istorii flory i
rastitel'nosti SSSR, Vol. 3, Moscow-Leningrad, Izd. AN
SSSR, 1958b.
Fedorovich, B.A., "The Origin of the Relief of the Takla-
Makan Desert and the Problems of Developing it," in the
book: Kun'lun' i Tarim, Moscow, Izd. AN SSSR, 1961.
_____. "Sand Topography of Asia as a Reflection of Atmos-
pheric Circulation Processes," in the book: Problemy
fizicheskoy geografii, Vol. 13, Moscow-Leningrad, Izd.
AN SSSR, 1948.
Fedorovich, B.A., and Yang T'ing-hsien, "New Data on the
Character and Amount of Glaciation of the Chinese Por-
tion of the Tien-Shan," in the book: Prirodnyye usloviya
Sin'tszyana, Moscow, 1960.
Fei Hung-nien, Rybolovstvo Kitaya (Fishing of China), Peking,
1955, (in Chinese).
_____. "The Tasks of Zoology Workers in the Area of
Fishing," Kehsueh t'ungpao, 1954, No. 11, (in Chinese).
Feng Chung-yun, "Ways for Developing the Natural Riches of
the Heilungkiang," Vestnik AN SSSR, 1960, No. 3.
Feng Li-ming and Yang Yueh-an, "The Migrations of the Small
Yellow Perch and the Yellow Tail," Shengwuhsueh
t'ungpao, 1955, No. 3, (in Chinese).
Fiziko-geograficheskoye rayonirovaniye Kitaya (The Physical
Geographical Zoning of China), No. 1, translated from
the Chinese, Moscow, IL, 1957.
Fu Le-huan, "On the Questions of the Sources of the Hwang Ho,"
Kehsueh t'ungpao, 1954, No. 10, (in Chinese).
Fu Shu-hsia, Paprotnikovoobraznyye Kitaya (Pteridophyta of
China), Peking, 1954, (in Chinese).
Geografiya Tayvanya (The Geography of Taiwan), a collection
of articles, Peking, 1955, (in Chinese).
Geologicheskaya struktura Kitaya (The Geological Structure of
China), Peking, Kehsueh Publishing House, 1959, (in
Chinese).

Gerasimov, I. P., "Basic Features in the Development of the Features of the Turan," Tr. In-ta geogr. AN SSSR (Transactions of the Geography Institute of the USSR Academy of Sciences), No. 25, Moscow-Leningrad, Izd. AN SSSR, 1937.

———. "The Loesses of China and Their Origin," Izv. AN SSSR, seriya geogr., 1955, No. 5.

Gerasimov, I. P., and Ma Yung-chih, Geneticheskiye tipy pochv na territorii Kitayskoy Narodnoy Respubliki i ikh geograficheskoye rasprostraneniye (Genetic Soil Types on the Territory of the Chinese People's Republic and Their Geographical Distribution), Moscow, Izd. AN SSSR, 1958.

Glebov, M. D., "The Meliorative Significance of the Sungari River and the Water Regime of the Sungari and Upper Argun' River Basins," Vestn. Man'chzhurii (The Herald of Manchuria), 1934, No. 6.

Gordeyev, T. P., Geobotanicheskiy ocherk rastitel'nosti Sev.-Vost. Kitaya i vostochnoy chasti Vnutrenney Mongolii (A Geobotanical Outline on the Vegetation of Northeast China and the Eastern Part of Inner Mongolia), Peking, "Science" Publishing House, 1957.

———. "An Outline of the Soils of Northeastern China and the Eastern Part of Inner Mongolia," T'ijang hsuehpao, 1954b, Vol. 2, No. 4, (in Chinese).

———. "Where is the Eastern Limit of the European Black Earth Zone?" T'ujang hsuehpao, 1954a, Vol. 2, No. 6, (in Chinese).

Gorshkov, G. P., "Problems of Seismotectonics and Seismic Zoning for the Territory of the Chinese People's Republic," Byull. soveta po seysmologii (Bulletin of the Seismology Council), Vol. 7, Moscow, Izd. AN SSSR, 1960

Grane, G. I., "On the Significance of the Glacial Age for the Morphology of the Northeast Altay," Zap. Zap.-Sib Otd. Russk. Geogr. ob-va (Notes of the Western Siberian Section of the Russian Geographical Society), 1916, Vol. 38.

Grubov, V. I., "A Conspectus of the Flora of the Mongolian People's Republic," Tr. Mongol'skoy Komissii AN SSSR (Transactions of the Mongolian Commission of the USSR Academy of Sciences), No. 67, Moscow-Leningrad, Izd. AN SSSR, 1955.

———. "A List of Plants of Dzungaria (China) Collected by V. S. Moiseyenko in 1951-1954," Botanich. materialy gerbariya Botanich. in-ta AN SSSR (Botanical Materials from the Herbarium of the Botanical Institute of the USSR

Academy of Sciences), Vol. 19, Leningrad, Izd. AN SSSR, 1959b.

_____, Opyt botaniko-geograficheskogo rayonirovaniya Tsentral'noy Azii (The Experience of Botanical-Geographic Zoning of Central Asia), Leningrad, 1959a, (mimeographed).

Grumm-Grzhimaylo, G. Ye., "The Tsaidam," Entsiklopedicheskiy slovar' Brokgauza i Yefron (The Encyclopaedic Dictionary of Brockhaus and Efron), Vol. 74, St. Petersburg, 1903.

Grushvitskiy, I. V., "The 'Adventitious' Roots of the White Elm," Soobshch. Dal'ne-Vostochnogo filiala AN SSSR (Statements of the Far Eastern Affiliate of the USSR Academy of Sciences), No. 7, Vladivostok, Maritime Publishing House, 1956a.

_____ "The Epiphyte Valley," Priroda (Nature), 1956b, No. 6.

Guru, P., Aziya (Asia), Moscow, Foreign Languages Publishing House, 1956.

He Ch'eng, "Mechanical Water Supply and the Use of Underground Water," Jenmin jihpao, September 8, 1961, (in Chinese).

He Ching-Hai and Shih Hua, "The Red Earths of China," T'ujang hsuehpao, 1954, No. 2, (in Chinese).

He Ching-hai, Shih Hua, Lu Hsing-cheng, Kung Tse-t'ung, Liang Kui, and Chang Hsiao-nien, "The Soils of Hainan Island," T'ujang hsuehpao, 1958, No. 31, (in Chinese).

Hou Hsueh-yu, "On the Question of Land Utilization in the Northeast," Kehsueh t'ungpao, 1951, February, (in Chinese).

_____, "Vegetation Associations in the South of Kweichow Province," Chiwu hsuehpao, 1952, Vol. 1, No. 2, (in Chinese).

Hou Kuan-chou, Flora Kaunchzhou (The Flora of Kwangchow), Peking, 1956, (in Chinese).

Hsi Ch'eng-p'an, "Problems of Melioration and the Utilization of Waste Salt Lands in the Maritime Regions of Shantung," Tujang hsuehpao, 1953, No. 2, (in Chinese).

Hsia K'ai-ju, "The Deposits of the Hwang Ho River in the Chialuho Basin," Tili hsuehpao, 1953, Vol. 19, No. 2, (in Chinese).

Hsiao Chien-ch'un, "The Natural Conditions and Agriculture of the Tibetan Uplands," Kehsueh t'ungpao, 1954, No. 10 and Tili hsuehpao, 1954, Vol. 20, No. 4, (in Chinese).

Hsieh Chia-jung, "On the Direction of Prospecting on the Basis
of Certain Patterns in the Location of Mineral Deposits
in China," Tichih hsuehpao, 1953, Vol. 32, No. 3, (in
Chinese).

"The Hsifeng Experimental Anti-erosion Station of the Com-
mittee to Control the Hwang Ho; Willow Silt Filters,"
Kehsueh tachung, 1960, No. 1, (in Chinese).

Hsin K'uei-te and Jen Ch'i-chia," The Distribution of Permafrost in Northeast China," Tichih chihshih, 1956, No. 10,
(in Chinese).

Hsiung Yung-hsien, "Traces of Glaciation along the Foothills
of the Chiutseshan Mountains in Sungp'ang," Tichih
lunp'ing, 1945, Vol. 10, No. 3-4, (manuscript, in
Chinese).

Hsu, Chun-ming, Ostrov Khanyan (Hainan Island), Kwantung
Jenmin Publishing House, 1958, (in Chinese).

_____ . Sb. statey po geografii Yuzhnogo Kitaya (A Collection of Articles on the Geography of South China),
Shanghai, 1957, (in Chinese).

Hsu Shu-ying, Hsu Ming-ying, and Kao Yu-hsi, "The Climate
of Hainan Island," Ch'ihsiang hsuehpao, 1954b, Vol. 25,
No. 3, (in Chinese).

Hsu Shu-ying, Kao Yu-hsi, Yang Chien-ch'u, and Yeh Tu-cheng,
"Preliminary Analysis of the Meteorological Conditions
of the Hwang Ho River Basin," Tili hsuehpao, 1954a,
Vol. 20, No. 1, (in Chinese).

Hsui Hsiu-ying, "The Carrying of Moisture over the East of
China," Kehsueh t'ungpao, July 12, 1957, (in Chinese).

Hu Hsien-hsiu, Kharakter Kitayskoy flory (The Character of
Chinese Flora), Peking, Chinese Academy of Sciences
Publishing House, 1937, (in Chinese).

_____ . Osobennosti lesov yugo-vostochnykh provintsii
Kitaya (Particular Features of the Forests in the South-
eastern Provinces of China), Shaighai, 1925, (in
Chinese).

Hu Huan-yung, "The Transformation of the Hwang Ho," Tili
chihshih, 1954, No. 1, (in Chinese).

Hu Shan-mei, "The Rivers of Fukien and the Hydroresources,"
Tili chihshih, 1959, No. 9, (in Chinese).

Huang Chi-ch'ing, "Basic Sedimentation Regions in East
China and their Features," Tichih chihshih, 1957, No. 5,
(in Chinese).

_____ . "Certain Features in the Tectonics of China,"
Geologicheskiye znaniya (Geological Knowledge), 1956,
No. 8, (in Chinese).

_____ . "Certain Features of Geotectonics in China," in the book: Voprosy sovremennoy zarubezhnoy tektoniki (Problems in Modern Foreign Tectonics), Moscow, IL, 1960.

Huang Jung-yun, "The Thermal Balance of the Earth's Surface in Kwangtung Province," Tili hsuehpao, 1960, No. 3, (in Chinese).

Huang Ping-wei, "The Causes and Forms of Erosion in the Loess Region of Shensi-Kansu," Tili hsuehpao, 1953, Vol. 19, No. 2, (in Chinese).

_____ . "Soil Erosion in the Loess Regions of Shansi-Kansu," Voprosy geografii, Coll. 35, Moscow, Geografgiz, 1954.

Huang Po-ch'in, Osnovnyye cherty tektonicheskogo stroyeniya Kitaya (Basic Features in the Tectonic Structure of China), translated from the English and with a foreword by N. S. Shatskiy, Moscow, IL, 1952.

Huang T'i-jung, "Marine Fishing in the Tonkin Gulf," Tili chihshih, 1955, No. 3, (in Chinese).

Hung Shih, "Fur Resources of China," Jenmin jihpao, March 13, 1963, (in Chinese).

Ikonnikov, S. S. , "New Data on the Flora of the Pamir," Problemy botaniki (Problems of Botany), Vol. 5, Moscow-Leningrad, Izd. AN SSSR, 1960a.

_____ . "On the Materials Concerning the Flora of Northwest China," Dokl. AN Tadzh. SSR (Reports of the Tadzhik Academy of Sciences), 1957, No. 20.

_____ . Sostav i analiz flory Pamira (The Composition and Analysis of the Pamir Flora), Dissertation Resumé for the degree of Candidate of Biological Sciences, Leningrad, 1960b.

Il'inskiy, A. P. , Rastitel'nost' zemnogo shara (Vegetation of the World), Moscow-Leningrad, Izd. AN SSSR, 1937.

Illyustrirovannaya flora derev'yev i kustarnikov Severo-Vostochnogo Kitaya (Illustrated Flora of Trees and Shrubs in Northeast China), Mukden, Publishing House of the Chinese Academy of Sciences, 1955, (in Chinese).

Ivanov, A. Kh. , "On Glaciation in the Northeastern Part of the Mongolian Altai," Trudy Mongol'skoy komissii AN SSSR (Transactions of the Mongolian Commission of the USSR Academy of Sciences), No. 38, Moscow-Leningrad, 1949.

Ivanov, G. I. , "The Soils of the Hankai Plain and the Ussuri River Valley, Their Development and Utilization," Tr. Tret'ye sessii ob"yedinennogo sovetsko-kitayskogo uchenogo soveta po probleme r. Amur, Vol. 3, Moscow, 1959, (mimeographed).

Jen Mei-e, "A Brief Description of the Geology and Topography of the Northeast, " Tili chihshih, November, 1953, (in Chinese).

Jen Mei-e, et al. , "The Geography of the Nanssuhu Region Lying in the Northern part of Kiangsu Province and in Shantung Province," Tili hsuehpao, 1954, Vol. 20, No. 2, (in Chinese).

Kalantyr', M. S. , Introduktsiya evkomii v SSSR (The Introduction of Eucomia into the USSR), (Dissertation Resumé), Leningrad, 1961.

Kaminskiy, A. A. , "On the Climate of the Tsaidam, " Tr. ekspeditsii Russk. geogr. o-va, sovershennoy v 1899-1901 gg po ruk P. K. Kozlova (Transactions of the Expedition of the Russian Geographical Society Made in 1899-1901 under the Leadership of P. K. Kozlov), Vol. 1, Part 2, St. Petersburg, 1906.

Kan Hsien-kang, Fizicheskaya geografiya Severo-zapadnogo Kitaya (The Physical Geography of Northwest China), Hsian, 1958, (in Chinese).

Kao Chen-hsi, "Certain Attestation to New Tectonic Movements close to Peking, " Tichi chishih, 1957, No. 1, (in Chinese).

Kao Hoi-min, "To Raise the Fertility of the Middle and Low Grade Lands, " Jenmin jihpao, April 17, 1962, (in Chinese).

Kaplin, A. , "The Fur Wealth of China, " Okhota i okhotnich'ye khozyaystvo (Hunting and Game Management), 1956, No. 4.

Kazakova, N. M. , "Certain Data on the Ancient Glaciation of China, " in the book: Geomorfologiya i paleogeografiya Azii (The Geomorphology and Paleogeography of Asia), Moscow, Izd. AN SSSR, 1955.

_____ . "Characteristics of the Natural Condition in North-East China in line with the Development of Agriculture and Forestry, " in the book: Voprosy geografii sel'skogo khozyaystva Kitayskoy Narodnoy Respubliki, Moscow, Izd. AN SSSR, 1959.

Kazakova, N. M. , Nikol'skaya, V. V. , Timofeyev, D. A. , and Chichagov, V. P. , "The Experience of Analyzing the Quantitative and Qualitative Indices in the Physical Geographical Zoning of the Argun' Area, " Voprosy fizicheskoy geografii (Problems of Physical Geography), Moscow, Izd. AN SSSR, 1958.

Ke Chia-lung, "Checking the Yungtingho River," Narodnyy
Kitay, 1953, No. 2.

Kes', A. S., "On the Question of the Origin of the Loess Beds
of North China," Tr. Komiss. po izucheniyu chetvertich.
perioda (Transactions of the Commission to Study the
Quaternary Period), Vol. 14, Moscow, Izd. AN SSSR,
1959a.

_____ . "On the Structure of the Topography of the Loess
Province of North China," Izv. AN SSSR, seriya geogr.,
1959b, No. 5.

Kitay (China), (a collection of articles), Moscow, Publishing
House of the Large Soviet Encyclopaedia, 1953.

Kitayskiy geograficheskiy atlas geograficheskogo o-va "Ya-
guan" (The Chinese Geographical Atlas of the "Yakuan"
Geographical Society), 4th Ed., Shanghai, 1951, (in
Chinese).

Klingen, M., Sredi patriarkhov zemledeliya narodov Blizhnego
i Dal'nego Vostoka (Among the Farming Patriarchs of
the Peoples of the Near and Far East), Part 3, China,
St. Petersburg, 1899.

Klimaticheskiy atlas Kitaya (Climatic Atlas of China), Peking,
Vol. 1, Publishing House of the Meteorological Admin-
istration of the People's Military Revolutionary Commit-
tee, Institute of Geophysics of the Chinese Academy of
Sciences, 1953, (in Chinese).

Ko Ching-hoi, "On Enumerating the Runoff Resources of China,"
Tili hsuehpao, 1957, Vol. 23, No. 1, (in Chinese).

_____ . "The Hydrology of China's Rivers," Tili chihshih,
1958, No. 3, (in Chinese).

_____ . "The Surface Runoff of China," Tili hsuehpao, 1955,
Vol. 21, No. 4, (in Chinese).

Ko Hung-chun and Hsieh Chou-p'ing, "The Geomorphological
Zoning of the Tungpei," Chungko tissuchi yenchiu, 1958,
Vol. 1, No. 1-2, (in Chinese).

Ko Ling-chih, "The Quaternary Glacial Relief of the Eastern
Spur of the Tapashan," Tili, 1943, Vol. 3, No. 3-4,
(in Chinese).

Komarov, V. L., "Botanical Trips of Important Russian Expeditions into Central Asia," Part I, the Trips of N. M.
Przheval'skiy, in: Tr. Gl. botanich. sada (Transactions
of the Main Botanical Garden), Vol. 34, No. 1, Petrograd, 1920.

_____ . "The Flora of Manchuria," Vols. 1, 2, 3, Tr. Peterb.
botanich. sada (Transactions of the Petersburg Botanical
Garden), Vols. 20-25, St. Petersburg, 1901-1907.

_____ . "Introduction to the Floras of China and Mongolia, "
Tr. Peterb. botanich. sada, St. Petersburg, Vol. 29,
No. 1-2, 1908.

_____ . Proiskhozhdeniye kul'turnykh rasteniy (The Origin
of Cultivated Plants), 2nd Ed. , Moscow-Leningrad,
Agricultural Publishing House, 1938.

_____ . "Types of Vegetation of the Southern Ussuri Region, " Trudy poch. -botan. ekspeditsii po issled.
koloniz. rayonov Aziatsk. Rossii (Transactions of the
Soil-Botanical Expedition to Study the Colonization of
Regions in Asiatic Russia), Part 2, No. 2, Petrograd,
1917.

Korneyev, K. S. , "The Water Resources of the Chinese People's
Republic and Their Utilization, " Gidrotekhnika i melio-
ratsiya (Hydraulic Engineering and Melioration), 1958,
No. 8.

Korovin, Ye. P. , "The Betpak-dala as a Particular Type of
Desert, " Tr. Botan. in-ta AN SSSR (Transactions of
the Middle Asiatic State University), series 8b, No. 27,
1935.

Korovin, Ye. P. , and Kashkarov, D. N. , "Types of Turkestan
Deserts, " Tr. Botan. in-ta AN SSSR (Transactions of
the Botanical Institute of the USSR Academy of Sciences
Series 3, Geobotany, No. I, Leningrad, Izd. AN SSSR,
1934.

Korzhinskiy, S. I. , "The Vegetation of Russia, " Entsiklopedicheskiy slovar' Brokguaz i Efron, 1899, Vol. "Russia, "
pp. 47-49.

Kovda, V. A. , Ocherki Prirody i pochv Kitaya (Essays on the
Nature and Soils of China), Moscow, Izd. AN SSSR, 1959.

Kovda, V. A. , Bekker, Z. E. , Sal'nikov, S. Ye. , Zimovets,
B. A. , and Vasilevskaya, V. A. , "Genetic Features of the
Amur Area Soils, " Sb. nauchn. dokladov Kompl. Amur-
skoy ekspeditsii (Collection of Scientific Reports of the
Multi-Field Amur Expedition), Vol. 1, Peking, 1958,
(in Chinese).

Kovda, V. A. , Liverovskiy, Yu. A. , and Sung Ta-ch'eng,
"Essay on the Soils of the Amur Area, " Izv. AN SSSR,
seriya biol. , 1957, No. 1.

Kozlov, P. K. , "Mongolia and the Kam, " Trudy ekspeditsii
RGO (Transactions of the Expedition of the Russian Geographical Society), Vol. 1, 2, St. Petersburg, 1905-1906.

_____ . Mongolia i Amdo i mertvyy gorod Khara-Khoto
(Mongolia, the Amdo and the Dead City of Khara-Khoto),
Moscow, Geografgiz, 1947a.

Kozlova, Ye. V., "Bird Fauna of the Tibetan Uplands, its Kindred Relationships and History," Tr. Zool in-ta AN SSSR (Transactions of the Zoological Institute of the USSR Academy of Sciences), Vol. 9, No. 7, Moscow-Leningrad, Izd. AN SSSR, 1952.

Krasnov, A. N., Chaynyye okrugi subtropicheskikh oblastey (Tea Districts of the Subtropical Areas of Asia), China, India, Ceylon, Kolkhid, St. Petersburg, 1898.

_____. "From a Trip to the Far East of Asia," Zemle-vedeniye (Geography), 1894, No. 1, Book 2.

Kratkiy Klimaticheskiy atlas Kitaya (A Brief Climatic Atlas of China), Peking, 1959, (in Chinese).

Krishtofovich, A. N., "The Development of the Botanical-Geographic Provinces in the Northern Hemisphere since the End of the Cretaceous Age," Sov. botanika (Soviet Botany), 1936, No. 2.

_____. Geologicheskiy obzor stran Dal'nego Vostoka (A Geological Review of the Nations of the Far East), Moscow-Leningrad, Geological Prospecting Publishing House, 1932.

_____. "The Origin of Flora in the Angara Dry Land Area," in the book: Materialy po istorii flory i rastitel'nosti SSSR (Materials on the History of Flora and Vegetation of the USSR), No. 3, Moscow-Leningrad, Izd. AN SSSR, 1958.

_____. Paleobotanika (Paleobotany), Moscow-Leningrad, State Geological Publishing House, 1941.

Kurdyukov, K. V., "Ancient Lake Basins in Southeast Kazakhstan and the Climatic Conditions During Their Existence," Izv. AN SSSR, seriya geogr., 1952, No. 2.

Kurentsov, A. I., "Relics in the Fauna of the Hsihot'e-Alin'," Komarovskiye chteniya (Komarov Readings), No. 7, Vladivostok, Maritime Region Publishing House, 1959.

Kurs ekonomicheskoy geografii Kitaya (A Course of Economic Geography of China), Vol. 2, Peking, 1958, (in Chinese).

Ku Shen-hsiu, "The Nature of the Tibetan Uplands," Priroda, 1955, No. 2.

Kuznetsov, N. T., "Ancient Glaciation of the Mongolian Altay," in the book: Voprosy geologii Azii, Vol. 2, Moscow, Izd. AN SSSR, 1955.

_____. "Hydrological Observations in the Kun'lun," in the book: Kun'lun i Tarim (The Kun'lun and the Tarim), Izd. AN SSSR, 1961.

_____. "The Rivers of Northern Sinkiang," Priroda, 1960, No. 1.

Kuznetsov, N. T., and Hu Chung-p'ei, "Hydrological Condi-
    tions in the Southwestern part of Dzungaria," Izv. AN
    SSSR, seriya geogr., 1959, No. 2.
Kuznetsov, N. T., and Murzayev, E. M., "Lacustrine
    Developmental Stages in the Quaternary Age of the
    History of Central Asia," Tr. Laborat. ozerovedeniya
    (Transactions of the Laboratory for Limnology), Vol.
    15, Moscow, Izd. AN SSSR, 1962.
Kyuner, N. V., Opisaniye Tibeta (A Description of Tibet),
    Part 1, No. 1, Vladivostok, 1907.
Labetskiy, O., "Developing the Virgin Lands of China,"
    Ekonomika sel'skogo khozyaystva (The Economics of
    Agriculture), 1961, No. 6.
Lavrenko, Ye. M., "On the Savanna Vegetation Along the Red
    River in the South of Yunnan Province," Tr. Mosk.
    o-va ispyt. prirody, Biology Section, Vol. 3, Collection
    of works on geobotany, botanical geography, plant tax-
    onomy and paleogeography, Moscow, MOIP Publishing
    House, 1960.
_____. "The Paleotropical Area," Bol'shaya sov. entsi-
    klopediya (The Large Soviet Encyclopaedia), Vol. 31,
    Moscow, 1955.
Lavrent'yev, P. F., "Modern Glaciation in the Dzungarian
    Alatau," Izv. Vsesoyuz. geogr. o-va, 1958, Vol. 90,
    No. 2.
Lavrov, V. V., Morskoy paleogen Zaural'skikh ravnin i yego
    kontinental'nyye ekvivalenty (The Marine Paleogene of
    the Transural Plains and Its Continental Equivalents),
    Alma-Ata, Kazakh Academy of Sciences Publishing
    House, 1957.
Lebedev, V. G., "Geomorphological Observations in the Karst
    Region of Kwangsi Province," in the book: Speleologiya
    i karstovedeniye (Speleology and Karst Studies), Mos-
    cow, MOIP Publishing House, 1959a.
_____. "On the Origin of the Great Bend of the Hwang Ho,"
    Izv. Vsesoyuz. geogr. o-va, 1961, Vol. 93, No. 6.
_____. "The Role of Important Tectonic Movements in the
    Formation of the Relief of the Shansi Plateau," Nauchn.
    dokady vyssh. shkoly geol.-geogr. nauki (Scientific
    Reports of the Higher School for Geological-Geographi-
    cal Science), 1959b, No. 2.
Lesa i pochvy Kitaya (The Forests and Soils of China), a geo-
    graphical collection, translated from the Chinese, Mos-
    cow, Foreign Languages Publishing House, 1955.
Lesnoye Khozyaystvo Man' chzhurii (Forestry of Manchuria),
    Mukden, 1948, (in Chinese).

Li Ch'en-san, "The Topography of Taiwan," Tili chihshih,
1954, No. 11, (in Chinese).

Li Ch'en-san, Chiao Ke-shih, and Ch'en Ssu-chiao, "The History of the Development of the Hydrographic Network of
the Yangtzekiang," Tili, 1944, Vol. 4, No. 3-4, (in
Chinese).

Li Ch'en-san and Kao Yung-yuan, "The Glacial Relief of the
Tapashan Mountains in the Region of Kuanshan," Tili,
1942, Vol. 2, No. 1-2, (in Chinese).

Li Ch'i-wen, "The Influence of the Tibetan Uplands on the
Climate of South China," Tili chihshih, 1959, Vol. 10,
No. 7, (in Chinese).

Li, J. S., and Li, I. I., "The Sinian Glaciation of China," in
the book: Mezhdunarod. geol. kongress, Trudy 17-y
sessii Mezhdunarodnogo geologich. kongress, 1937 g.
(The International Geological Congress, Transactions
of the 17th Session of the International Geological
Congress of 1937), Vol. 6, Moscow, State Geological
Prospecting Publishing House, 1940.

Li Jui, "A Grandiose Plan for Construction on the Hwang Ho
River," Narodnyy Kitay, 1955b, No. 16.

_____. "The Water Resources and Hydroelectric Construc-
tion of China," Gidrotekhnich. stroitel'stvo (Hydroengineering Construction), 1955a, No. 4.

Li Lien-tse, "The Natural Zoning of the Tibetan Uplands,"
Tili hsuehpao, 1954, Vol. 20, No. 3, (in Chinese).

Li P'u, "Certain Information on the Geology of the Eastern
Part of Tibet," Kehsueh t'ungpao, 1955, No. 7, (in
Chinese).

_____. "The Physical Geographic Conditions and Natural
Resources of the Sikiang-Tibetan Uplands," Kehsueh
t'ungpao, 1954, No. 2, (in Chinese).

Li Shan-p'ang, et al., "The Map for the Seismic Zoning of
China and its Explanation," Tich'iu wuli hsuehpao, 1957,
No. 2, (in Chinese).

Li Shih-ying, "Particular Features in the Formation of the
Vegetation Cover of the Northern Slopes of the K'unlun
Range and its Relationship to the Aridness," Chiwuhsueh
hsuehpao, 1960, No. 9 (I), (in Chinese).

Li Ssu-Kuang, Geologiya Kitaya (The Geology of China), Moscow, IL Foreign Languages Publishing House, 1952.

Li T'ao, "Certain Questions of the Hydrography of Sinkiang
and the Utilization of the Rivers," Tili chihshih, 1958a,
No. 6, (in Chinese).

_____. "Recent Tectonic Movements in Eastern Yunnan,"
Quaternaria Sinica, 1958, Vol. 1, No. 2, (in Chinese).

Liang Jen-ts'ai, Huang Mien, and Shen Wei-ch'eng, Yuzhnyy Kitay (South China), Moscow, IL, 1962.

Lin Chou, "The Hunting and Game Resources of China," Jen-min jihpao, October 10, 1962, (in Chinese).

Lindberg, G. U., "The Geomorphology of the Bottom of the Surrounding Seas of Eastern Asia and the Distribution of Freshwater Fishes," Izv. Vse-soyuz. geogr. o-va, 1946, Vol. 78, No. 3.

_____. "Patterns in the Distribution of Fishes and the Geological History of Far Eastern Seas," in the book: Ocherki po obshchim voprosam ikhtiologii (Essays on General Problems of Ichthyology), Moscow-Leningrad, Izd. AN SSSR, 1953.

Lir, E. S., "On the Circulation of Air in Southeast Asia, Meteorol i. gidrol (Meteorology and Hydrology), 1936, No. 2.

Liu Cheng-ch'an, "The Glacial Relief in the Basin of the Tat'-ungho along the Southern Foothills of the Ch'ilienshan," Tichih lunp'ing, 1946, Vol. 2, No. 3-4, (in Chinese).

Liu Ch'eng-chung, "The Present Glaciers of the Tien-Shan," Tili chihshih, 1960, No. 2, (in Chinese).

Liu Hai-p'eng, Obrazovaniye zhelezistykh kor v pochvennykh profilyakh Futszyani (The Formation of Ferruginous Crusts in the Soil Profiles of Fukien), 1948, Vol. 1, No. 1, (in Chinese).

Liu Hsien-t'ien, "Features of Nature in Inner Mongolia," Tili chihshih, 1955, No. 10, (in Chinese).

Liu Hsin-wu, "Particular Features of the Yungtingho River and Improving its Water Regime," Tili chihshih, 1953, No. 5, (in Chinese).

Liu Yu-ch'uan, "Means of Development for Forestry in the Chinese People's Republic," Lesnoye khozyaystvo, 1959, No. 10.

Liverovskiy, Yu. A., and Rubtsova, L. P., "The Soil-Geographical Zoning of the Amur Area," in the book: Voprosy prirodnogo rayonirovaniya sovetskogo Dal'nego Vostoka v svyazi s rayonnoy planirovkoy (The Problems of Natural Zoning of the Soviet Far East in Line with Regional Planning), Moscow, 1962.

Lo K'ai-fu, "A Draft for the Physical Geographical Zoning of China," in the book: Fiziko-geograficheskoye rayonirovaniye Kitaya.

Lo Lai-hsing, "How to Understand the Features of Rivers," Tili chihshih, 1954a, No. 12, (in Chinese).

_____. "The Hydrography of the Hanshui River," Tili, 1948, Vol. 6, No. 1, (in Chinese).

————. "The Problem of Shifting Sands Between Yuling and
　　　Chingpien," Kehsueh t'ungpao, 1954b, No. 3, (in Chinese).

Lo Lai-hsing and Ch'i Yen-nien, "Ravine Formation in the Re-
　　　gions of the Loess Hills and Samples of Computing the
　　　Amount of Erosion," Tili hsuehpao, 1953, Vol. 19, No.
　　　2, (in Chinese).

L'vovich, M. I., "Elements of the Water Regime of the World's
　　　Rivers," Tr. Nauchno-issled. uchrezhd. Gidromet.
　　　sluzhby, series 4, Hydrology, No. 18, Sverdlovsk-
　　　Moscow, 1945.

Ma T'ing-ying, "Changes in the Climate of Asia in the Recent
　　　Geological Era, the Causes for the Retreat of the Glaciers
　　　in the Quaternary Periods and the Question of the Relief
　　　of the Sea Bottom," Tichih lunp'ing, 1938, Vol. 3, No. 2,
　　　(in Chinese).

Ma Yung-chih, "The Formation of Chinese Loess," Tichih
　　　lunp'ing, 1944, Vol. 9, No. 3-4, (in Chinese).

Ma Yung-chih and Wen Chen-wang, "The Principle of Soil Zoning
　　　Set for the Purposes of Developing Agriculture," T'ujang
　　　hsueh pao, 1958, Vol. 6, No. 3, (in Chinese).

Margolin, A. B., Priamur'ye (The Amur Region), Moscow,
　　　Geografgiz, 1957.

Masibroda, V. Ye., "The Absolute Elevation of the Turfan De-
　　　pression," in the book: Voprosy geografii (Problems of
　　　Geography), Coll. 2, Moscow, Geografgiz, 1949.

————. "The Aeolian Relief of the Turfan Depression and
　　　the Western Pei-Shan as a Reflection of Local Atmos-
　　　pheric Circulation," Izv. AN SSSR, seriya geogr., 1952,
　　　No. 2.

"Materials on the Research on the Hwang Ho River in the Area
　　　of Kueite-Ninghsia," Kehsueh t'ungpao, 1953, No. 7,
　　　(in Chinese).

Materialy po fizicheskoy geografii Severnogo Kitaya (Materials
　　　on the Physical Geography of North China), series of
　　　authors, Peking, "Science" Publishing House, 1957,
　　　(in Chinese).

Materialy po geologii i poleznym iskopayemym vostochnoy
　　　chasti Tibeta (Materials on the Geology and Minerals of
　　　Eastern Tibet), Peking "Science" Publishing House,
　　　1959, (in Chinese).

Muranov, A. P., Reka Khuankhe (Zheltaya reka) (The Hwang
　　　Ho River [The Yellow River]), Leningrad, Gidro-
　　　meteoizdat, 1957.

————. Reka Yantszy (The Yangtze River), Leningrad,
　　　Gidrometeoizdat, 1959.

Murzayev, E. M. , "The Geographical Features of the K'unlun, " in the book: Kun'lun' i Tarim (The K'unlun and Tarim), Moscow, Izd. AN SSSR, 1961.

_____. Mongol'skaya Narodnaya Respublika (The Mongolian People's Republic), Moscow, Geografgiz, 1952.

_____. "On Certain Causes for the Meandering of Rivers on Desert Plains, " Izv. AN SSSR, seriya geogr. , 1960, No. 2.

_____. Severo-Vostochnyy Kitay (Northeast China), Moscow, Izd. AN SSSR, 1955.

Nagibina, M. S. , "The Geological Structure of the Northern Tungpei, " Tr. Tret'yey sessii ob"yedinennogo sovetsko-kitayskogo uchenogo soveta po probleme r. Amur, Moscow, 1959 (mimeographed).

Nauchnyye rezul'taty puteshestviy N. M. Przheval'skogo. Otdel meteorologicheskiy, obrabotal A. I. Voyeykov (Scientific Results of the Travels of N. M. Przheval'skiy. Meteorological Section Edited by A. I. Voyeykov), St. Petersburg, 1895.

Nenarokomov, A. V. , Lesnoye khozyaystvo Kitaya (Forestry of China), Moscow, Lumber and Paper Technical Publishing House, 1957,

Nesteruk, F. Ya. , "Water Control in China, " in the collection Iz istorii nauki i tekhniki Kitaya (From the History and Technology of China), Moscow, Izd. AN SSSR, 1955.

Nikalayev, N. I. , "Problems in Studying the Geomorphology and Neotectonics of China, " Tr. Mosk. geol razved. in-ta (Transactions of the Moscow Geological Prospecting Institute), Vol. 28, Moscow, State Geological Technical Publishing House, 1960.

Nikol'skiy, G. V. , Reka Amur i yeye presnovodnyye ryby (The Amur River and Its Freshwater Fishes), Moscow, MOIP Publishing House, 1948.

Obruchev, V. A. , "The Cumulose Sands as a Particular Type of Sand Accumulation, " in the book: Izbr. raboty po geografii Azii (Selected Works on the Geography of Asia), Vol. 3, Moscow, Geografgiz, 1951b.

_____. "Indications of the Ice Age in Northern and Central Asia, " Izv. Russk. Geogr. o-va, 1895, Vol. 31, No. 3; Izv. Russk. Geogr. o-va, Vol. 3, 1951e.

_____. "The Loess of North China, " Tr. komissii po izucheniyu chetvertichnogo perioda, Vol. 14, Moscow, Izd. AN SSSR, 1959.

_____. "On the Processes of Weathering and Winnowing in Central Asia, " in the book: Izbr. raboty po geografii

Azii (Selected Works on the Geography of Asia), Vol. 3,
Moscow, Geografgiz, 1951c.
_____. "On the Question of the Origin of Loess," in the book:
Izbr. raboty po geografii Azii, Moscow, Geografgiz, 1951a.
_____. "The Orography of Central Asia and Its Southeastern
Border," Izv. Russk. Geogr. o-va, 1895, Vol. 31, No. 3;
Izv. Russk. Geogr. o-va, Vol. 3, 1951d.
_____. "Pages from my Life," Izv. Russk. Geogr. o-va,
Vol. 1, 1951.
_____. Pogranichnaya Dzhungariya (Border Dzungaria),
No. 1, Tomsk, 1912; No. 2, 3, Tomsk, 1914; No. 3,
Leningrad, Izd. AN SSSR, 1932.
_____. "The Problem of Loess," Izv. Russk. Geogr. o-va,
1895, Vol. 31, No. 3; Izv. Russk. Geogr. o-va, Vol. 3, 1951f.
_____. Tsentral'naya Aziya, Severnyy Kitay i Nan'shan'
(Central Asia, North China and the Nanshan), Vol. 1-2,
St. Petersburg, 1900, 1901.
_____. Vostochnaya Mongoliya (Eastern Mongolia), Moscow-
Leningrad, Izd. AN SSSR, 1947.
_____. "The Young Volcanic Area of the Greater Khingan," in
the book: Voprosy geografii, Coll. 12, Moscow, Geografgiz,
1949.
Oliferov, A.N., "Controlling Erosion in the Chinese People's
Republic," Lesnoye khozyaystvo, 1959, No. 9.
Paleogeograficheskiy atlas Kitaya (Paleogeographic Atlas of
China), ed. by Liu Hung-Yun, Peking, "Science" Publishing
House, 1959, (in Chinese).
Pal'gov, N.N., "A Major Area of Present Glaciation in the
Dzungarian Alatau," Izv. Vsesoyuz. geogr. o-va, 1949, Vol.
81, No. 1.
P'an Te-yang, Less (Loess), Peking, "Geology" Publishing
House, 1958, (in Chinese).
P'an T'ien-shou, "The Present and Future of Navigation on the
Hwang Ho," Tili chihshih, 1955, No. 10, (in Chinese).
Panfilov, D.V., Nasekomyye v tropicheskikh lesakh Yuzhnogo
Kitaya (Insects in the Tropical Forest of South China),
Moscow University Publishing House, 1961.
_____. "On the Geographical Distribution of Bumblebees in
China," Acta geographica sinica, 1957, Vol. 23, No. 3,
(in Chinese).
_____. "The Position of the Boundary Between Tropical and
Subtropical Landscapes in Eastern Asia," Izv. AN SSSR,
seriya geogr., 1959, No. 3.
_____. "The 'Stone Forests' in the South of China," Priroda,
1958, No. 9.

Pavlinov, V. N., "Certain Data on the Genesis of Chinese Loess," Tr. komissii po izucheniyu chetvertichnogo perioda, Vol. 14, Moscow, Izd. AN SSSR, 1959.

P'en Chien, Kitayskiye lekarstvennyye rasteniya (Chinese Medicinal Plants), Publishing House of the Chinese Academy of Sciences, 1955, (in Chinese).

Petrov, M. P., "Botanical Research in the Northern Part of Central China," Botanich. zhurn. (Botanical Journal), 1959a, Vol. 44, No. 8.

_____. "A Study of the Sandy Deserts and Semideserts of China in Line with Their Development," Izv. AN Turkm. SSR (News of the Turkmen Academy of Sciences), 1959b, No. 3.

_____. "The Vegetation of the Deserts in Central Asia (Ordos, Alashan and Peishan) and the Particular Features of its Distribution," Botanich. zhurn., 1959c, Vol. 44, No. 10.

Pevtsov, M., "The Climate of Kashgaria (Eastern Turkestan)," Meteorol. vestn. (The Meteorological Herald), Vol. 4, St. Petersburg, 1894.

Pevtsov, M. V., Puteshestviye po Kitayu i Mongolii (A Journey Through China and Mongolia), Moscow, Geografgiz, 1951.

_____. Puteshestviye po Vostochnomu Turkestany, Kun'-lunyu, severnoy okraine Tibetskogo nagor'ya i Chzhungarii v 1889 i 1890 gg. (A Journey Through Eastern Turkestan, the K'un'lung, the Northern Edge of the Tibetan Uplands and Dzhungaria in 1889 and 1890), St. Petersburg, 1894.

_____. Puteshestviye v Kashgariyu i Kun'-lun' (A Journey to Kashgaria and the K'unlun), Moscow, Geografgiz, 1949.

Pogosyan, Kh. P., "Modern Ideas on General Atmospheric Circulation," in the book: A. I. Voyeykov i sovremennyye problem klimatologii, Leningrad, Gidrometeoizdat, 1956.

Polyanskiy, V. I., V tropkakh yuzhnogo Kitaya (In the Tropics of South China), Leningrad, Leningrad University Publishing House, 1960.

Popov, M. G., "Between Mongolia and Iran," Tr. po prikladnoy botanike, genetike i selektsii, 1931, Vol. 26, No. 3.

_____. "On the Use of the Botanical-Geographic Method in Plant Taxonomy," Problemy botaniki, Vol. 1, Moscow-Leningrad, Izd. AN SSSR, 1950.

Popov, V. V., and Fedorov, A. A., "Chinese-Soviet Floristic

and Faunistic Research in Yunnan, " Izv. AN SSSR, seriya biol. , 1958, No. 6.

Potanin, G. N. , "A Trip to the Northern Part of the Greater Khingan During the Summer of 1899, " Ivz. Russk. geogr. o-va, 1901, Vol. 37, No. 5.

Preobrazhenskiy, A. V. , "Forest Planting and Forestry in the Northeast of China, " Sb. statey Leningr. obl. pravl. nauchn. -tekhn. o-va lesn. prom. (A Collection of Articles by the Leningrad Oblast Board of the Scientific-Technical Society for the Lumber Industry), No. 3, Leningrad, 1958.

Prirodnyye usloviya Sin'tszyana (The Natural Conditions of Sinkiang), Moscow, Izd. AN SSSR, 1960.

Provintsiya Sychuan' (Szechwan Province), Shanghai, 1956, (in Chinese).

Przheval'skiy, N. M. , "From Kul'dzhi Over the Tien-Shan to Lob-nor and Across Dzungaria to Kuch'eng, " Izv. Vses. geogr. ob-va, 1940, Vol. 72, No. 4-5.

_____ . Iz Zaysana cherez Khami v Tibet (From Zaysan Across the Khami to Tibet), Moscow, Geografgiz, 1946a.

_____ . Mongoliya i strana tangutov (Mongolia and the Land of the Tanguts), Moscow, Geografgiz, 1946b.

_____ . Ot Kyakhty na istoki Zheltoy reki (From Khyakhta to the Sources of the Yellow River), Moscow, Geografgiz, 1948.

Rass, T. S. , Mirovoy promysel vodnykh zhivotnykj (World Hunting of Aquatic Animals), Moscow, Soviet Science, 1948.

Ratsek, V. I. , "Glaciation of Peak Victory (Tienshan Glaciation Focus), " Geogr. sbornik Geogr. o-va SSSR, Vol. 4, Glaciology, Moscow-Leningrad, Izd. AN SSSR, 1954.

Regional'naya stratigrafiya Kitaya (The Regional Stratigraphy of China), Moscow, IL, 1960.

Richardo, P. U. , Tropicheskiy dozhdevoy les (The Tropical Rain Forest), Moscow, IL, 1961.

Roborovskiy, V. I. , Puteshestiviye v Vostochnyy Tyan'-Shan' i Nan'-Shan' (A Journey to the Eastern Tien-Shan and Nan-Shan), Moscow, Geografgiz, 1949.

_____ . "The Report of the Head of the Expedition of V. I. Roborovskiy," Vols. 1-3, St. Petersburg, 1900, 1901 (Tr. eksped RGO po Tsentr. Azii, Sovershennoy v 1893-1895 gg. [Transactions of the RGO Expedition Through Central Asia Made in 1893-1895], Vol. 1, No. 1-3.)

Rodevich, V. M. , Sungari ot istoka do vpadeniya v Amur. Na

osnovanii materialov po issledovaniyu reki Sungari
partiey Ministerstvo putey soobshcheniya v 1904 g.
(The Sungari from the Source to the Entrance into the
Amur. On the Basis of Materials on the Research on
the Sungari River by a Party of the Ministry of Com-
munication in 1904), Parts 1-3, St. Petersburg, 1906.
Rozov, N. N. , "The Soil Map of the Chinese People's Re-
public from the Geographic Atlas Published by 'Yahuang, '"
Pochvovedeniye (Soil Science), 1954, No. 1.
Rubtsov, L. I. , "Results of Introducing Trees and Shrubs in
the Sukhumi Subtropical Arboretum, " Tr. Introduk.
pitomnika subtropicheskikh kul'tur (Transactions of the
Introductory Nursery for Subtropical Crops), No. 2,
Sukhumi, 1937.
Saburenkov, N. M. , "Fishing in the Chinese People's Repub-
lic," Rybnoye khozyaystvo (Fisheries), 1961, No. 9.
Sapozhnikov, V. V. , Mongol'skiy Altay v istokakh Irtysha i
Kobda (The Mongol Altay and the Sources of the Irtysh
and Kobda), Tomsk, 1911. Repeat Edition on the Rus-
sian and Mongolian Altay, edited and commentary by
V. A. Obruchev, Moscow, Geografgiz, 1949.
Selivanov, Ye. I. , "Landforms of the Aeolian Sand Accumu-
lation in the Western Part of Central Asia, " Vestn.
Mosk. un-ta (Herald of Moscow University), Series 5,
Geography, 1961, No. 2.
_____ . "On the Question of Ancient Glaciation of Central
Asia, " Izv. Vsesoyuz. geogr. o-va, 1959a, Vol. 91,
No. 6.
_____ . "On the Paleogeography of the Tarim Depression,"
Dokl. AN SSSR, 1959b, Vol. 127, No. 4.
Seliverstov, Yu. P. , "Present and Ancient Glaciation on the
Saur Range, " in the book: Voprosy geografii Kazakhstana
(Problems of Kasakhstan Geography), No. 9, Alma-Ata,
Izd. AN SSSR, 1962.
Selyaninov, G. T. , "The Boundaries of the Subtropics, " in the
book: Materialy po agroklimaticheskomu rayonirovaniyu
subtropikov SSSR (Materials on the Agroclimatic Zoning
of the Soviet Subtropics), Leningrad, 1936.
Seng Ch'u, "Orogenic Phases in China," Tr. XVIII sessii
Mezhdunarodnogo geologicheskogo kongressa (Trans-
actions of the 17th Session of the International Geologi-
cal Congress), 1937, Vol. 2, Moscow, State Geological
Technical Publishing House, 1939.
Severnyy Kitay. Ekonomicheskaya geografiya (North China.
Economic Geography), Moscow, 1958.

Shan Ming and Chuang Chi-p'ing, "Soils of the Amur Basin and Their Utilization in Agriculture," Sb. nauchnykh dokladov komplesknoy Amurskoy ekspeditsii, Vol. 1, Peking, 1958, (in Chinese).

Shen Tao-chi and She Chi-hsiang, "The Turfan Depression," Tili chihshih, 1959, No. 3, (in Chinese).

Shen Yu-ch'ang, "The Hydrography of Lake Tunt'ing," Tili hsuehpao, 1950a, No. 16, (in Chinese).

_____. "The Topography of the Border Regions of Szechwan and Kweichow," Tili hsuehpao, 1950b, No. 3-4, (in Chinese).

Shih Ch'eng-hsi, "The Experience of Classifying the Rivers of the Chinese People's Republic," Tr. Tret'yego Vsesoyuzn. gidrol s"yezda (Transactions of the Third All-Union Hydrological Congress), Vol. 7, Section on General Hydrology, Leningrad, Gidrometeoizdat, 1959.

Shih Ya-feng, Rel'yef Kitaya (The Relief of China), Peking, 1955, (in Chinese).

Shih Ya-feng, Ch'en Meng-hsiung, Li Wei-chi, and I Shih-ming, "Preliminary Research on the Physical Geography (Predominantly Geomorphology) of the Tsinghai Lake and its Surroundings," Tili hsuehpao, 1958, Vol. 24, No. 1, (in Chinese).

Shih Ya-feng and Ch'en Shu-p'eng, "The Profile of the Tapeishan," Tili hsuehpao, 1954, No. 9, (in Chinese).

Shih Ya-feng and Wang Chung-t'ai, "Present Glaciation of the Ch'ilienshan," Tili chihshih, 1959, No. 2, (in Chinese).

Shipulin, F.K., "Basic Features of the Geological Structure of Mongolia," Sovetskaya geologiya, 1947, No. 24.

Shtegman, B.K., "Bases of the Ornithogeographical Division of the Paleoarctic," in the book: Fauna SSSR (The Fauna of the USSR), Vol. 1, No. 2, "Birds," 1938.

Shuvalov, S.A., "On the Soils of the Farming Regions of Central China," Pochvovedeniye, 1959, No. 11.

Sinitsyn, N.M., and Sinitsyn, V.M., "The Tien-Shan. The Most Important Tectonic Elements," Izv. AN SSSR, seriya geol., 1958, No. 4.

Sinitsyn, V.M., "Basic Elements in the Geological Structure of the Gobi," Byull. Mosk. o-va ispyt. prirody, Geology Section, 1956a, Vol. 31, No. 6.

_____. "Basic Features in the Tectonics of China," Voprosy Geologii Azii, Vol. 2, Moscow, Izd. AN SSSR, 1955.

_____. "Geographical Observation in Alpine Asia," Izv. AN SSSR, seriya geogr., 1958, No. 3.

_____. "The Geological History of the Lobnor Depression and Lake Lobnor," Izv. AN SSSR, seriya geol., 1954b, No. 6.

_____. "The Geotectonic Factor in the Change of Central Asiatic Climate," Byull. Mosk. o-va ispyt. prirody, Geological Section, 1949, Vol. 24, No. 5.

_____. "The History of the Arid Area of Central Asia During the Mesocenozoic," in the book: Doklady na yezhegodnykh chteniyakh pamyati V. A. Obrucheva (Reports at Yearly Lectures in the Memory of V. A. Obruchev), Moscow-Leningrad, Izd. AN SSSR, 1961.

_____. "New Information on the Active Volcano in Central Asia," Priroda, 1954c, No. 9.

_____. "On the Geological Boundary of the K'uenlung and Tien-Shan Structures in the Pamiro-Alai Convergence," Izv. AN SSSR, seriya geol., 1945, No. 6.

_____. "On the History of the Tarim Stable Mountain Area," Izv. AN SSSR, seriya geol., 1948a, No. 1.

_____. "On the Quaternary History of the Tarim Depression," Byull. Mosk. o-va ispyt. prirody, Geology Section, 1947b, Vol. 22, No. 3.

_____. Ordos i Ala-Shan'. Geograficheskoye i geologicheskoye opisaniye (The Ordos and Ala-Shan. A Geographical and Geological Description), Moscow, Izd. AN SSSR, 1954d.

_____. "Several Remarks on the Orographic Taxonomy of the Central Asiatic Ranges," Izv. AN SSSR, seriya geol., 1948b, No. 3.

_____. "The Structural-Orographic Scheme of the Chinese Tien-Shan," Izv. AN SSSR, seriya geol., 1947a, No. 4.

_____. "The Structure and Development of the Chinese Platform," Izv. AN SSSR, seriya geol., 1948c, No. 6.

_____. "The Tectonic Nature of the K'uen-Lun Arc," Dokl. AN SSSR, 1956b, Vol. 106, No. 5.

_____. Tsentral'naya Aziya (Central Asia), Moscow, Geografgiz, 1959.

_____. Turfan-Khamiyskaya vpadina i Kashun'skaya Gobi (The Turfan-Khami Depression and the Kashun Gobi), Moscow, Izd. AN SSSR, 1957.

_____. Vostochnyy Tyan'-Shan'i Bei-Shan' (The Eastern Tien-Shan and Pei-Shan), Moscow, Izd. AN SSSR, 1954a.

Skvortsov, B. V., "The Vegetation of the Barga," Vestnik Man'chzhurii, (The Herald of Manchuria), 1930, No. 6.

Smirnov, A. M., "Basic Problems in the Geology of Manchuria," Zap. Kharbinskogo o-va yestestvoispytateley i etnografov

(Notes of the Harbin Naturalist and Ethnographer Society), Harbin, 1954.

_____. "The Development of the Relief and Hydrological Network on the Tungpei Plain," Chungko tissutse yenchiu, 1958, Vol. 1, No. 2, (in Chinese).

Sobolevskiy, G.K., "On the Present and Ancient Glaciation in the Western K'uen-Lun," Izv. Russk. geogr. o-va, 1918, Vol. 54, No. 1.

Sochava, V.B., "Problems in the Florogenesis and Phylo-cenogenesis of the Manchurian Mixed Forest," in the book: Materialy po ist. flory i rast. SSSR, Vol. 2, Moscow-Leningrad, Izd. AN SSSR, 1946.

Sorochan, O.G., "Certain Ideas on the Nature of the Summer Monsoon of Eastern Asia," Tr. Gl. geofizich. observatorii, No. 71, Leningrad, Gidrometeoizdat, 1957.

Ssu Hsi-ming and Ma Jui-chiun, "The K'aifeng Relief," Tili hsuehpao, 1958, No. 1, (in Chinese).

Stanyukovich, K.V., "The Vegetation Cover of the Eastern Pamir," Zap Vsesoyuzn. geogr. o-va (Notes of the All-Union Geographical Society), New Series, Vol. 10, Moscow, Geografgiz, 1949.

Strokovskiy, V., "Outline of the Urumchi Climate," Izv. Imp. Akad. nauk (News of the Imperial Academy of Sciences), Series 6, 1912, No. 4.

Su Ming, "The Control of Floods on the Yangtze River," Narodnyy Kitay, 1952, No. 9-10.

Sukachev, V.N., "In the Tropical Forests of China, (From Impressions of 1956-1957)," Vestn. AN SSSR, 1958. No. 5.

Sun Ch'eng-lieh, "The Physical Geography of the Hanshui Basin," Tili chihshih, 1955, No. 8, (in Chinese).

Sun P'an-shou, et al., Tsentral'nyy Kitay (Central China), Moscow, 1961.

Sun Shu and Khodak, Yu. A., "Basic Features in the Geological Structure and Metallogeny of the Lesser Khingan, Changkuants'ailing, and Wangtashan," Tr. Tret'yey sessii ob"yedinennogo sovetsko-kitayskogo uchenogo soveta po probleme r. Amur, Vol. 2, Moscow, 1959, (mimeographed).

Sung Chao-ch'un, "Neotectonic Movements in Northeast China and their Role in Physical Geography," Tili hsuehpao, 1959, Vol. 25, No. 6, (in Chinese).

Sung Chia-t'ai, "To Use the Land Fully and Rationally," Tili chihshih, 1956, No. 4, (in Chinese).

Sung Ta-ch'eng, "The Properties and Fertility of Soils, the

Principles of Natural and Agricultural Zoning in the
    Amur Basin, " Tr. Tret'ye sessii ob"yedinennogo sovet-
    sko-kitayskogo uchenogo soveta po probleme r. Amur.
    Vol. 3, Moscow, 1959, (mimeographed).
Sung Ta-ch'uan, "Soils of the Amur Basin and Their Agricul-
    tural Development, " Nauch. dokl. o kompl. issledov.
    basseyna Amura (Scientific Reports on the Integrated
    Research on the Amur Basin), Peking, 1958, (in Chinese).
Sung Ta-ch'uan, Cheng Chao-shun, Hsiung Yeh-chi, Yen Chang-
    sheng, and Sung Chia-t'ai, "The Tsaidam Depression, "
    Tsentr. un-t, geogr. otd., in-ta tochnykh i yestestv. nauk,
    June, 1944, (in Chinese).
Tai Yen-nien, "How the Chingkiang Reservoir was Built, "
    Narodnyy Kitay (People's China), 1952, No. 17.
Takhtadzhyan, A. L., "The Ecological Evolution of the Angio-
    sperms and the Problem of the Origin of Temperate
    Flora, " Delgatskiy s"yezd Vses. botanich. ob-va (Dele-
    gates Congress of the All-Union Botanical Society),
    Report Theses, 1957.
_____. "On the Question of the Origin of the Temperate
    Flora of Eurasia," Botanich. zhurn., 1957, Vol. 42,
    No. 11.
T'ang Ch'i-ch'eng, "The Tarim River," Tili chihshih, 1958
    No. 12, (in Chinese).
T'ang Ch'i-hsiang, "The Great Canal, " Narodnyy Kitay, 1955,
    No. 22.
T'ang Yung-luan, Landshafty p-va Leichzhou i ikh izmeneniye
    (The Landscapes of the Leichow Peninsula and the
    Changes in Them), Shanghai, Hsin chihshih Publishing
    House, 1957, (in Chinese).
Teng Tse-hoi, "On a Full Plan for Checking the Hwang Ho
    River and Utilizing its Water Resources, A Report at
    the 2nd All-China Meeting of National Representatives, "
    Supplement to the magazine Narodnyy Kitay, 1955, No. 21.
Ting I, et al., "On the Problem of Developing the Production
    of Mineral Fertilizers, " Jenmin Jihpao, November 15,
    1962, (in Chinese).
Tolmachev, A. I., "The Latitudinal Limits for the Distribution
    of Plants on Sakhalin, " Geogr. sbornik Vsesoyuz. geogr.
    o-va (A Geographical Collection of the All-Union Geogra-
    phical Society), Vol. 8, Moscow-Leningrad, Izd. AN
    SSSR, 1956b.
_____. O flore o-va Sakhalin (On the Flora of Sakhalin
    Island), Moscow-Leningrad, Izd. AN SSSR, 1959,
    (Komarov Lectures, No. 12).

_____. "Vertical Distribution of Vegetation on Sakhalin," Geogr. sbornik Vsesovuz. geogr. o-va (A Geographical Collection of the All-Union Geographical Society), Vol. 8, Moscow-Leningrad, Izd. AN SSSR, 1956a.

Trudy Tibetskoy ekspeditsii 1889-1890 gg. pod nachal'stvom M. V. Pevtsova (Transactions of the Tibetan Expedition of 1889-1890 under the Leadership of M. V. Pevtsov), Part 1, St. Petersburg, p. 895.

Ts'ui Chi-chiu, "Particular Features of Glaciers in the Muztagat and Kongur Mountains and the Conditions for Developing and Using Them," Tili hsuehpao, 1960, Vol. 26, No. 1, February, (in Chinese).

T'ung Ch'eng-k'ang, "The Turfan Depression," Tsentr. un-t, geogr. otd. In-ta tochnykh i yestestv. nauk (Central University, Geographical Department, Institute of Precise and Natural Sciences), October, 1949, (in Chinese).

Vavilov, N. I., "Centers of Origin for Cultivated Plants," Tr. po prikladnoy botanike, genetike i selektsii (Transactions on Applied Botany, Genetics and Selection), 1926, Vol. 16, No. 2.

_____. "The Role of Central Asia in the Origin of Cultivated Plants," Tr. po prikladnoy botanike, genetik i selektsii, 1931, Vol. 26, No. 3.

Vitvitskiy, G. N., "The Circulation of Air over China," Izv. AN SSSR, seriya geogr., 1956, No. 2.

_____. Klimaty zarubezhnoy Azii (The Climates of Foreign Asia), Moscow, Geografgiz, 1960.

_____. "The Limits for the Distribution of the Summer Monsoon in Eastern Asia, Tr. Vsesoyuz. nauchnogo meteorologich. soveshchaniya (Transactions of the All-Union Scientific Meteorological Meeting), Vol. 4, Climatology Section, Leningrad, Gidrometeoizdat, 1962.

Vlodavets, V. I., "On Certain Features in the Cenozoic Volcanism of the Darigan Area of Mongolia," Voprosy geologii Azii (Problems in the Geology of Asia), Vol. 2, Moscow, Izd. AN SSSR, 1955.

Voronov, A. G., "Biocenological Observations in the Subtropical Forests of Yunnan," Tr. Mosk. ob-va ispyt. prirody (Transactions of the Moscow Naturalist Society), Biology Section, Vol. 3; Collection of works on the geobotany, botanical geography, plant taxonomy and paleogeography, Moscow, MOIP Publishing House, 1960.

Vostochnyy Kitay (Eastern China), Moscow, Geografgiz, 1955.

Voyeykov, A. I., "The Climate in the Monsoon Area of Eastern Asia," Izv. Russk. Geogr. ob-va, 1879, Vol. 15, No. 5.

_____. "The Climate of Manchuria," Vestn. Man'chzhurii
(The Herald of Manchuria), Harbin, 1932, No. 1-6;
Voprosy vodnykh resursov Kitaya (Problems in the
Water Resources of China), Collection in 4 Vols.,
Shanghai, 1939 (in Chinese).

Vul'f, Ye. V., "Essays on the History of the Flora in Eastern
Asia," Izv. Gos. geogr. o-va (News of the State Geographical Society), 1939, Vol. 71, No. 10.

_____. Istoricheskaya geografiya rasteniy (istoriya flor
zemnogo shara) (The Historical Geography of Plants
[A History of World Floras]), Izd. AN SSSR, 1944,
Moscow-Leningrad.

Vyalov, O. S., "A Concise Review of the Orography and Hydrography of Northwest Dzungaria," Voprosy geografii
(Problems of Geography), Coll 35, Moscow, Geografgiz,
1954.

_____. "A Flight over the Dzungarian Plain," Uch. zap.
L'vovskogo un-ta (Scientific Notes of L'vov University),
Vol. 39, Geological Collection, No. 3, L'vov, L'vov
University Publishing House, 1956.

Wang An-ch'iu, "The Mountain Region of the Eastern Part of
the Tungpei," Tili chihshih, 1956, No. 6, (in Chinese).

Wang Chu-ch'uan, "The Experience of Neotectonic and Seismological Zoning of China (Establishing the Neotectonic
and Seismological Regions)," in the book: Tr. Pervogo
soveshchaniya po neotektonike Kitaya (The Transactions
of the First Meeting on Neotectonics in China), Moscow,
Gosgeoltekhizdat (State Geological Technical Publishing
House), 1960.

Wang Hsiu-chang, Govorov, I. N., Radkevich, Ye. A., and
Smirnov, A. M., "Metallogenic Features in the Border
Regions of Northeast China and the USSR," Tr. Tret'yey
sessii ob''yedinennogo sovetsko-kitayskogo uchenogo
soveta po probleme r. Amur (Transactions of the Third
Session of the Combined Soviet-Chinese Study Council
on the Problem of the Amur River), Vol. 2, Moscow,
1959, (mimeographed).

Wang Huang-Yun, "An Initial Discussion on the Problem of
Shifting the Water From South to North," Kehsueh
t'ungpao, 1959, No. 8, (in Chinese).

Wang Mine, "Soil Erosion in the Hwang Ho River Basin and
Meliorative Works," Tili chihshih, 1952, No. 2,
(in Chinese).

Wang Ta-ch'un, Chu Shang-ch'ing, et al., "Deep in the
Sikiang-Tibetan Plateau Area," Vokrug sveta (Around
the World), 1954, No. 9-10.

Wang, Yueh-lun, "Certain Data on the Neotectonic Movements in China," in the book: Tr. Pervogo soveshchaniya po neotektonike Kitaya, Moscow, Gosgeoltekhizdat, 1960.

Wu Ch'uan-chiun, Tibetskiy okrug pr. Sikan (The Tibet District of Sikiang Province), Peking, 1955, (in Chinese).

Wu Ch'uan-chiun, et al., Ekonomicheskaya geografiya Kitayskogo Priamur'ya (Economic Geography of the Chinese Amur Area), Moscow, Geografgiz, 1960.

Wu Ch'uan-chiun, Sung Ch'en-lieh, Teng Ching-chung, and Wang Ming-yeh, Ekonomicheskaya geografiya zapadnykh rayonov srednego techeriya Khuanhe (The Economic Geography of t Western Regions of the Middle Hwang Ho), Peking, "Kehsu Publishing House, 1956, (in Chinese).

Wu Chuang-ta, Tayvan' (Taiwan), Translated from the Chinese, Moscow, IL, 1955.

Wu Chung-lun, "On the Characteristics of Developing Forestry in the Chinese People's Republic," in the book: Voprosy ekonomiki i povysheniye produktivnosti lesnogo khozyaystva v stranakh narodnoy demokratii (The Problems of Economics and Raising the Productiveness of Forestry in the People's Democracies), Moscow-Leningrad, State Lumber and Paper Publishing House, 1960.

Yakovlev, A. A., Klimaticheskiy obzor Severnoy Man'chzhurii po dannym meteorolgicheskikh stantsii KEZhD (A Climatic Review of Northern Manchuria from the Data of the Meteorological Stations of the Chinese Eastern Railway), Harbin, 1934.

Yang Chi-ch'eng, "The Tarim River," Tili chihshih, 1958, No. 12, (in Chinese).

Yang Chung-chien, "The Loess of China," Priroda, 1957, No. 5.

Yang Chung-chien and Sun Meng-lin, "New Findings of Fossil Ostriches in China and Their Stratigraphic Significance," Tr. komissii po izucheniyu chetvertichnogo perioda, Vol. 14, Moscow, Izd. AN SSSR, 1959.

Yang Huai-shen, et al., "The Discovery and Study of Quaternary Glacial Deposits in the Lower Yangtze," Kehsueh t'ungpao, 1957, No. 8, (in Chinese).

Yang Huai-shen and Yang Hsen-yuan, "Periglaciation Phenomena of Quaternary Glaciation in the Lower Yangtze," Quaternaria sinica, Vol. 1, No. 2, (in Chinese).

Yang Jen-chang, "The Climate of the Northeast," Tili hsuehpao, 1950, Vol. 16, September, (in Chinese).

_____. "The Hydrography of Northeast China and Irrigation Construction," Tili chihshih, 1953, Vol. 4, No. 1, (in Chinese).

_____. "The Natural Landscape to the West of the T'olaiho River in the Tsaidam," Tili hsuehpao, 1959, Vol. 25, No. 6, (in Chinese).

Yang Tse, "The Genesis of the Loess Deposits of North China," Tr. komissii po izucheniyu chetvertichnogo perioda, Vol. 14, Moscow, Izd. AN SSSR, 1959.

Yanshin, A. L., "The Geology of the Northern Aral Area. Stratigraphy and the History of the Geological Development," Materialy k poznaniyu geol. stroyeniya SSSR (Materials in Understanding the Geological Structure of the USSR), No. 15, MOIP Publishing House, 1953.

Yaroshenko, P.D., "The Forest Steppe of the Soviet Far East and the Nearby Regions of Northeast China," in the book: Voprosy sel'skogo i lesnogo khozyaystva Dal'nego Vostoka (Problems of Agriculture and Forestry in the Far East), No. 2, Vladivostok, Maritime Publishing House, 1958.

Yatsenko-Khamelevskiy, A.A., and Baydalina, N.A., Opredelitel' i kratkaya kharakteristika osnovnykh lesopromyshlennykh drevesin V'yetnama (Guide and Brief Description of the Basic Lumber Trees of Vietnam), Leningrad, Publishing House of the Forestry Academy imeni Kirov, 1959.

Yeganov, E.A., "On the Piedmont Deposits of the Tsaidam and the Basic Features of its Development in the Quaternary Age," Tichih hsuehpao, 1960, No. 2, (in Chinese).

_____. "The Tsaidam Depression," Priroda, 1959, No. 9.

Yeh Su-ju and Liu Hsien-t'ien, Fizicheskaya geografiya Kitaya (The Physical Geography of China), Peking, 1959, (in Chinese).

Yeh T'u jeng and Ku Chen-ch'ao, "The Influence of the Tibetan Uplands on the Atmospheric Circulation and on the Weather of China," Izv. AN SSSR, seriya geogr., 1956, No. 2.

Yen Ch'in-shan, "The Barkhans of the Northern Shensi and Their Origin," Tili chihshih, 1954a, No. 8, (in Chinese).

_____. "The Glacial Relief in the Region of the Greater Khingan," in the book: Voprosy geografii, Coll 35, Moscow, Geografgiz, 1954c.

_____. "The Shifting Barkhans Between Yulin and Tung-pien and Their Reformation," Kehsueh t'ungpao, 1954b, No. 11, November, (in Chinese).

Ying Chung-chao, "Charasteristics of the Thermal and Water Balance of the Territory of China," Tr. Glavn. geofizich.

observatorii (Transactions of the Main Geophysical Observatory), 92, Leningrad, Gidrometeoizdat, 1959.

Yunatov, A.A., "Basic Features of the Vegetation Cover of the Mongolian People's Republic," Tr. Mongol'skoy komissii, Vol. 39, Moscow-Leningrad, 1950, Izd. AN SSSR.

_____. "The Basic Patterns of the Vegetation Cover in the Northern Part of Central Asia," in the book: Voprosy botaniki, Coll 2, Moscow-Leningrad, Izd. AN SSSR, 1954.

_____. "On Certain Ecological-geographic Patterns of the Vegetation Cover of the Sinkiang-Uigur Autonomous Region," in the book: Prirodnyye usloviya Sin'tszyana, Moscow, Izd. AN SSSR, 1960.

_____. "On the Understanding of the Vegetation Cover in the Western Kun'lun and Nearby Part of the Tarim Depression," in the book: Kun'lun' i Tarim, Moscow, Izd. AN SSSR, 1961.

Yusov, B.V., Tibet, Moscow, Geografgiz, 1958.

Zabirov, P.D., Oledeneniye Pamira (Glaciation of the Pamir), Moscow, Geografgiz, 1955.

Zarubezhnaya Aziya (Fizicheskaya geografiya) (Foreign Asia [Physical Geography]), Moscow, Pedagogical Publishing House, 1956.

Zaslavskiy, M., "Organizing Erosion Control in Communist China," Zemledeliya i zhivotnovodstvo Moldavii (Farming and Livestock Raising in Moldavia), 1959, No. 2.

Zaychikov, V.T., Bluzhdayushchaya reka Khuange (The Wandering Hwang Ho River), Moscow, Geografgiz, 1956.

_____. "The Natural Zoning of the Chinese People's Republic," Vestn. AN SSSR, 1959, No. 9.

_____. Puteshestvenniki drevego Kitaya i geograficheskiye issledovaniya v Kitayskoy Narodnoy Respublike (Travelers of Ancient China and Geographical Research in the Chinese People's Republic), Moscow, Geografgiz, 1955.

Zaykov, B.D., "The Mean Runoff and its Distribution over the Year on the Territory of the USSR," Tr. nauchn. issled. uchrezhd. gidromet. sluzhby (Transactions of the Scientific-Research Institutions of the Hydrometeorological Service), Moscow-Leningrad, Series 4, No. 24, Gidrometeoizdat, 1946.

Zenkova, V.A., "Glaciers in the Headwaters of the Baskan River of the Dzungarian Alatau," Geogr. sbornik Vses.

geogr. o-va (A Geographical Collection of the All-Union Geographical Society), Vol. 4, "Glaciology," Moscow-Leningrad, Izd. AN SSSR, 1954.

Zhukovskiy, P. M., Kul'turnyye rasteniya i ikh sorodichi (Cultivated Plants and Their Relatives), Moscow, "Soviet Science" Publishing House, 1950.

Zhukovskiy, Ye., "The Urkushar and Darbuljin Apples," Plodovodstvo (Fruit-raising), 1893, No. 1.

Zonn, S. V., "The Soils in the Eastern Part of the Sikiang-Tibetan Uplands and the Pattern of Their Distribution," T'ujang hsuehpao, 1959b, Vol. 7, No. 12, (in Chinese).

_____. V tropikakh Yuzhnogo Kitaya (In the Tropics of Southern China), Geografgiz, 1959a.

Zubov, Yu. P., Koldanov, V. Ya., and Solov'yev, K., "The Restoration of Larch Forests in the Greater Khingan," Lesnoye khozyaystvo, 1959, No. 9.

Non-Cyrillic Sources

Academia Sinica, Staff Members, On the General Circulation
    Over Eastern Asia. Tellus (Stockholm), 1957, Vol. 9,
    No. 4; 1958, Vol. 10, No. 1.
Allen, G.M., The Mammals of China and Mongolia, pp. 1-2,
    New York, 1938-1940.
Anderson, Y.G., Essays on the Cenozoic of Northern China.
    Mem. Geol. Surv. China, A. No. 3, 752 pp. Peking,
    1923.
Barbour, G.B., "Analysis of Lushan Glaciation Problem,"
    Bulletin of the Geological Society of China, 1934, Vol. 13.
Bartz, F., Das Tierleben Tibets und des Himalayagebirges.
    Leipzig, 1935.
Beard, J.S., "Climax Vegetation in Tropical America," Eco-
    logy, 1944, Vol. 25, No. 2.
Bentham, G., Flora Hongkongensis. London, 1861.
Bretschneider, E.V., History of European Botanical Dis-
    coveries in China. Vol. 1-2. London, 1898.
Chan Kuo-te, "On the Geotectonic Nature of the Southeastern
    Coastal Region of China," Scientia Sinica, 1958, Vol. 11,
    No. 1.
Chang, H.T., The Vegetation of Luichou Peninsula. Report
    on Plant Ecology and Geobotany, Academia Sinica, Pub-
    lication Commission, 1957, No. 17, (in Chinese).
Chang, H.T., Wang, P.S., and Cheng, C.C., The Mangrove-
    Vegetation of China. 1957, (in Chinese).
Chang Ping-chen, "Air Masses Interactions and the Weather
    of China." In Collected Scientific Papers. Meteorology.
    1919-1949. Peking, 1954.
Chen Chao-liu, "Amphibians of Western China. Zoology Mem-
    oirs," Chicago, Natural History Museum, Fieldiana,
    1950, Vol. 2.
Chen-Cheng-siang, "The Climate and Climatic Regions of
    Taiwan," Malayan Journal of Tropical Geography (Singa-
    pore), 1955, Vol. 5, March.
Ch'ên Fêng-huei, "A Preliminary Study on the Vegetation of the
    China Po-hu Lake and its Vicinity in the Northeastern
    Part of Kirin Province, Manchuria," Bulletin of the Fan
    Memorial Institute of Biology. Botanical Ser., 1934,
    Vol. 5.
Cheng, T.U., "Check List of Chinese Birds," Transactions of
    Chinese Association for the Advancement of Sciences,
    1947, Vol. 9.

Ching, R. C., "The Studies of Chinese Ferns, " I. Sinensia,
1930, Vol. 1; II-V, Bulletin of the Fan Memorial Insti-
tute of Biology. Bot. ser., 1930-1931, Vol. 1-2;
VI-VIII, Sinensia, 1931-32, Vol. 1-3; IX-X, Bulletin
of the Fan Memorial Institute of Biology. Bot. ser.,
1933, Vol. 4; XI, Contributions from the Institute of
Botany. National Academy of Peiping, 1933, Vol. 2.
Chu Chung-hsiang and Tshou Yen-cheng, "A Survey of Plant
Communities in Yulung Mountains, Likiang, Yunnan, "
Acta Scientiarum Naturalium Universitatis, Yunnan,
1947, (in Chinese).
Chu Coching, "Southeast Monsoon and Rainfall in China, " In
Collected Scientific Papers. Meteorology. 1919-1949.
Peking, 1954.
Chun Woon-Yeung and How Toon-chew, "Contributions to the
Flora of South China, " Acta Phytotaxonomica Sinica,
1958, Vol. 7, No. 1, (in Chinese).
Chun, W. Y., "New Species of Machalus from South China, "
Acta Phytotaxonomica Sinica, 1953, Vol. 2, No. 2,
(in Chinese).
"Claves Familiarum Generumque Plantarum Sinicarum, " Acta
Phytotaxonomica Sinica, 1953, Vol. 3; 1954, Vol. 4, (in
Chinese).
Corner, E. J. H., "The Durian Theory of the Origin of the
Modern Tree, " Annals of Botany, New. ser., 1949,
Vol. 13.
_____. "The Evolution of Tropical Forests, " In Evolution
As a Process. Ed. by J. Huxley, a. o. 2d ed., 1958.
Cressey, G. B., Land of the 500 Million. New York, 1955.
Dao Schin-yen and Chen Lung-shun, "The Structure of General
Circulation Over Continent of Asia in Summer, " Acta
Meteorologica Sinica, 1957, Vol. 28, No. 3, (in Chinese).
Diels, L., "Beiträge zur Flora des Tsin Ling Schan und andere
Zusätze zür Flora, " Botanische Jahrbucher, 1905, Bd.
36, Beiblatt, No. 82.
_____. "Die Flora von Central China, " Nach der vorhändenen
Literatur und neu mitgeteilten original Materiale. Engler's
Bot. Jahrbücher. Bd. 29, 1901.
Dunn, S. T., and Tuscher, W. J., "Flora of Kwangtung and Hong-
kong (China), " Bulletin of Miscellaneous Information.
(Royal Botanic Gardens, Kew), Additional series, 1912,
Vol. 10.
Fang Wen-p'ei, Icones Plantarum Omeinsium. Vol. 1-2,
Chengtu, 1944-1945.

Fang, W. P., "Notes on Dendrobentamia," Acta Phytotaxonomica, 1952, Vol. 2, No. 2, (in Chinese).

Fang, Y., "Timber Studies of Chinese Trees." I-VII. Bulletin
of the Fan Memorial Institute of Biology. Botanical
ser., 1932-1935, Vol. 3-6.

Flohn, H., "Hochgebirge und Allgemeine Zirkulation. Die
Gebirge als Wärmequellen," Archiv für Meteorologie,
Geophysik und Bioklimatologie. Ser. A., 1953, Bd.
5, H. 3.

_____. "Neue Anschaungen über das Monsunklima Osta
Asiens," Geographische Rundschau, 1949, Jg. I, No. 1.

Flohn, H., and Oeckel, H., "Water Vapour flux during the Summer Rains over Japan and Korea," Geophysical Magazine
(Tokyo), 1956, Vol. 27, No. 4.

Forbes, F. B., and Hemsley, W. B., "An Enumeration of all
the Plants Known from China Proper, Formosa, Hainan,
Corea, and Luchu Archipelago, and the Island of Hong-
kong, Together with Their Distribution and Synonymy,"
Journal of the Linneau Society of Botany. London, 1886-
1906, Vol. 23, 26, 36.

Franchet, A., "Plantas Yunnanenses a cl. J. M. Delavay col-
lectas enumeravit novasque describit," Bulletin Société
Botanique de France, 1886, 33.

Furrill, W. B., "Plant Geography," Vistas Botany. London,
1959.

General Geological Map of China. Prepared under the Super-
vision of T. K. Huanh. Nanking, Geological Survey of
China, 1948.

Good, R., The Geography of the Flowering Plants. 2d ed.
London, New York, Toronto, 1953.

Gordeev, T. P., and Jernakov, V. N., "Materials Related to the
Study of the Soils and Plant Associations of Northeastern
China and Autonomous Region of Inner Mongolia, Collected
in 1950," Acta Pedol. Sinica, Vol. 2, No. 4, 1954.

Gundersen, A., Families of Dicotyledons. Waltham, Mass.
Chron. Bot. Co. N.-G., 1950.

Handel-Mazzetti, H., Naturbilder aus Südwest-China. Wien
und Leipzig, 1927.

_____. "Das nordwest-birmanischwestyunnanische Hochge-
birgegebiet," Vegetationsbilder, 1926/1927, H. 17.

_____. "Die pflanzengeographische Gliederung und Stellung
Chinas," Botanische Jahrbücher, 1931, Bd. 64, H. 4.

_____. Symbolae Sinicae botanische Ergebnisse der Expedi-
tion der Akademie der Wissenschaften in Weinnach Sudwest
China 1914-1918. Vol. 1-7. Wien, 1929-1937.

Hedin, S. A., "Southern Tibet." Vol. 6, Part 1. Die Meteoro-
logischen Beobachtungen. Stockholm, 1920.
Hou, H., "Distribution of Economic Plants in Southern Kwei-
chow Province with Special Reference to their Environ-
ment," Acta Phytotaxonomica Sinica, 1951, Vol. 1.
No. 2, (in Chinese).
_____. "Notes on the Preliminary Survey of the Medical
Plants in Szechuan and Kweichow," Acta Phytotaxonomica
Sinica, 1951, Vol. 1, No. 3-4, (in Chinese).
_____. "The Plants Communities of Southern Kweichow
Province," Acta Botanica Sinica, 1951, Vol. 1, (in
Chinese).
_____. Soils of North Central Kweichow. Publishings by
the National Geological Survey of China. Pehpe, Chung-
king, 1941, (in Chinese).
Hou, H., Lee, A. R., Lin, H. S., and Kuan, Y. Y., "A Pre-
liminary Study on the Plant Association of Peithaho,
Hopei Province," Acta Botanica Sinica, 1953, Vol. 2,
(in Chinese).
Hou Hsien-Yu, Chang Tu-chen, and Hsien pu-wang, The Vege-
tation of China to the Special Reference to the Main Soil
Types. Report for the 6th International Congress of
Soil Science, Peking, 1956.
Hou, K. H., and Chu, C. H., The Vegetation of Hainan Island
and Kwantung Province. Preliminary Report on Plant
Ecology and Geobotany. Academia Sinica. Publication
Commission, 1955, No. 4, (in Chinese).
How, T. C., and Ho, C. N., "Rhizophoroceae in Chinese Flora,"
Acta Phytotaxonomica Sinica, 1952, Vol. 2, No. 2, (in
Chinese).
Hsü Yinn-tze, "A Note on the Climatic Conditions of Lhasa,"
Bulletin of the American Meteorological Society, 1941,
Vol. 22, No. 2.
Hu, H. H., "Amesiodendron, a New Genus of Anacardiaceae
from Southwestern China," Bulletin of the Fan Memorial
Institute of Biology. Botanical Ser., 1935, Vol. 6, No. 4.
_____. "The Characteristics and Affinities of Chinese Flora,"
Bulletin of the Chinese Botanical Society, 1936, Vol. 2,
No. 2.
_____. "A Comparison of the Ligenous Flora of China and
Eastern North America," Bulletin of the Chinese Botani-
cal Society, 1935, Vol. 1, No. 2.
_____. "The Importance of Plant Ecology in China and a
Suggested Procedure of Study," Bulletin of the Department
of Biology of Yenching University, 1930, Vol. 1, (April).

_____. "The Nature of the Forest Flora of Southeastern China," Bulletin of the Peking Society of Natural History, 1929, Vol. 4.

_____. "Notulae Systematicae ad Floram Sinensem." I-IV, Journal of the Arnold Arboretum, 1930-1936, Vol. 11-13; V-X, Bulletin of the Fan Memorial Institute of Biology, Botanical Ser., 1934-1940, Vol. 5-10.

_____. A Preliminary Survey of the Forest Flora of Southeastern China. Contributions from the Biological Laboratory of the Science Society of China. Botanical series, 1926, Vol. 2. Abstracted in Proceedings of the Third Pan-Pacific Science Congress, 1928.

_____. "Prodromus Florae Sininsis," I. Contributions of the Biology Laboratory Science Society of China, 1929, Vol. 5; II. Bulletin of the Fan Memorial Institute of Biology. Botanical Ser., 1929, Vol. 1.

_____. "Rehderodendron, A New Genus of Styracaceae from Szechwan," Bulletin of the Fan Memorial Institute of Biology. Botanical Ser., 1932, Vol. 3.

_____. "Sinmerrillia, a New Genus of Celastraceae," Bulletin of the Fan Memorial Institute of Biology. Botanical Ser., 1937, Vol. 8.

_____. "Sinojackia, a New Genus of Styracaceae from Southeastern China," Journal of the Arnold Arboretum (Harvard University), 1928, Vol. 9, No. 3, (July).

_____. "Sinojohnstonia, a New Genus of Boraginaceae from Szechuan," Bulletin of the Fan Memorial Institute of Biology. Botanical Ser., 1936, Vol. 7, No. 5.

_____. "Tienmia, a New Genus of Orobanchaceae of South-Eastern China," Bulletin of the Fan Memorial Institute of Biology. Botanical Ser., 1939, Vol. 9, No. 1.

Hu, H.H., and Cheng, W.C., "On the New Family Metasequoiceae and on Metasequoia Glyptostroboides, a Living Species of the Genus Metasequoia Found in Szechuan and Hupeh," Bulletin of the Fan Memorial Institute of Biology. New ser., 1943, Vol. 1, No. 2.

Hu, H.H., and Ching, R.C., Icones Filicum Sinicarum. Vol. 2-4, Nanking, 1930-1937.

Huntington, E., The Pulse of Asia. Boston and New York, 1907.

Icones Plantarum Sinicarum. Ed. H.H. Hu and W.-Y. Chun. Fasc., 1-5, Shanghai, 1927-1937.

Jong Pin-chen, "The Kunming Quasistationary Front," Journal of the Chinese Geophysical Society, 1950, Vol. 2, No. 4.

Kao Fan, "Building China's Forests," China Monthly Review,
    July, 1952.
Kao Yu-hsie, "General Circulation of the Lower Atmosphere
    Over the Far East," In Collected Scientific Papers.
    Meteorology, 1919-1949. Peking, 1954.
Kitagawa, M., Lineamenta florae Manshuriae. Report of the
    Institute of Scientific Research, Manchou kuo, 1939,
    No. 43.
Koo Chen-Chao, "The Upper Wind Structure Over Western
    China in Winter," Science Record (Peking), 1951, Vol. 4,
    No. 2.
Kostermans, A. F. G. H., Lanraccae-Rcinwardtia, Vol. 4, No.
    2, 1957.
Ku Tschen-tschan, "Der dynamische Einfluss des Hochlander
    von Tibet auf die Ostasiatische Zirkulation," Acta
    Agronomica (Budapest), 1950/1951, Bd. 1, fasc. 1-2.
Lee, J. S., Quaternary Glaciations in the Lushan Area, Cen-
    tral China. Monographs of the Institute of Geology.
    Academia Sinica. Ser. B, 1947, Vol. 2.
_____. "Vestiges of Corrie. Glaciation of the Kweichow
    Plateau," Bulletin of the Geological Society of China,
    Ser. B, 1947, Vol. 27.
Lee Shih-ying, Wang An-chiu, Tsai Wei-chi, Huang Ta-haing,
    and Wang Ching-jui, "The Tsaidam Basin with Regard
    to the Natural Regionalization of China," Acta Geogr.
    Sinica 23 (3): 329-342 (chin.), 342-343 (engl. abstr.).
    1957.
Li Lien-chien, "Soils of Junging-Kwangsi," Soil Bulletin, 1936,
    No. 16, (Oct.).
Loczy, L., Beschreibung der geologischen Beobachtungen und
    deren Resultate. Die wiss. Ergebnisse der Reise des
    gr. Bela Sechenyi in Ost Asien 1877-1880. Bd. I, Wien,
    1893, pp. 307-845.
Lu, A., "A Brief Survey of the Climate of Lhasa," Quarterly
    Journal of the Royal Meteorological Society, London,
    1939, Vol. 65, No. 281.
_____. "Chinese Climatology," In Collected Scientific Pa-
    pers. Meteorology. 1919-1949. Peking, 1954.
_____. "The Cold Waves of China," In Collected Scientific
    Papers. Meteorology. 1919-1949. Peking, 1954.
Lu, T. J., The Boulder Clay and its Associated Topographic
    Features in the Southern Slope of Tapiehshan. Contri-
    butions of the Natural Research of Institute of Geology.
    Academia Sinica, 1948, Vol. 8.

Matsumuru, J., and Hayata, B., "Enumeratio Plantarum in insula Formosa sponte crescentium hucusque rite cognitarum adjectis discriptionibus et figuris specierum pro regione novarum," Journal of the College of Science, Imperial University of Tokyo, 1906, Vol. 22.

Merrill, E.D., "An Enumeration of Hainan Plants," Lingnan Science Journal. Canton, 1927, Vol. 5.

_____. "Die Pflanzengeographische Scheidung von Formosa und den Philippinen," Botanische Jahrbücher, 1923, Bd. 58.

Merrill, E.D., and Walker, E.H., A Bibliography of Eastern Asiatic Botany. Boston, 1938.

Meusel, H., "Bilder aus der Waldvegetation Süd und Mittel China," Urania, 1958, No. 2.

_____. Fortschritte der Pflanzengeographische Forschung in China. Wissenschaftliche Zeitschrift der Martin-Luther Universität Halle Wittenberg. Mathematisch-naturwissenschaft-liche Reine. 1956/1957, Jg. 6, H. 6.

Nichols, J.T., Fresh-water fishes of China. New York, 1943.

Norin, E., "Quaternary Climatic Changes within the Tarim Basin," Geographical Review, 1932, Vol. 22.

Norlindh, T., Flora of the Mongolian Steppe and Desert Areas. Report of the Scientific Expedition, North-Western Province of China, 1949, No. 31.

Osgood, W., The Mammals of China, Chicago, 1943.

Pendleton, R.L., Ch'ang, L.C., Chen, R., and Hou, K.C., "A Reconnaissance Soil Survey of the Harbin Region," Soil Bulletin, 1935, No. 11.

The Plant Communities of Tinghuschan, Kaoyei Hsien, Kwantung Province. Contributions from the Cungschan University, 1955, Vol. 3, (in Chinese).

Pumpelly, R., "Relations of Secular Rock Disintegration to Loess, Glacial Drift and Rock Basins," Am. Journ. of Science and Arts, Vol. 27, 1879.

Puri, C.S., Indian Forest Ecology. II. Calcutta, 1960.

Ramage, C.S., "Relationship of General Circulation to Normal Weather over Southern Asia and Western Pacific During the Cool Seasons," Journal of Meteorology, 1952, Vol. 9, No. 6.

Regel, A., "Reise von Kuldscha zum Sairam-Nor, Issyk-Kul, Turfan," Gartenflora, 1877, Vol. 26; 1878, Vol. 27; 1881, Vol. 30.

Richthofen, F.V., "China," Ergebnisse Einiger Reisen und darauf gegrundeter Studien. Bd. 1, 11. Berlin, 1877, 1882.

Sargent, C.S., Plantae Wilsonianae. An Enumeration of the
    Woody Plants Collected in Western China for the Arnold
    Arboretum of Harvard University During the Years
    1907, 1908 and 1910 by E.H. Wilson. Vol. 1-3. Boston,
    1911-1917.
Schweinfurth, U., "Die horizontale und vertikale Verbreitung
    der Vegetation in Himalaja," Bonner Geographische
    Abhandlungen, 1957, H. 20.
Skrine, C.P., "The Alps of Qungur," The Geographical Jour-
    nal. London, 1925, Vol. 66, No. 5.
Steward, A.N., Manual of Vascular Plants of the Lower
    Yangtze Valley, China. Corvallis, 1958.
Sun, T.C., "Glacial Features in North-Western Kuangsi," Bul-
    letin of the Geological Society of China. Ser. B, 1944,
    Vol. 24, No. 1-2.
Sung Shio-wang, "The Extratropical Cyclones of East China
    and Their Characteristics," In Collected Scientific Pa-
    pers. Meteorology. 1919-1949. Peking, 1954.
Szepanik, E.F., "The Fisheries of Mainland China," Fishing
    News International, 1961, Vol. 1, No. 1.
Tafel, A., Meine Tibetreise, Eine studienfahrt durch das
    nordwestliche China und durch die Innere Mongolei in
    das östliche Tibet. Bd. 1, Berlin, 1914.
Takhtajan, A., Die Evolution der Angiospermen. Jena, 1959.
Tao Schin-yen, "The Mean Surface Air Circulation Over China,"
    In Collected Scientific Papers. Meteorology. 1919-
    1949. Peking, 1954.
Teng, S.C., "Forest Geography of the East-Tibetan Plateau,"
    Botanical Bulletin. Academia Sinica, 1948, Vol. 2, No. 1.
    _____. "A Provisional Sketch of the Forest Geography of
    China," Botanical Bulletin .Academia Sinica, 1948,
    Vol. 2.
Teng Shu-ch'iin, "The Forest Regions of Kansu and Their Eco-
    logical Aspects," Botanical Bulletin. Academia Sinica,
    1947, Vol. 1, No. 3.
Thopson, B.W., "An Essay on the General Circulation of the
    Atmosphere Over South-East Asia and the West Pacific,"
    Quarterly Journal of the Royal Meteorological Society
    (London), 1951, Vol. 77, No. 334.
Thorp, Y., Geography of the Soils of China. Nanking, China,
    1936.
Ting, V.K., Geology of the Yangtze Estuary. Shanghai, 1919,
    (Harbour Investigation ser. I, Rep. 1).
Trinkler, E., Tarimbecken und Taklamakan Wüste. Zeit-
    schrift der Gesellschaft fur Erdkunde zu Berlin, 1930,
    Bd. 65, H. 9/10.

_____. Tibet. Sein geographisches Bild und seine Stellung im Asiatischen Kontinent. Mitteilungen der Geographischen Gesellschaftin München, 1921/1922, Bd. 15.

Troll, C., Die Tropischen Gebirge. Ihre dreidimensionale klimatische und pflanzengeographische Zonierung. Bonner Geographische Abhandlungen, 1959, H. 25.

"The Tsaidam Basin with Regard to the Natural Regionalization of China," Acta Geographica Sinica, 1957, Vol. 23, No. 3, (in Chinese).

Tu Chang-wang, "The Air Masses of China," In Collected Scientific Papers. Meteorology. 1919-1949. Peking, 1954.

Tu Chang-wang and Hwang Sze-sung, "The Advance and Retreat of the Summer Monsoon in China," In Collected Scientific Papers. Meteorology. 1919-1949. Peking, 1954.

Walker, E.H., "Plants Collected by R.C. Ching in Southern Mongolia and Kansu Province, China." Contributions from the United States National Herbarium, 1941, Vol. 28.

Wang, H.P., Li, S.G., and Hwang, A Preliminary Observation on the Growth Cunninghamia lanceolata in Relation to Its Environment. 1954.

Ward, F.K., "Botanical and Geographical Explorations in Tibet, 1935," Geographical Journal (London), 1936, Vol. 88.

_____. "A Sketch of the Geography and Botany of Tibet, Being Materials for a Flora of that Country," The Journal of the Linn. Society Botany, 1935, Vol. 50, No. 333.

Weigold, H., Südost Tibet als Lebensraum. Hannover, 1935, (Jahrbuch der Geographische Gesellschaftzu Hannover 1934-1935).

Willis, Bailey, and Blackwelder, E., Research in China. Vol. 1 p. 353. Washington, 1907.

Wilson, E.H., A Naturalist in Western China. Vol. 1-2. London, 1913.

Winkler, H., Die Pflanzendecke Sudost-Borneos. Botanische Jahrbücher, 1914, Bd. 50.

Wissman, H. von, Die quartare Vergletscherung in China. Zeitschrift der Gesellschaft für Erdkunde zu Berlin, 1937, H. 7/8.

_____. "The Pleistocene Glaciation in China," Bulletin of the Geological Society of China, 1937, Vol. 17, No. 2.

Wong, W.U., "The Mesozoic Orogenic Movement in Eastern

China," Bulletin of the Geological Society of China,
1928, Vol. 8.
Yang, H.H., Fang, C., and Yeh, K.Y., Ecological Study of
Cunninghamia lanceolata (Lamb.) Hook. in China.
Forest Ecology Laboratory, CPSRI, China, Peking,
1958.

GEOGRAPHIC NAME INDEX

GEOGRAPHIC NAME INDEX